CW00968213

FLORA
OF THE
ISLE OF MAN

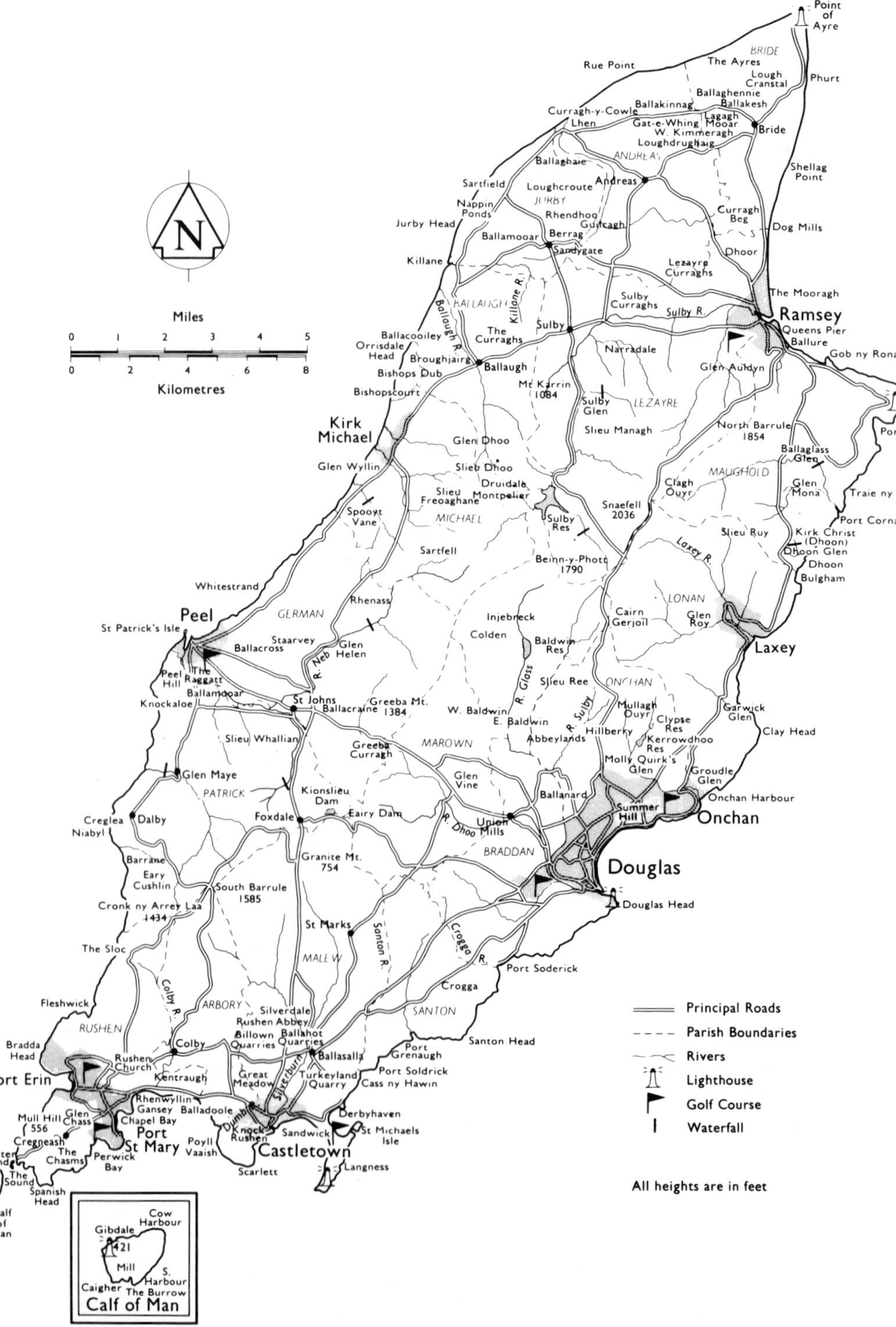
Point of Ayre
BRIDE
The Ayres
Rue Point
Lough Cranstal
Phurt
Ballaghennie
Ballakinnag
Ballakesh
Curragh-y-Cowle
Lhen
Gat-e-Whing
Lagagh Mooar
W. Kimmeragh
Bride
Loughdrughaig
ANDREAS
Ballaghaie
Shellag Point
Sartfield
Loughcroute
Andreas
JURBY
Nappin Ponds
Rhendhoo
Curragh Beg
Jurby Head
Guilcagh
Dog Mills
Ballamooar
Berrag
Sandygate
Dhoor
Killane
Lezayre Curraghs
Ballaugh R.
Killane R.
BALLAUGH
Sulby Curraghs
Sulby R.
The Mooragh
Ramsey
Queens Pier
Ballure
Ballacooiley
Orrisdale Head
The Curraghs
Sulby
Narradale
Gob ny Rona
Broughjairg
Ballaugh
Bishops Dub
Glen Auldyn
Bishopscourt
Mt Karrin 1084
Sulby Glen
LEZAYRE
Kirk Michael
Glen Dhoo
Slieu Managh
North Barrule 1854
Port M
Ballaglass Glen
Glen Wyllin
Slieu Dhoo
MAUGHOLD
Druidale
Clagh Ouyr
Slieu Freoaghane
Montpelier
Glen Mona
Traie ny Ha
Spooyt Vane
MICHAEL
Sulby Res
Snaefell 2036
Port Cornaa
Slieu Ruy
Kirk Christ (Dhoon)
Laxey R.
Dhoon Glen
Sartfell
Dhoon
Beinn-y-Phott 1790
Bulgham
Whitestrand
LONAN
Rhenass
Peel
GERMAN
Cairn Gerjoil
Glen Roy
Injebreck
St Patrick's Isle
Staarvey
Glen Helen
Colden
Baldwin Res
Laxey
Ballacross
R. Neb
R. Glass
Peel Hill
The Raggatt
Slieu Ree
ONCHAN
Ballamooar
R. Sulby
Knockaloe
St Johns
Ballacraine
Greeba Mt. 1384
W. Baldwin
Mullagh Ouyr
Garwick Glen
E. Baldwin
Clypse Res
Clay Head
Slieu Whallian
Hillberry
Abbeylands
Kerrowdhoo Res
Greeba Curragh
MAROWN
Molly Quirk's Glen
Groudle Glen
Glen Maye
Glen Vine
Kionslieu Dam
Onchan Harbour
PATRICK
Ballanard
Summer Hill
Creglea
Dalby
Foxdale
Eairy Dam
Onchan
Niabyl
R. Dhoo
Union Mills
BRADDAN
Barrane
Granite Mt. 754
Douglas
Eary Cushlin
South Barrule 1585
Cronk ny Arrey Laa 1434
Douglas Head
St Marks
Crogga R.
The Sloc
Santon R.
MALEW
Port Soderick
Colby R.
Crogga
Fleshwick
ARBORY
Silverdale
SANTON
RUSHEN
Rushen Abbey
Billown Quarries
Ballahot Quarries
Bradda Head
Colby
Santon Head
Rushen Church
Ballasalla
Port Grenaugh
Port Erin
Kentraugh
Great Meadow
Silverburn
Turkeyland Quarry
Port Soldrick
Cass ny Hawin
Rhenwyllin
Gansey
Balladoole
Derbyhaven
Mull Hill 556
Glen Chass
Chapel Bay
Dumb
Knock Rushen
Sandwick
St Michaels Isle
Cregneash
Port St Mary
Poyll Vaaish
Castletown
Kitterland
The Chasms
Perwick Bay
Scarlett
Langness
The Sound
Spanish Head
Calf of Man
Cow Harbour
Gibdale
421
Mill
S. Harbour
Caigher
The Burrow
Calf of Man
N
Miles
0 1 2 3 4 5
0 2 4 6 8
Kilometres
Principal Roads
Parish Boundaries
Rivers
Lighthouse
Golf Course
Waterfall
All heights are in feet

FLORA
OF THE
ISLE OF MAN

By

D. E. Allen, M.A., F.L.S.

With the assistance of

Larch S. Garrad, Ph.D., A.M.A., F.S.A.
and Marjorie Devereau

First published 1984
ISBN 0 901106 23 2

The Manx Museum,
Douglas,
Isle of Man.

Printed by Titus Wilson & Son Ltd., 28 Highgate, Kendal, Cumbria.

DEDICATED

TO THE MEMORY OF

William Stanley Cowin (1908-1958)
Ralph Howarth (1889-1954)
Alexander Dalrymple Walker (1896-1961)

generous hosts and valued field companions

FOREWORD

The Manx Museum is proud to undertake the publication of "Flora of the Isle of Man", in the knowledge that this long-awaited volume will form the definitive publication in a fundamental branch of Manx studies for many years to come. It can indeed be regarded as an important aspect of the life work of a distinguished botanist.

I first heard of David Allen and his outstanding interest in the botany of the Isle of Man when, in 1950, as a young graduate I was called for interview for the Deputy Directorship of the Manx Museum, and found myself in a waiting room which was festooned with drying botanical specimens. This, for me, novel experience I later learned was due to the Manx Museum playing host to a conference of the Botanical Society of the British Isles, and the conference delegate who had left the strongest impression on the local people with whom he had come into contact was an enthusiastic sixth-form schoolboy called David Allen. There is considerable personal satisfaction for me, when approaching my retirement from the Directorship of the Manx Museum, in penning this Foreword to the product of his labours over the intervening thirty-four years. Throughout that period, through his many visits and correspondence, one has been impressed and inspired by the persistent dedication of a scholar who has pursued his field of study with such sustained diligence.

The author pays detailed acknowledgment to the earlier botanists who have worked in the Isle of Man, and in particular to the contemporaries with whom he has co-operated so closely, above all Miss Marjorie Devereau and my colleague on the staff of the Manx Museum, Dr. Larch Garrad, whose names appear with that of the author on the title page. It is gratifying too to note the tribute to Messrs. Will Cowin, Ralph Howarth and A. D. Walker, all of whom I had the pleasure of working with in my early days at the Manx Museum.

The systematic list of plants of course will stand as the definitive statement on Manx botany for the decades ahead, but it is particularly reassuring that this is preceded by a masterly review of the geography of the Island in relation to the history of the development of its flora. The significant late-glacial and post-glacial history of the Isle of Man and the vitally important date of its severance from Britain are topics that the author and I have discussed and corresponded about many times over the past thirty years, with the crucial relevance that they hold for both botany and prehistory alike. While there is of course no substitute for the detailed mastery of the essential basic elements of any academic discipline, the treatment of these broader questions demonstrates the very real benefits that derive from interdisciplinary studies. This is perhaps particularly clear in an island situation. The botanical contribution to such studies is clearly significantly advanced by the publication of this major work.

A. Marshall Cubbon
Director, Manx Museum
July 1984.

PREFACE

It is remarkable that an island so promisingly positioned, so readily accessible and so multitudinously visited should have been till now without a comprehensive account of its flowering plants and ferns. This has not been for want of attempts. Since a Welshman drew up the first list just over two hundred years ago at least two Manxmen, a Merseysider and a Londoner have set out to this end. But for one reason or another, as explained later in these pages, the efforts of most of these came to very little and nothing comparable with the Floras that have existed for many years for so many of the counties of Britain ever managed to emerge.

It was following a visit in the spring of 1949 that I resolved to try to fill the gap. I was then looking around for some new area to encompass and explore and, having been born and brought up on the Lancashire coast, I had that almost proprietary interest in the Island characteristic of Lancastrians. Unbeknown to me the latest and most nearly successful in the series of would-be providers of a Flora, C. I. Paton, had then only a few more months to live, so that by the time I was ready to start work in the field the Island was botanically 'vacant', quite fortuitously, for the first time in a generation.

Considering my presumptuousness, the welcome I received from the Island's naturalists could hardly have been more encouraging. Without the help of those who lived there a Flora compiled by means of mere holiday visits, as this one has been, could not have helped but be glaringly deficient. Many plants reveal their presence only briefly and then disappear. Many others are to be found only after time-consuming, and maybe repeated, searches. All through the years it has again and again been borne in on me how deeply handicapped is the investigator who cannot watch over what he studies through each and every season. Even when he does come, the time he can spare for exploring each locality is heartbreakingly limited. Forever conscious of the shortness of the time at his disposal, he feels bound to be always working fresh country, in the hope of lighting on that paradise of rarities he knows must be lurking just over the next hill. Those day-long sessions ensconced in a single field patiently mastering the complexities of a hybrid swarm or some elusive variation, so necessary for a properly deep knowledge, are not normally for him. Nor, for that matter, is the disciplined drudgery of recording by grid-squares, with its need to devote all-too-precious hours to moor after monotonous moor and pasture after monotonous pasture.

For these reasons I count myself more than fortunate to have secured such willing and active resident collaborators. Outstanding among these, in the later stages of the project, have been Marjorie Devereau and Larch Garrad. All-penetrating in their coverage, raining records upon me, wresting reports of finds from others, their assistance has been beyond measure and is abundantly testified to in the number of localities that stand to their initials in this book. Nor has it ended there: they have read through every word of it in draft, making suggestions and repairing omissions, and have taken upon themselves the formidable task of typing out the manuscript. That their names appear alongside my own on the title-page is no more than their due, for it has been in large degree a joint creation.

Despite the frustrations of investigating a flora from a distance I have never regretted for one moment my decision to make the Island my subject of study all these years. All islands have a special fascination: they can be an adventure to get to; they are liable to harbour entities that occur nowhere else; they are satisfyingly well-defined areas; above all, they pose questions about how and when their present plants and animals came to arrive which lead to an unusually close concern with the work of specialists in other fields. Not the least rewarding aspect of the project has been the friendships I have made as a result with ornithologists and entomologists, with Quaternary researchers and pre- and mediaeval historians. Through these I have had the privilege of partaking of, and contributing to, that special encrustation of learning that forms around any island through the very interdependence of the studies that have it as their focus – and through which its culture is given added cohesion and enrichment.

The flora of the Island, while unusual in its geographical diversity, can boast very little in the way of the botanically spectacular. Its interest and appeal, rather, are more subtle. Because of the uniformity of so much of the Island geologically and the great range in rainfall within so small a compass, it must have few rivals as an exemplar of the influence of atmospheric moisture on plant distribution when unobscured by the effects of differences in the underlying rocks. Its paucity of lakes and ditches, too, has meant a corresponding paucity of native species peculiar to such places; so that when new stretches of such water are created, unusual openings for home-produced crosses result, permitting these to become established to an extent not commonly paralleled elsewhere. Islands, by virtue of their isolation, make excellent open-air laboratories at the best of times: other attractions such as these merely enhance their value scientifically. Which is one reason why care needs to be taken to ensure that their flora and fauna are minimally disturbed and enabled to continue.

Another reason for conservation is a more obvious one: its plant and animal life are an important part of what gives any area its distinctive character. The Isle of Man means more to those who live or holiday there than the shape of its hills, the style of its houses or the accent of its people;

it is also the tang of seaweed, the cry of herring gulls, golden sheets of gorse. No one who has walked its countryside can come away without such scents and sights and sounds staying permanently with them. And for my own part, at bottom, beneath the memories of rare plants discovered, of neatly closing the gap in some previously puzzling distribution, of working for the first time a hitherto untouched locality, it is the elemental essence that I shall forever be aware of having secretly taken in through all these years. The final debt I have to acknowledge is thus to the Island itself – for simply being what it is.

D.E.A.

CONTENTS

LIST OF FIGURES

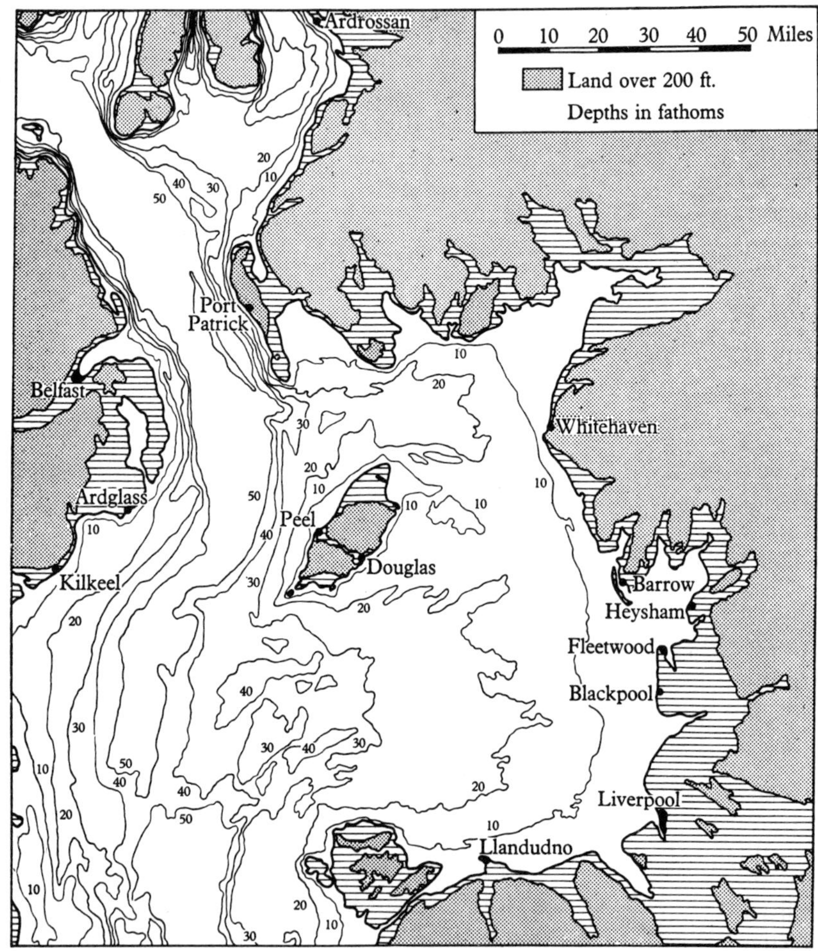

FIG. 1. The position of the Isle of Man

THE PHYSICAL SETTING

Size and position

The Isle of Man constitutes the western end of a submarine shelf which stretches out from Cumbria into the Irish Sea (Fig.1). The nearest coasts are those of Galloway, Cumberland and Ulster (in that order, North Wales being considerably more distant). Each of the surrounding land masses can been seen from the Island when conditions are clear, but Galloway, a mere 16 miles off, is close enough for even men working in the fields to be made out on occasions through strong glasses. The Island's northern tip is in fact nearer to Scotland than it is to its far south-western end – a point important to remember when considering the possibilities of dispersal across the sea.

Some 30 by 10 miles, the Island is around 227 square miles (58,793 hectares) in area. This is roughly the size of Middlesex and half as large again as the Isle of Wight and Rutland. Man is thus very much bigger than those who have never been there tend to suppose. A good deal of its interior being comparatively wild and rugged, it is possible to wander for miles without encountering another human being and easy for those unfamiliar with the terrain to find themselves lost.

Two subsidiary islets lie off the south-west tip: the Calf of Man, of 616 acres (249·3 hectares), and tiny Kitterland. Half-way up the west coast, at Peel, and in the south-east corner, at the north end of Langness, there are two further broken-off pieces, but these lie so immediately off-shore that they are connected by causeways and are islets in name only.

Relief, geology and land use

The hilliness of the southern three-quarters is the Island's most striking feature. The main high ground is aligned north-east/south-west and falls into three distinct sections: the Mull Hills (of which the Calf of Man is the offshore continuation), rising to 556 ft (169 m) at most; the Southern Hills, culminating in the 1,585 ft (483 m) of South Barrule; and the Northern Hills, the highest mass of all, with Snaefell (2,046 ft; 619 m) as their central point and perhaps the only summit that outsiders would be prepared to accept as a mountain in the real sense. Sharply separating the second two groups of hills is the remarkably narrow Central Valley.

As far as the botanist is concerned, the geology is very simple (Fig. 2). Almost all of that three-quarters of the Island which holds the hills consists of Manx Slates, resulting in siliceous soils which bear an acid-loving vegetation, with mainly few and monotonously repeated species. Just north of the Neb at Peel, on the mid west coast, there is a small belt

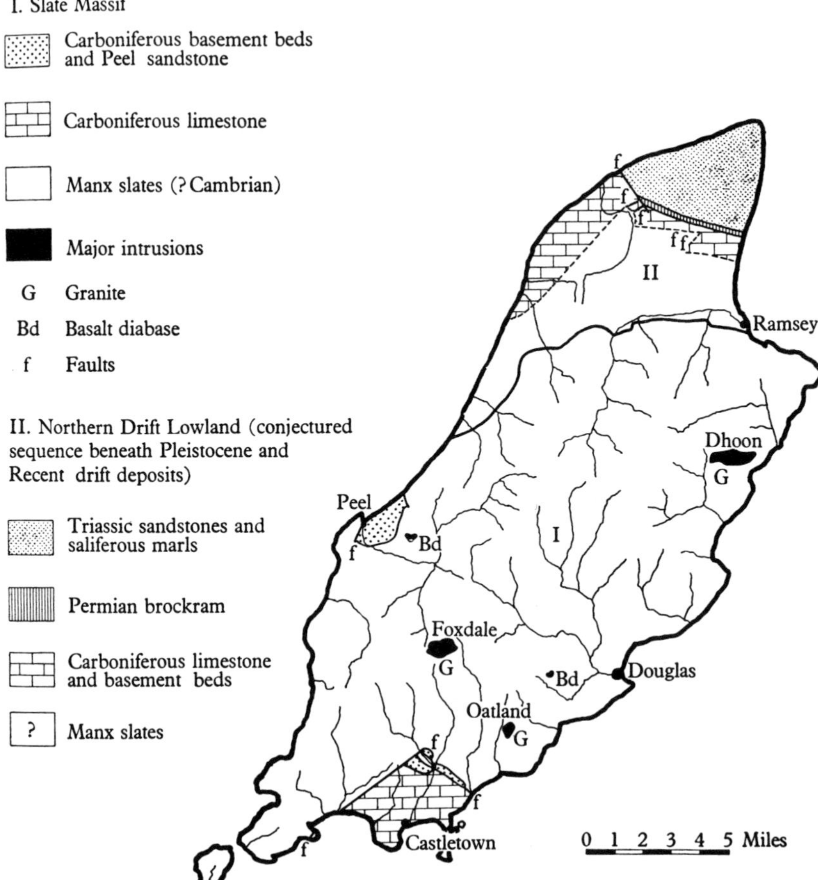

Fig. 2. Geology: major structural components

of sandstone, which finds some slight reflection in the flora locally. Around Castletown, in the south-east corner, Carboniferous limestone is to be found, but, disastrously for the botanist, is only exposed in quarries (though the oldest of these, long overgrown, do contribute a tiny, precious quota of lime-loving species). For the rest, there are just two or three outcrops of granite, of which hopes have been entertained but which appear to be quite irrelevant botanically.

At their northern edge the hills drop away with remarkable abruptness and the remaining quarter of the Island consists of a largely flat plain. This is made up of Quaternary drift deposits, in part a legacy of massive moraines, with an incomplete topping of more recent alluvium and a coastal fringe of blown sand. Sharply different in character from the rest of the Island, with extensive fen-like country and a welcome scatter of ponds and small peaty pools, this plain has been compared by visitors to Anglesey.

A covering of glacial drift also persists along the western side of the Island, penetrating from there up the main valleys towards Foxdale and to Greeba. Over the hills there is a comparable masking of the slate with a layer of peat. And in the south-east corner, dulling the influence of the limestone still further, there is a repeat on a small scale of the northern plain's blown sand and alluvium.

The morphological regions into which the Island can be divided as a

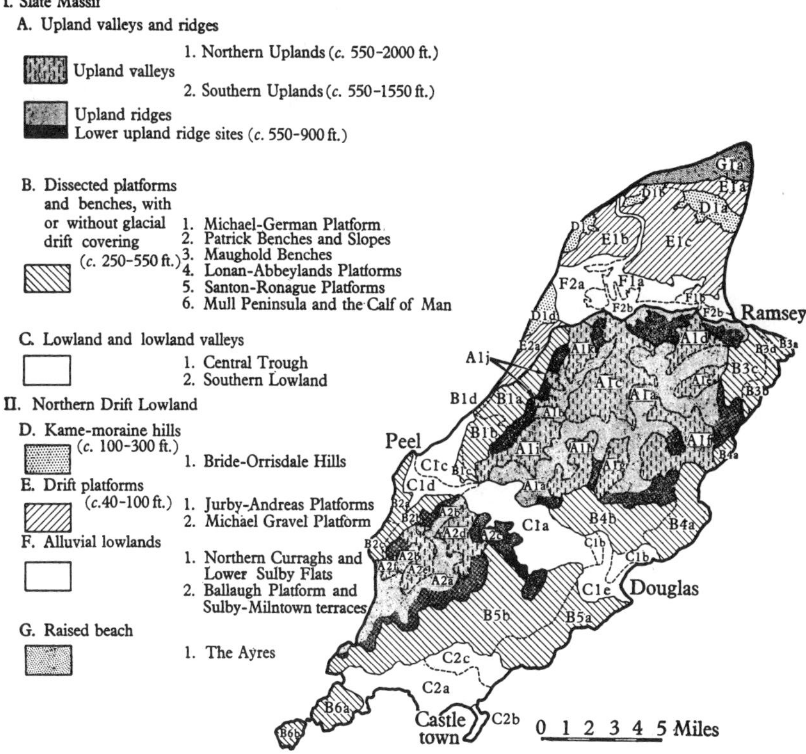

FIG. 3. Morphological regions

result are shown in Fig. 3. Fig. 4 in turn shows the pattern which these regions impose on present-day land use. Mainly unenclosed rough grazings cover about a quarter of the Island; of these, only about a quarter again are privately owned, the remainder being the former Crown and

Common Lands, now under the I.O.M. Forestry, Mines and Lands Board. A further tenth of the Island's surface is accounted for by enclosed rough grazings and another tenth by permanent grassland (Birch 1964). Thus nearly half the land can be wandered over freely or without reasonable objection: a marvellous contrast to all too many parts of Britain.

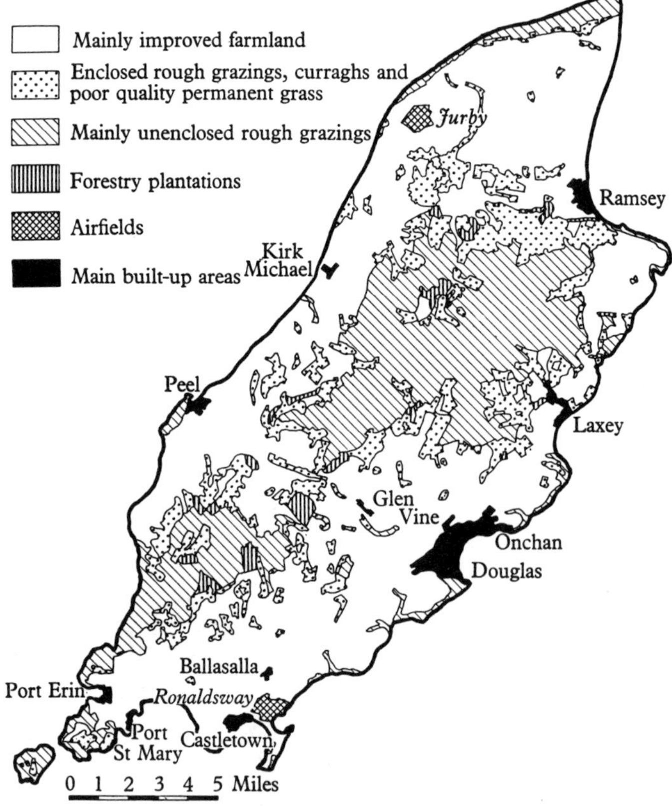

FIG. 4. Land use

Climate

A finger of warm water brought by the Gulf Stream pushes into the Irish Sea from the south and curls up close in round the east and then the north side of the Island. This produces a winter sea temperature several degrees warmer than Liverpool Bay or the Irish coast opposite (Colman 1953). As a result the climate is decidedly 'Atlantic', with all that this implies: normally mild winters and cool summers, a comparativ-ely high rainfall and very slight frosts. The cool summers make for late harvests and severely limit the fruit that can be ripened; the mild winters, on the other hand, allow some species to flower almost the whole year round. The vegetation tends to lushness, many exotics non-hardy in most of Britain flourish out of doors and the fauna and flora display a predominantly western aspect in their composition.

No part of the Island is more than six miles from the sea, which exerts a strong influence on temperature conditions on land in consequence. The main effect is that variations are reduced, so that Man has an especially equable temperature distribution both seasonally and daily (Birch 1960).

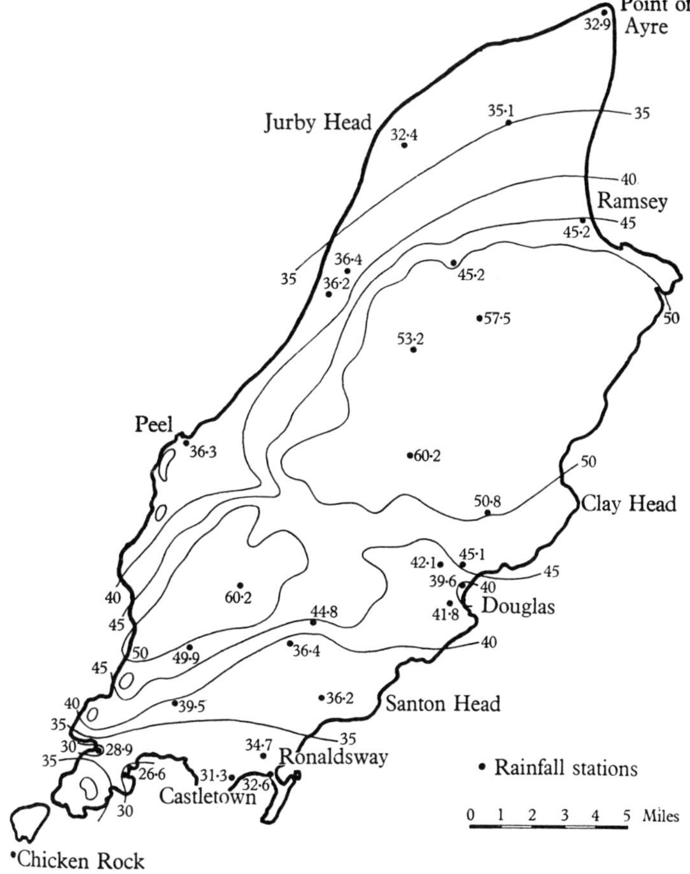

Fig. 5. Mean annual rainfall (inches)

Rainfall, by contrast, exhibits a marked degree of variation, especially between one part of the Island and another (Fig. 5). This makes it far and away the most important factor influencing, or even determining, plant distribution patterns. From annual means of nearly 90 inches in the hills, through totals of over 40 along much of the eastern side, the figures drop to as low as 26·6 at Port St. Mary. The southern plain has a mean of 35 or less, while its northern counterpart shades gradually from 45 immediately beneath the hills to a nearly comparable 32·9 farthest away from their influence at the Point of Ayre. These are very substantial differences to encounter within so confined an area. They explain why the floras of the far north and far south of the Island have many similarities; they also explain why, paradoxically, the east coast flora is noticeably richer in western species than that of its counterpart – presumably because the prevailing winds, from the west-south-west, continually blow across moisture-laden clouds from the hills above.

At Douglas, in one of the wettest parts of the lowlands, every year some rainfall is recorded on over half the days on average. 45% of the annual total there falls between mid-October and the end of January; by contrast, April–June has the lowest amount, in both intensity and incidence.

Long-term fluctuations in the Island's rainfall seem to be quite sizeable (unlike the temperature). This could be a cause of major instability in the wetland habitats; it could also have a multiplier effect on the reproductive capacity of species that are sensitively adjusted at the best of times to existence in this ever-quivering 'Atlantic' Zone. From an analysis of the nineteenth-century data Moore (1901) concluded that over the period 1830-70 rainfall became steadily heavier, but that from 1870 to 1895 it underwent a marked decline. More recent data reproduced by Stenning (1950), derived from monthly readings at Douglas, show a further decrease in 1906-35 as against 1881-1915, particularly in the months of May, July and August. Such a trend might well account for the spontaneous decline that seems to have taken place of many of the Island's more strongly 'Atlantic' plants – as well as for a corresponding increase of drier-demanding 'Germanic' ones that has lately become perceptible around the Irish Sea (Allen 1953).

In addition to their much heavier rainfall it is the hills, as one would expect, that experience the worst conditions more generally. Only there is fog common (its coastal equivalent is usually infrequent and confined to the south and south-east) and only there, too, in normal years, does snow persist.

The hills are far from alone, however, in experiencing high winds. Mostly these consist of westerlies; but east winds are not inconsiderable, especially in the spring. The destruction of the natural tree-cover has greatly intensified the adverse effects of wind and traditionally all building in the Island (including hedgebanks) has laid much emphasis on shelter in consequence. The high level of salt in the gales which sweep the west coast in particular is likely to compound the restrictive effects of this factor on plant distribution. Indeed the great differences in wind exposure between one locality and another suggest that this must play a major role, after rainfall, in influencing distribution patterns.

There is much yet to be learned about the Island's microclimates, those highly localised conditions which may greatly mitigate or intensify the tendencies overall. The heightening of moisture in the immediate vicinity of waterfalls and dripping rocks, for instance, is well evidenced by the predilection for such habitats of three Sedges (*Carex remota*, *C. laevigata* and *C. sylvatica*) and three Hawkweeds (*Hieracium vulgatum*, *H. cravoniense* and *H. perpropinquum*). The last two, characteristic species of Lakeland, in fact occur in such places in Man apparently exclusively. Closer study will no doubt reveal other, similar associations and help to elucidate many anomalies of distribution at present unexplained.

HISTORY AND COMPOSITION OF THE FLORA

After the ice

It can safely be assumed that the present-day native flora descends from that which colonised the area as the ice withdrew at the close of the last glaciation. It is conceivable that one or two arctic-alpines, such as the Least Willow (*Salix herbacea*) or the liverwort *Lepidozia pinnata*, which have survived high up on Snaefell, could have persisted through at least some of the glacial periods; but these can only have been very few – and may be discounted as special cases. For practical purposes the area was swept clean and repopulation had to begin quite afresh.

During the glaciation the seas had retreated far to the west and north, allowing all of the British Isles to be joined together by dry land and united in their turn to the Continent. When the ice-sheets retreated, their melt-waters made for a rapid rise in the sea, resulting in the severance one by one of the land connections that had been created. Recent research has revealed that the return to high temperatures was very much more rapid than has previously been supposed, the climate of Galloway (for instance) having already become as warm as it is there today by as early as 11,500 years ago. Such benign conditions can have been expected to bring an inrush of warmth-demanding plants and animals to colonise the vast, grassy plains that constituted the initial environment post-glacially. Because trees spread more slowly, there was a substantial, critical time-lag between the arrival of much of the temperate flora and fauna and the closing-in of the advancing forests. This time-lag, it has credibly been suggested, permitted the establishment in the British Isles in force of many light-demanding species which the subsequent forest blanket exiled to a few, specialised, marginal situations in so far as it did not eliminate them altogether. The celebrated flora of Teesdale, that anomalous rest-home of rarities, is now believed to have originated in this way. Limestone bluffs, with steep sides and shallow soils inimical to tree growth, are likely to have been particular harbourers of such refugees. Precipitous river-banks, sand-dunes and sea-cliffs are habitats which could have served this purpose too. Purple Milk-vetch (*Astragalus danicus*) and Field Mouse-ear (*Cerastium arvense*) are two Manx species that very probably fall into this category of pre-forest survivors. Both today are largely confined to the eastern side of Britain, with just a few isolated outposts in the west; while in Ireland the first is to be found only in the Aran Isles, the second hardly more widely. Their presence in Man is therefore surprising. But, significantly, the two grow in the Island in much the same places: in the short, dry, mainly coastal turf in the far south and in the north-west beyond Kirkmichael – just the kind of ground that can be assumed to have escaped any shading ever since this first became the coastline. Several other Manx species, among them Smooth Catsear (*Hypochoeris glabra*), Slender Sheep's Sorrel (*Rumex tenuifolius*) and Shepherd's Cress (*Teesdalia nudicaulis*), share that same smallish area in the north-west, are all similarly great rarities in Ireland, and may well owe their presence in the Island to this same effect.

By coincidence that area north of Kirkmichael has also produced most of what has been learned so far about the Manx flora at this earliest post-glacial period. From the fossil pollen and other fragments in the deposits in the cliffs there (Mitchell 1958, 1965; Dickson, Dickson & Mitchell 1970) 163 flowering plant and moss species have been identified. 46 of these are not now known in Man, at any rate as natives; but the fact that the remainder are is arresting confirmation of the temperature conditions attained here by 10-12,000 years ago. They include even the strongly western and southern Bog St. John's Wort (*Hypericum elodes*) and a species of Water Starwort, *Callitriche obtusangula*, which today scarcely extends to Scotland. It is startling to know that plants so familiar may have been trampled underfoot by the Giant Irish Deer that roamed the region for part of this period. So rich indeed in species by then does the flora prove to have been, and so numerous the ones with southern proclivities, that the team of researchers who carried out the work were led to suggest that the Island had already acquired in large part its present-day floristic composition.

Man becomes an island

This at once raises the central question: at what date was Man cut off from Britain? It has recently become clear that the rise in sea-level necessary for this occurred much earlier than had been thought. Recent study of estuarine deposits near Blackpool has established that even by 8,575 years ago the Irish Sea had already filled sufficiently to produce water at least 24 metres deep between Man and Cumbria. This is more than enough to have overwhelmed the land-connection in that area (which, in view of the much shallower depths between Man and the land to the east, is likely to have been the one that lasted longest). We thus have a firm terminal date for this key event. However, work elsewhere in Europe has shown that the rise in sea-level during the centuries preceding this was extremely rapid at first and then slowed down. So it may well be that the land-connection was broken even earlier, possibly around 9,000 years ago (Allen 1978a).

Despite this very early date the cutting-off of Man must still have occurred a long, long time after the cutting-off of Ireland – their joint monopoly of the Irish Stoat notwithstanding – if only because of the far deeper seas that separate that country from Britain. It is to be expected, therefore, that Man should have a number of species that are non-Irish: those putatively which lagged too far behind, for temperature or other reasons, in the general movement north in the wake of the glaciers to arrive in time for the Irish land crossing. Such species are indeed found, in many plant and animal groups, and four of them are flowering plants (disregarding the odd Hawkweed, Dandelion and Bramble, in view of the incompleteness with which the Irish microspecies of these are known). The credentials of these four, though, are less impressive than they at first sight look and only one, Marsh Valerian (*Valeriana dioica*), would seem to be an unassailable instance of an overland immigrant. The Isle of Man Cabbage (*Rhynchosinapis monensis*), the next most convincing, is a plant of shores and so could owe its presence here to the vagaries of sea currents. Yellow Vetch (*Vicia lutea*) is known in Man, significantly, virtually only about gulls' nests. And Dyer's Greenweed (*Genista tinctoria*), even more suspiciously, occurs in a chain of stations in just one district and may well be a relic of long-forgotten cultivation as a dye source. Even so it is odd that there are not more higher plants among this non-Irish element. Maybe there were some which died out before modern records began.

Forest history

Compared with the great attention that the Late-glacial deposits have received, those of the Island's younger periods have been unreasonably neglected. Precise knowledge of the train of events here from the arrival of the first forests is thus still slight (a useful summary of what we have learned to date is provided by Tooley 1978); but it is possible to make out the broad pattern, partly by analogy with elsewhere.

The first forests to form were dominated by Birches. Their reign was comparatively short, for soon the all-prevailing tree of the colder northern climates, the Scots Pine, arrived in irresistible strength, leaving the Birches to withdraw further northwards or high up on the hills as a terminating fringe. In the hills probable descendants of those original Birches linger on in Man still, as the clearly relic northern race, *Betula pubescens* subsp. *odorata*.

As the climate grew warmer, the Pines in turn began to give way to the broad-leaved deciduous trees. By 7,000 years ago the principal components of this 'mixed Oak forest' – Oak itself, Hazel, Wych Elm and Alder – had all reached Man and were beginning their rise to dominance of the lowlands. As the land-connection with Britain must long since have gone, their arrival, at any rate in quantity, was probably belated. Indeed from that point on the insular character of Man, with the restriction this imposed on replenishment, combined with its lack of calcareous soil can be expected to have led to considerable anomalies. One member tree of this forest grouping, Small-leaved Lime, may even have been excluded by the sea barrier altogether; for though one or two grains of its pollen have been detected in the Manx deposits, this is a sufficiently negligible number to suggest that they may have been brought merely by wind.

Effects of human influence

With periodic variations, in response to swings in temperature or rainfall or to other ecological happenings, this Oak-dominated forest reigned unchallenged till its eventual destruction by man. Down till as recently as the 1950s the myth held sway that the Island had always been more or less bare, in consequence of the high winds – so completely had all memory of its aboriginal state been lost. In the years since, evidence bearing on the course of that destruction has been accumulating (Allen 1956, Garrad 1974), but we are still very far from a coherent history. One major clue is the Wartime discovery by archaeologists that in the first few centuries BC and AD the Island's Celtic inhabitants had a ready enough timber supply to treat themselves to large round-houses requiring the use of tens of thousands of oak posts. As late as the eleventh century documentary records suggest there were still considerable woods. But by 1500, if not indeed far earlier, all the trees of any size appear to have gone. The modern reafforestation had its beginning a century and a half after that, but was not to gather pace till the later eighteenth century when much of the semi-natural woodland that exists today must have had its origin.

For the rest, man's influence on the flora has been direct and conspicuous even as it has gradually accelerated in intensity. Even the original Mesolithic colonists, arriving as early as 9,000 years ago (even before an island existed perhaps), would have disturbed the vegetation in some degree despite being without a farming economy. Indeed their middens may well have served as a novel, nitrate-rich habitat which first put various plants of natural habitats on their road to weed status in whole or part. The discovery of the pollen of Ribwort Plantain (*Plantago lanceolata*) in peat from Lough Cranstal in layers dating well back into Mesolithic times may be confirmatory evidence of this. The theory has recently been advanced that Mesolithic peoples also initiated the clearance of woodland, in order to hunt more easily, and so touched off the soil changes which led to the extensive formation of blanket-bog (as opposed to climatic deterioration, hitherto the supposed culprit for this). By contrast, the impact of early farming, which may have begun in the Island by 6,000 years ago, can too easily be exaggerated – except for its introduction of goats and sheep, the close grazing of which would at once have had a cataclysmic effect on vegetation. Grazing by stock, and latterly by the introduced rabbit as well, must always indeed have been by far the most adverse of human influences.

Composition of the flora

One argument regularly advanced for a very early-broken land-connection with Britain (or even none at all) was the alleged exceptional poverty of the Island in species. Usually this argument was based on glaring gaps in the best-known groups, in particular the larger vertebrates (some of which we now know were once present but have become extinct). It conveniently overlooked that many other groups, likely to be more representative, were still known very imperfectly; it also overlooked that Man is not only too small to provide a sufficiency of the ecological niches needed, but it also lacks certain important habitats more or less completely. It has hardly any salt marsh, no true fens, virtually no exposed rock at high levels, no slow-flowing rivers, no upland meadowland, virtually no natural woodland and no sizeable expanses of natural fresh water. Except for the last two there is no reason to suppose that the situation was any different at earlier periods either. Furthermore, of particular importance botanically, Man has next to no calcareous soil. Once all these handicaps have been taken into account, its species totals are in fact not unimpressive. In every plant and animal order (except the wholly freshwater ones) that has so far been adequately worked, with a striking consistency Man proves to have two-thirds of the Irish total and two-fifths of the British (Allen 1962a).

The misleading effect of not comparing like with like is well illustrated by a study made by Birks & Deacon (1973) of the degree of floristic affinity between different regions of the British Isles, based on the data in the *Atlas of the British Flora*. Twelve regions were distinguished for this purpose, one of which was the Isle of Man alone. While this was refreshingly unusual recognition of the Island's distinctiveness, not unpredictably Man proved grossly out of line, displaying little resemblance to any other region.

The Island makes up for its paucity of habitats with an especially rich geographical representativeness. Thanks to its intermediate position it is the meeting-ground, not only of western and eastern species, but of northern and southern ones as well. Although it cannot compete with the ultra-admixture of the west of Ireland, where Mediterranean species grow side by side with arctic-alpines, it can produce many unexpected bedfellows, offering rare opportunities for studying how such normally far-removed species interact when they occur together.

The western element in the flora is probably the most obvious: certainly, it is the one that strikes newcomers to the Island first. Widespread species like the Spring Squill (*Scilla verna*), English Stonecrop (*Sedum anglicum*), Wall Pennywort (*Umbilicus rupestris*), Western Gorse (*Ulex gallii*), Sheepsbit (*Jasione montana*) and Bog Pimpernel (*Anagallis tenella*) give an immediate 'Atlantic' flavour to the scene. Less obtrusive, but more intensely western in their British Isles distribution, are Sea Storksbill (*Erodium maritimum*), Pale Flax (*Linum bienne*), Whorled Caraway (*Carum verticillatum*), Portland Spurge (*Euphorbia portlandica*), Dotted Sedge (*Carex punctata*) and Hay-scented Buckler-fern (*Dryopteris aemula*). A Fumitory, *Fumaria muralis* subsp. *boraei*, a Bramble, *Rubus briggsianus*, and a Toad Rush, *Juncus foliosus*, express the same theme more esoterically. Ivy-leaved Bellflower (*Wahlenbergia hederacea*) and Maidenhair Fern (*Adiantium capillaris-veneris*), also highly characteristic, are now treasured rarities, while the Pale Heath Violet (*Viola lactea*) is feared extinct.

In almost every instance where recent, closer study has revealed that a long-familiar British species has an over-looked near-twin with a preponderantly western distribution, it is the latter which has proved to be the prevailing, if not the only one in Man. Thus the Polypody is *Polypodium interjectum* in the main, among the rushes *Juncus kochii* almost wholly replaces *J. bulbosus*, the only Ivy looks like being *Hedera hibernica*, the only Harebell *Campanula giesekiana*. And below the specific level the same pattern is reproduced: the False Oat (*Arrhenatherum elatius*) is almost wholly the bulbous form, the Water Purslane (*Lythrum portula*) tilts towards the extreme with long outer calyx-teeth.

Yet apart from the freakish occurrence of the Dense-flowered Orchid (*Neotinea maculata*) the flora contains no genuine representative of the so-called 'Lusitanian' element that is such a striking, and controversial, ingredient in that of southern and western Ireland. Though bearing the name *Pinguicula lusitanica*, Pale Butterwort is much more broadly western; and O'Kelly's Spotted Orchid (*Dactylorhiza fuchsii* subsp. *okellyi*), while otherwise Irish almost exclusively, is evidently locally-evolved and unlikely to be on the Continent. At least one Bramble, *Rubus lettii*, is known only in Ireland outside Man, but this clearly falls into a peculiar category. The Island just does not have that extra measure of mildness that permits so many natives of the southern Biscay region to be also quite contentedly Irish. With the one exception again of the Dense-flowered Orchid, all of the western element in Man is unambiguously part of one purely British Isles distributional continuum.

Next most conspicuous of the elements is probably the northern one. Even without inspecting the upland flora, most of which naturally belongs to this, the visitor will receive sharp reminders of the latitude on any average walk. In place of *Rosa canina* and *R. tomentosa* the hedges will be gay with *R. dumalis* and *R. villosa* subsp. *mollis*, in place of *Dactylorhiza praetermissa* the rich purple Orchid of marshy places will be *D. purpurella*, in place of *Carex acutiformis* the big Sedge of watersides will be *C. rostrata*. Shady areas will produce Wood Horsetail (*Equisetum sylvaticum*), bogs Common Butterwort (*Pinguicula vulgaris*), cultivated ground Intermediate Dead-nettle (*Lamium molucellifolium*), bushy places almost everywhere a Bramble with flowers like pink apple blossom, *Rubus errabundus*. Among the rarities, as well, there is a goodly sprinkling of northern species:

Marsh Hawksbeard (*Crepis paludosa*), Bay Willow (*Salix pentandra*), Chestnut Sedge (*Blysmus rufus*), White Sedge (*Carex curta*) and Lesser Clubmoss (*Selaginella selaginoides*) – to mention just a few. The Oyster Plant (*Mertensia maritima*) and Seaside Centaury (*Centaurium littorale*) are teetering on the verge of abandoning such southern shores, while Variegated Horsetail (*Equisetum variegatum*) would appear to have done so already. On the other hand a Bramble otherwise confined to the Clyde Area and the Hebrides, *Rubus hebridensis*, is widespread enough to be described as common.

This last, though, is perhaps more rightly seen as one of a dozen or so species which cannot be assigned neatly to either of the foregoing elements but which constitute a linking group between the two. These include Bog Myrtle (*Myrica gale*), Burnet Rose (*Rosa pimpinellifolia*), Heath Pearlwort (*Sagina subulata*) and the Island's principal Water Milfoil, *Myriophyllum alterniflorum*.

In the same way there are numerous species that cannot fairly be categorised as either truly eastern or truly southern. Indeed, so extensive is this merging that it is feasible only to talk in terms of an overall south/east element: the 'Germanic' Type, in the terminology introduced by H. C. Watson. Several of these species, as one might guess, are very close here to the northern limit of their British Isles range – notably Small-flowered Buttercup (*Ranunculus parviflorus*), Fenugreek (*Trifolium ornithopodioides*), one of the Water Starworts (*Callitriche obtusangula*), Golden Dock (*Rumex maritimus*), Calamint (*Calamintha sylvatica* subsp. *ascendens*) and Autumn Lady's Tresses (*Spiranthes spiralis*). Oddly, though, the only plants for which Man is well to the north of the rest of their range are both strongly western species: Pale Flax (*Linum bienne*) and the Pale Heath Violet (*Viola lactea*). This is a useful reminder that failure to penetrate this far north can be for quite different reasons: low summer temperatures, high rainfall, inadequate sunlight – or any combination of these or other, subtler factors. In Ireland quite a number of species which also occur in Man are more or less confined to its south-eastern corner, unexpectedly; one or two of these are strongly 'Atlantic', the majority 'Germanic'.

The 'Germanic' element in Man is a particularly large one, most species characteristic of the sandy areas of the far north and south of the Island (which coincidentally enjoy both the highest temperatures and the lowest rainfall) being referable to this. Many of the weed species also belong here. Other sample members not so far mentioned are the Bee Orchid (*Ophrys apifera*), Pyramidal Orchid (*Anacamptis pyramidalis*), Great Broomrape (*Orobanche rapum-genistae*), Pink Water Speedwell (*Veronica catenata*), Narrow Water Plantain (*Alisma lanceolatum*), Lesser Hawkbit (*Leontodon taraxacoides*), Common Dodder (*Cuscuta epithymum*), Great Pond Sedge (*Carex riparia*) and Reflexed Meadow-grass (*Puccinellia distans*). Sea Wormwood (*Artemisia maritima*) nicely contrasts with the Oyster Plant as a seashore species that is withdrawing southwards. The Grey Sallow (*Salix cinerea* subsp. *cinerea*), the 'Germanic' counterpart of the Common Sallow (subsp. *oleifolia*), also merits notice for being otherwise almost confined in the British Isles to the Fenland of East Anglia.

These three elements are not the only ones that can be distinguished once recourse is had to the groups with numerous microspecies, the far more restricted ranges of so many of which afford opportunities of finding links between Man and far more narrowly delimited areas. Two Brambles, for instance, *Rubus bartonii* and *R. lentiginosus*, are otherwise wholly or mainly confined to North Wales. Another, *R. cumbrensis*, is so far known only around the north-east corner of the Irish Sea. Such valuably finer discrimination more than justifies the exceptional effort the mastering of these difficult genera demands.

HABITATS

The plant ecology of Man has yet to be adequately studied. Despite its poverty in habitats the Island has plant communities of a variety and complexity sufficient to require the attention of specialists for many years. In the meantime a privately-circulated survey by the Institute of Terrestrial Ecology (Perkins and Buse 1974) provides a useful, if inevitably cursory overview, including some species lists. More specialised studies have appeared on The Ayres and other coastal habitats in the north (Hartley & Wheldon 1914b, Moore 1931, Garrad 1972c), the Ballaugh Curraghs (Wheldon 1909-10), the maritime heaths around Port Erin (Russell 1967) and the upland and lowland acidic wetlands (Osvald 1949).

It is possible in these pages to do no more than indicate the extent to which various habitats are represented and some of their salient features, while also pointing out certain communities of particular interest which seem to merit closer study.

THE COAST

1. *Dunes, sand-cliffs and sandy shores.* The west coast from south of Kirk Michael north to the Point of Ayre and round to Ramsey is sandy in varying degrees. The greater part consists of sand-cliffs ('brooghs'), the rest, from Sartfield to just south of the Point of Ayre, of fixed dunes. Till early this century there were also fixed dunes on the north side of Ramsey harbour, including slacks which seem to have been of importance floristically; most, however, were obliterated by the making of the Mooragh Park. Another set of low dunes on Douglas foreshore was similarly destroyed by the building of the promenade and the expansion of the town seawards. Blown sand reappears just east of Castletown, where golf links have been created out of consolidated dunes, and as a tiny patch further along the south coast by Kentraugh.

On the whole both surviving dune systems are floristically most disappointing. The damp hollows on the Castletown one just manage *Gentianella campestris* and the others, along the Ayres, are mostly little better. Contrary to the assertion of Hartley & Wheldon, however, the latter do produce a few approaches to genuine slacks seawards of Ballaghennie and Ballakinnag as well as near Sartfield; apart from *Salix repens* their main 'indicator' is *Carex serotina*. There is reason to believe that the flora of both the dunes themselves and of the damp hollows has been growing markedly richer in recent years. Seven of the rarer Orchid species are now known, for example, whereas *Anacamptis pyramidalis* was the only one to be reported up to 1923 – when it was a first record for Man. In part the increase in records may merely reflect a previous failure to appreciate the Ayres' potential, in part the myxomatosis epidemic must have been responsible; but as even the *Salix repens* is spreading, some wider factor must be involved as well.

On sandy fore-shores *Mertensia maritima* is the prize rarity. *Orobanche minor* on *Eryngium maritimum* by Ramsey Mooragh is also noteworthy.

2. *Rocky shores and sea-cliffs.* These take over from the sandy coast at Ramsey and continue almost uninterruptedly right round to just north of Peel. Along the south coast from Port St. Mary eastwards cliffs give way to low rocks – but without losing *Crithmum maritimum.* The flora is fairly uniform and limited, among regular species *Spergularia rupicola* and *Eupatorium cannabinum* being more especially Manx. *Polypodium interjectum* and *Osmunda regalis* in a few places add their fronds to those of the widespread *Asplenium marinum*, while the cave-dwelling *Adiantum capillus-veneris* also occurs along one short stretch. *Limonium binervosum* has its sole Manx station on high cliffs near Port St. Mary.

Wet crevices and brackish rock-pools, filled by spray and rain-water but not normally washed by the tide, support a more interesting community, rich in sedges and rushes. This includes *Samolus valerandi*, *Triglochin maritima*, *Spergularia salina*, *Puccinellia maritima*, *Glaux maritima*, *Limonium vulgare* (in two places), *Juncus maritimus*, *J. gerardii*, *J. bufonius*, *Schoenus nigricans*, *Eleocharis multicaulis*, *Scirpus maritimus*, *S. cernuus*, *Carex otrubae*, *C. distans*, *C. extensa*, *C. demissa* and *C. punctata*. *Potamogeton pectinatus* shares the pools at Scarlett with *Chara aspera*. Most of these are more usually typical of salt marsh, for the lack of which in Man this habitat to some extent makes up.

3. *Shingle beaches.* Mostly only the small fringing type occurs, but its flora is comparatively rich. In addition to the usual species *Glaucium flavum* and, rarely, *Hyoscyamus niger* are characteristically Manx. Gravel workings at West Kimmeragh, Bride, more than a mile inland, have produced a semblance to shingle beach on which the otherwise wholly coastal *Glaucium flavum* has become established. At Port Cornaa *Umbilicus rupestris*, *Valeriana officinalis*, *Veronica officinalis* and *Stachys palustris* constitute unusual additions. Another interesting stretch occurs south of the Point of Ayre lighthouse, holding *Filago* species, *Ornithopus perpusillus* and the very rare *Gnaphalium sylvaticum*.

4. *Salt marshes.* The very few salt marshes are all small, the largest being along the estuary of the Sulby River at Ramsey. One formerly round the Dubbyr Mooar at the mouth of the Ballaugh River was swept away by storms; *Trifolium fragiferum* and unknown species of *Limonium* and *Salicornia* are on record from it. All the rest are in the south: at Port Erin, Poyllvaaish, Knock Rushen, Castletown inner harbour, west Langness and Derbyhaven. The flora is as rich as can be expected, but may be

expanding – if the recent resurgence of *Halimione portulacoides* and *Limonium vulgare* represents anything more than the usual floristic fluctuation to which tide-dispersed communities are subject. The belated arrival, in the early 1970s, of *Spartina anglica*, that superlative mud-binder, could make for dramatic changes should it become well-established.

5. *Maritime sward.* A short grassland community occurs round most of the coast, occupying the normally very narrow, outermost margin of closed vegetation, where the high exposure inhibits the development of heath. This shares many constituents with ordinary Bent-Fescue grassland but on the whole is quite distinct. *Festuca rubra* is the dominant species and *Plantago coronopus* next most abundant. *Bellis perennis* is a regular, apparently indigenous member, as too is *Plantago lanceolata* – which suggests that Quaternary researchers need to be more cautious about interpreting its pollen as an indicator of human activity. *Euphrasia confusa* and *E. tetraquetra* (often crossing), *Scilla verna*, *Thymus praecox*, *Catapodium marinum*, *Koeleria macrantha* and *Carex caryophyllea* are among the many other characteristic species.

6. *Maritime heath.* Abutting on the maritime sward is a zone of heathland of varying extent and composition, mostly heavily grazed and frequently burnt. Round most of the coast this consists of a mixed community in which *Ulex gallii*, *Erica cinerea* and *Calluna vulgaris* are co-dominant. Attempts have been made to discriminate sub-categories reflecting the local dominance of one of these over the other two, but it is doubtful whether this is practicable. On the Ayres, uniquely in the Island, the heath is rich in lichens, which in one area towards the eastern end take over dominance and justify the distinguishing of lichen heath as a community of its own.

LOWLAND GRASSLAND

Covering the greatest area of the Island, this falls broadly into two categories: wild, and improved or cultivated. The first consists of rough grazing, wet grazing, bracken, and tall shrub; the second of improved grazing, arable and hay. Apart from the wet grazing (much of which borders curraghs) and some of the arable they are on the whole of slight interest floristically. Hay meadows are very largely confined to the north, where through the beneficial proximity of the curraghs they harbour a few noteworthy species, in particular *Parentucellia viscosa*. Some of the improved grazing may be worth more careful study than it has appeared to deserve: one dampish field below the Glen Mona Hotel was found to have the strange make-up of *Leontodon taraxacoides* in abundance, *Centaurium erythraea*, *Euphrasia nemorosa*, a slender form of *Potentilla anglica* and *Trifolium repens*.

A stretch of grassland of outstanding interest, however, is that which clothes a tract of sandy country seaward of Ballaugh, around Ballacooiley and Broughjairg Beg. This was apparently once a line of fixed dunes, but presumably because of heavy grazing (mainly by rabbits) heathland has not developed and the area resembles instead the Breckland of East Anglia. Bracken is as yet confined to its fringes but ominously advancing. The community is rich in small annuals and supports the main Manx populations of *Rumex tenuifolius* (common), *Viola tricolor* subsp. *tricolor* (frequent) and *Hypochoeris glabra* as well as the sole ones of *Teesdalia nudicaulis*. The dominant grass is *Anthoxanthum odoratum*, with *Deschampsia flexuosa*, *Aira praecox* and *Holcus mollis* not much less abundant.

The small area of basic grassland overlying the lime quarries west of Ballasalla and their vicinity still awaits study.

LOWLAND HEATH

In the absence now of natural woodland gorse heath would be the terminal covering of all the drier parts of the lowlands, were it not kept in check by grazing and burning. Both Gorse species, the introduced *Ulex europaeus* as well as the native *U. gallii*, play the major part in this together with *Erica cinerea* and *Calluna* variously as co-dominants. Other common participants are *Teucrium scorodonia*, *Potentilla erecta*, *Hypericum pulchrum* and *Galium hercynicum*. In one small area in Lonan, between Grawe farm and the church, a remarkable *Calluna* lowland heath has survived, outstanding for its abundance of the very distinctive Bramble, *Rubus sprengelii*, here in virtually its only Manx locality.

BRACKEN

As elsewhere, Bracken is spreading (despite considerable expenditure on control attempts) and now covers as much as 4% of the Island's land surface. It is especially concentrated on the slopes of the foothills and the west coast. Supposedly all-smothering, it has lately been found affording necessary shelter for an abundance of *Platanthera chlorantha* on a hillside at Rhenass.

WETLANDS

1. *Pools and reservoirs.* The Island no longer possesses what can properly be described as natural lakes. A large portion of the northern curraghs was evidently at one time a single expanse of open water, a grant of one-half of the fishery of it having been made as late as 1505. 'Ellan' in curragh place-names today indicates the islands of higher ground that stood out of this. Gradually, helped by drainage, the curragh vegetation has encroached and prevailed, until today the best that the northern plain can boast are three or four lakelets. Lough Cranstal, which formerly covered a large area near the Point of Ayre, is now a dense reedswamp (holding, uniquely in Man, *Carex riparia*, in great plenty).

All over the north there is a generous scatter of pools (or 'dubs') of various sizes. Some are shrunken remnants of the old natural lakes (many of them 'kettle holes'), some probably stand as they were aboriginally, others are the flooded relics of the excavating of the local *Chara* 'marl' for use as a fertiliser or clay for brickmaking, still others are minor duck- and goose-ponds which may have been purposely dug as water supplies for stock or for the retting of flax. The different types have markedly different floras and part of their fascination is the difficulty of predicting which new one will prove to be which. All but some of the smallest must have been investigated in the past thirty years and a rich harvest has resulted, including several species not known hitherto as Manx. *Apium inundatum*, unrecorded before 1919, yet now in most, has apparently undergone a great recent spread; but *Scirpus fluitans* and *Veronica scutellata* have also been found far more widely than previous records suggested. It may be that a run of dry seasons led to the abnormal exposure of mud, with much greater chances of dispersal by moorhens and other birds in consequence.

Everywhere else natural pools of any kind are extremely scarce. Two near Ballacross, outside Peel, are isolated recurrences of one of the common types in the north and have a comparable flora accordingly. The only others of significance are all flooded quarries or clay-pits: by Peel power station, brackish ones at Scarlett and near the Point of Ayre, the rest near Ballasalla; another till recently at Gansey, which held *Myriophyllum verticillatum*, has unfortunately been filled in.

Making up for this lack to some extent, and for the virtual absence of upland tarns, the rest of the Island has several sizeable reservoirs. In all of these the water is acid. One of the oldest, north of Onchan, dating from 1875, has acquired *Rorippa sylvestris*. Baldwin (or Injebreck) Reservoir, very much larger, was built only in 1900-5 and has yet to attract much interest; its chief speciality is a profusion of *Littorella uniflora*. The big new Sulby Dam, opened in 1983, may one day rival it.

2. *Ditches.* The drainage of the larger curraghs has led to the creation of several botanically rich watercourses. The longest, the Lhen Trench, had a mill-dam at its mouth till 1922 which held plants of interest. Regular cleaning out has rendered them a peculiarly unstable habitat and this has provided a vacant niche in which two sterile hybrids have flourished: that between the two *Alismas* in the north and that between the two Water *Veronicas* west of Castletown. The trenches at the latter drain an alluvial flood-plain occupied by a lakelet in the seventeenth century which is now the marshland of Great Meadow. In the north, within the area of the curraghs themselves, the local conditions render the drains more acid, sufficient to yield *Utricularia* species.

3. *Rivers and streams.* All the Manx rivers are too fast-flowing to allow of much weed. Water *Ranunculi* grow in only one, the Colby River, and that at its mouth. The sides and banks are on the whole equally

disappointing floristically. River shingle is often exposed and colonised by a distinctive vegetation, in which the alien *Polygonum cuspidatum* is widely prominent.

4. *Marshes.* The prevailing acid conditions greatly restrict the areas capable of supporting these. They are best developed around Peel and along the alluvial flood-plain between Castletown and Colby (where *Carex disticha* is characteristic and has its Manx headquarters). *Iris pseudacorus* is usually prominent, *Equisetum palustre* and *Carex hirta* sometimes abundant, and *Dactylorhiza fuchsii*, *Myosotis discolor* and *Glyceria plicata* among the more interesting associates. A different, smaller type of marsh, with its own special community, occurs round the flushes and trickles which the rock- and sand-cliffs extensively harbour. A further community has been noted in one or two spots in the far south: in this *Cerastium glomeratum* tends to be abundant and *Glyceria declinata*, *Plantago major*, *Gnaphalium uliginosum*, *Stellaria alsine*, *Myosotis laxa* subsp. *caespitosa* and *Veronica serpyllifolia* are among its companions.

5. *Curraghs.* A Manx word meaning boggy ground in general, this has usefully come to be applied to a particular ecological formation highly characteristic of the Island (and responsible for much of its best botanising). True fen cannot develop here in the absence of sufficiently non-acid ground-water, and its place in the vegetational sequence characterising the gradual filling-in of lakes is accordingly taken by a complex of swamp and bog communities with willow carr as their centrepiece.

The main mass of curraghs occurs along the south edge of the northern plain, especially in its western portion. A second large strip gives character to the Central Valley. The flora is too extensive to be cited even in outline: the reader is referred to Wheldon (1909-10) for the most complete list. *Myrica gale* is the most typical indicator species.

6. *Gareys.* Another useful Manx word which has come to denote wet, rushy areas with willow scrub but dry enough to be grazed and so prevented from developing into curraghs. They range from small patches to very extensive areas. Mapping of their distribution by Garrad (1972b, 141) has revealed that they are noticeably commoner along the southern end of the hills, reflecting less steep slopes there. *Carum verticillatum*, characteristic of the northern curraghs, recurs abundantly in some of these.

7. *Calcareous mires.* In the areas bordering on the Lhen Trench the ground-water is somewhat alkaline, perhaps through the influence of the Late-glacial deposits of *Chara* 'marl' once dug for thereabouts. This has permitted the development of one or two approaches towards fen, notably by The Guilcagh, at Loughcroute and near Ballaghaie. Overlooked till very recently, these swampy patches are peculiar in Man in possessing *Carex diandra* (in abundance), *C. dioica*, *C. serotina* subsp. *serotina*, *Sagina*

nodosa and *Selaginella selaginoides*. *Dactylorhiza incarnata* subsp. *incarnata* and *Schoenus nigricans* are also characteristic.

8. *Bogs*. In the lowlands valley-bogs are the prevailing form of acidic wetland, occurring wherever there are wet depressions in heathland or rough grazings or where streams flush. Some are quite extensive: by Staarvey (282845), south of Baldrine (423805) and at Clay Head, for instance. Several of the typical 'Atlantic' species such as *Ranunculus lenormandi*, *Anagallis tenella*, *Pinguicula lusitanica* and *Juncus foliosus* are characteristic of the community, which in exceptionally wet conditions can extend to *Myosotis secunda*, *Potentilla palustris* and even *Menyanthes*.

WOODLAND

The natural climax vegetation of the Manx lowlands is Sessile Oak-wood. Apart from relic scrub on the east coast cliffs and one or two other putative fragments this survives now only in 'ghost' form, as the ground flora of the planted-up glens. This is as poor in species as it must always have been, especially in the high-rainfall districts. At the north end of the hills, at the mouths of Sulby Glen and Narradale, *Veronica montana* and *Moehringia trinervia* betray an area of more amenable conditions – just as *Bromus ramosus* appears in the south at the mouths of Glen Maye and Silverdale. Populations here and there of the indigenous, northern race of *Anthriscus sylvestris* are probably relics of birchwood, while seemingly relic Oak-Hazel woods occur in lower Glen Maye and upper Glen Auldyn.

Broad-leaved plantations are numerous and have been the cause of the introduction of 'wild garden' species in the past. These include *Carex pendula*, *C. sylvatica* and *Poa nemoralis*. The conifer plantations which now cover about 3% of the Island appear to be devoid of interest floristically.

THE UPLANDS

1. *Upland grassland*. 2. *Upland heath*. Rough grazing, much of it dominated by *Nardus stricta*, covers almost exactly half the uplands but except beneath South Barrule seems of negligible interest. *Calluna* heath, which there comes into its own, accounts for much of the rest. With this are considerable stands of *Vaccinium myrtillus* and, very locally, of *Empetrum nigrum* and *Luzula sylvatica*; other species, however, are extremely few. *Erica tetralix* is noticeably more widespread on the southern hills, adding to the impression that these have a history of much less intensive grazing.

3. *Blanket-bog*. Compared with Ireland, this plays a rather minor role. The peat of the Manx blanket-bog appears to be uniformly very shallow and a monotous Scirpetum caespitosi is the dominant community. *Eriophorum vaginatum* forms stands in places.

4. *Montane vegetation*. The virtual absence of exposed rock at high levels means that this is almost wholly lacking. What little does exist is thanks

entirely to the altitude. *Salix herbacea* and *Deschampsia flexuosa* subsp. *montana* are in some quantity on Snaefell, while North and South Barrule have *Vaccinium vitis-idaea*. *Festuca vivipara* (in the 1770s), *Viola lutea* and *Antennaria dioica* were once known as well, but have presumably been eliminated by grazing. Another long-lost species is *Saxifraga aizoides*. *Cryptogramma crispa* is very scarce high up but occurs profusely on substitute screes in South Barrule slate quarries.

MAN-MADE HABITATS

1. *Hedgebanks.* Hedgerows of the English type are mostly confined to the populated areas. Elsewhere, as in Galloway and most of Ireland, the hedges are sod banks, surmounted with *Ulex europaeus* or Hawthorn – a topping which sometimes becomes thin and ragged. These have a rich flora, reproducing many of the herbs of the lowland heath and supporting always at least three or four species of Bramble.
2. *Walls and roofs.* The Manx stone walls (and roofs too) are often capped with a layer of vegetation, but except near the sea this seldom holds unusual species. The older, dry-stone walls, now scarce, are the haunt of *Polypodium vulgare*: the mortared walls, by contrast, hold *P. interjectum* in often great profusion. The introduction of lime-mortar provided a habitat for the much rarer and more calcicole *P. australe* too, as well as for *Poa compressa* and *Asplenium* species. *Sempervivum tectorum*, once widely planted on roofs for superstitious reasons, is still to be found on one or two old cottages or adjacent old stonework.
3. *Roadsides.* Extensive stone-walling means that roadside verges are precluded in many parts; the sod-hedges are not conducive to verge development either. But in some areas of the north, in Andreas and Jurby, very wide verges exist and house interesting species (e.g. *Orobanche minor* and *Genista tinctoria*). Visitors may be struck by the great scarcity or absence of such common English plants as *Anthriscus sylvestris*, *Alliaria petiolata* and *Lamium album*.
4. *Paths and tracks.* These support a distinctive community, of which the jewel is the gradually-spreading American invader, *Juncus tenuis*. An earlier-arrived alien, *Matricaria matricarioides*, is now almost ubiquitous on such ground.
5. *Railways.* 47 miles of railway track were laid between 1872 and 1883, slate chippings (and not clinker ash, as in Britain) being used as the foundation. At least in recent years little or no attempt has been made to keep this weed-free and many species characteristic of dry, open ground were attracted to this new habitat in considerable profusion. *Knautia arvensis* and *Linaria vulgaris* even owed an extensive diffusion to it. Not until 1960, however, was this flora examined more than cursorily and it was then realised that it included certain rarities partly or wholly exclusive in Man to this habitat (Allen 1962b). *Kickxia elatine*, a cornfield weed

elsewhere in the British Isles, was found established for considerable distances along four widely-separated stretches; *Filago minima*, *Euphorbia exigua* and *Spergularia rubra* each turned up too in several places. The branch line to Foxdale was further distinctive in having an abundance of the normally coastal *Plantago maritima*. Appropriately, in view of its endearing peculiarity generally, the Manx railway entirely lacked the common counterpart in Britain of *K. elatine*, the closely-related *Chaenorhinum minus* (although, ironically, this made a fleeting Wartime appearance on the line at Peel Road Station). Sadly, all except the stretch from Douglas to Port Erin became defunct during the 1960s, the lines were removed and the track became overgrown or converted to footpaths.

The electric tramway linking Douglas and Ramsey, which was built to supplement the railway network and opened in 1899, has always been kept clean of weeds in contrast. Its only notable contribution botanically has been the very local adventive, *Hieracium vagum*, which abounds round Laxey on its banks.

6. *Gardens and parks*. These afford three separate habitats: lawns, in which *Veronica filiformis* is a new and especial pest; shrubberies, with *Circaea lutetiana* and *Lapsana communis* as the most characteristic species; and flower-beds, a haunt of *Veronica agrestis* much more often than arable fields. The arable flora in Man is not a rich one to recruit from, but this is increasingly made up for by the flow of additional species accidentally brought from 'Across' in soil round the roots of nursery plants. *Datura stramonium*, *Scutellaria galericulata* (only known as a garden weed, in Onchan), *Ranunculus ficaria* subsp. *bulbifer*, *Galinsoga ciliata*, *Mercurialis annua* and *Conyza canadensis* have apparently all arrived through this means.

7. *Refuse tips*. Recent years have brought an immense increase in municipally-handled refuse, with the consequent need for larger tips, and the widespread post-war use of commercial bird-seed mixtures considerably extended the floristic potential of these. Those at Douglas and Ramsey were particularly productive of records from 1960; but sadly, like most of the railway, they are now no longer.

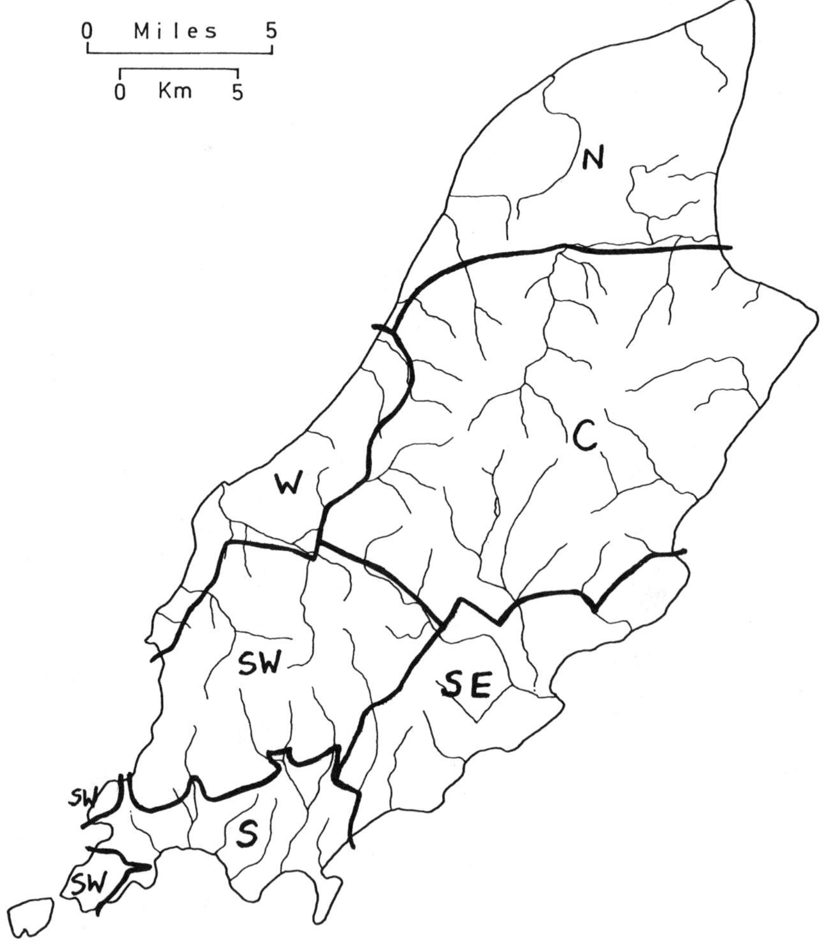

FIG. 6. The districts

THE DISTRICTS

It has been traditional for writers of county Floras to divide up their area into a number of districts, normally based on river-basins, in order to give long strings of localities cited under many species some geographical grouping and so enable the broad pattern of distribution to be made out at a glance. For an area so small as Man such a procedure is perhaps superfluously elaborate; nevertheless by providing each record with a context in which it can be placed it clearly has much merit. Man, moreover, offers the unusual opportunity of giving the districts more significance by aligning them with natural eco-geographical sub-divisions.

The six districts which have been adopted are shown in Fig. 6. Their respective boundaries are:–

N The area lying north of the Ramsey–Kirkmichael road (A3) as far as Ramsey pier in the east and the next stream north of Glen Wyllin on the west. It thereby corresponds more or less exactly with the start of the sand and the end of the hills.

W The area of lowish rainfall and, in part, sandy soils bounded by the Kirkmichael–St. John's–Dalby road. The boundary skirts St. John's to the east, running from Ballacraine to the junction to the south, thence north and then west along the A30 to meet the Peel road by Knockaloe; then it turns south down the A27 as far as Dalby, but instead of concluding with the Niarbyl lane (which would cause ambiguity for the Niarbyl records) it branches off down the Eary Cushlin track as far as Barrane and thence parallel to the Niarbyl lane to the sea.

SW The area of the Southern Hills, bounded on the north by the St. John's–Dalby line just described, on the south by the 250-foot contour (and so taking in Bradda Hill, the Mull Peninsula and the Calf as well), on the east from the point where that contour meets the road north of Blackhill, Malew, up through St. Mark's along the A26 to Glen Vine and thence back to Ballacraine.

S The area of Rushen below the 250-foot contour – until that cuts the road by Orrisdale, Malew. From there it continues down on to the A5, thence briefly east to the Santon Burn and so to the sea.

SE Douglas and its southerly hinterland: a zone intermediate between the extreme dryness of the far south and the much more moist area to the north. The northern boundary runs from Glen Vine north-east to the A23, along that as far as the crossroads below Abbeylands, thence east along the minor road to Hillberry. There it takes up the

Ballacottier lane round to its intersection with Molly Quirk's Glen, whence it follows the stream to the A2. It continues north along the A2 as far as the double bend beyond Baldrine and thence down the lane to Garwick Bay.

C The remaining area consisting of the Northern Hills and the narrow, especially moist lowland strip to their east.

The visitor with little time will find that **N**, **S** and the lowland part of **C** together house the majority of the Island's species.

THE DISCOVERERS OF THE FLORA

The Isle of Man, considering its isolation, first features in the literature of British botany remarkably early. Indeed, apart from those English counties lucky enough to have been visited by William Turner in the mid-sixteenth century, it compares well with anywhere in the British Isles in the antiquity of its original records.

As elsewhere, these are of Tudor date. They are only two and both are unlocalised, yet their existence shows that, even at that period, Man formed part of a wider scientific world. This it owed, almost certainly, to its status as a 'dependency' of Lancashire – by virtue of being a personal appanage of the Earls of Derby. Thomas Cogan, whose long-selling handbook of hygiene for students, *The Haven of Health* (1584), mentions Samphire as ". . . very plentiful about the Ile of Man, from whence it is brought to divers parts of England, preserved in Brine", was, significantly, a Manchester headmaster and physician. A Lancastrian, too, was the possible author of the next record: Thomas Hesketh (1561–1613), a physician and surgeon of Clitheroe. In his celebrated *Herball, or Generall Historie of Plants* (1597) John Gerard figures two forms of Plantain reputed to be ". . . strangers in England, notwithstanding I have heard say they growe upon the rocks in Scylla, Garnsey, and the Isle of Man." Such an observation, unlike Cogan's, implies a visit to the Island by someone with botanical knowledge. Gerard himself was a Londoner from his teens and relied largely on Hesketh for his North of England information. While there is no evidence that Hesketh's fieldwork ranged as far as Man, it is suggestive that his sister-in-law was one of the Stanleys, the Island's then-resident owners.

After that all was obscurity again for more than sixty years. Then, in July, 1660, Man at last emerged, unambiguously, into the scientific light. On one of their mounted forays through Britain, which first revealed the main broad outlines of its natural history, the Cambridge divine, John Ray (1627–1705), and his young patron, Francis Willoughby (1635–1672), found the lure of this unexplored island irresistible. They are believed to have crossed from Ravenglass to Ramsey, where, promptly upon landing, they were greeted by a yellow flower quite new to them. To this Ray gave the name *Eruca monensis* and as the Isle of Man Cabbage it has been known ever since. It was doubtless in the cornfields thereabouts that they also noted Pennycress, perhaps on account of its unusual plenty. The specimen that Willoughby took of this miraculously still survives: facing p. 831 in the third volume of his collection, now in Nottingham University Library, one of the all-too-few gatherings he took the trouble to localise. Also in the corn was a noteworthy grass, '*Festuca altera*', almost certainly the Black Oat, a weed they are unlikely to have become familiar with in England. On their visit to the Calf (attested by Willoughby's later description of its "Puffins") they probably saw the Royal Fern on the rocks, a habitat in which Ray reported it as growing "very plentifully . . . about the Isle of Man." Here too, perhaps, they found another of the novelties of their trip, the Sea Storksbill. Strangely, they missed many other of the Island's specialities. This suggests that the visit was brief, hurried and even unplanned.

So disappointing a haul can scarcely have encouraged others to brave the rigours of the crossing. True, Thomas Lawson, a Quaker schoolmaster in Lakeland, wrote to Ray on 9 April 1688 that he intended going over "at Pentecost" to observe the Cabbage; but there is no evidence that he ever realised that intention. Indeed, the only other botanist definitely known to have reached the Island in that early period arrived there accidentally, when storms forced his ship to put in at Ramsey, in September 1702. This was Gedeon Bonnivert, a lieutenant in the army of William of Orange and a veteran of the Battle of the Boyne. Alas, he had time only to note in his journal (now in the British Library) that Wall Pennywort grew "on all the walls of the houses between every stone", before his ship put out again.

As long as botanists were themselves everywhere great rarities, the chances of somewhere so out-of-the-way receiving their attention continued to be slight. Equally, so small and isolated a community stood little chance of giving rise to botanists of its own. Even as late as 1770 the Vicar-General was forced to admit: "I cannot learn that we have any person in the Island who applies himself to the study of the Natural History thereof, or that has made any material collection."

As these words were being penned, however, the subject was bursting into fashion. The taste for the Picturesque had brought the cultivated classes out on tours and led them to perceive the attractions of the countryside more closely. Furthermore, the great simplification that botany underwent at the hands of Linnaeus was sufficient to convert many of these cultivated travellers into plant-hunters.

The leading pioneer of this opening-up of the wilds was a member of the North Wales gentry, Thomas Pennant, perhaps best remembered today as the man to whom Gilbert White wrote many of the letters that make up *The Natural History of Selborne*. A relentless traveller, Pennant's fact-finding tours of the lesser-known regions of the kingdom aimed to fill in the details where Ray and Willoughby had been able merely to indicate the outlines. At home with zoology and antiquities, he was nevertheless no botanist and for the accounts of the plants of the areas he surveyed he necessarily relied on friends.

Thus when, in 1774, he decided that it was the Isle of Man's turn, an

Anglesey minister, the Rev. Hugh Davies (1739–1821), was invited to accompany him in this capacity. This was a sound choice, for Davies later proved himself a conscientious and accurate observer. Certainly, he worked hard during the week in mid-August that they were over (receiving as his reward the elusive Lesser Twayblade near Snaefell), for Pennant sent him back again on his own the following June in order to finish off. "By his labours," Pennant was to recall in his autobiography, "a Flora of the island is rendered as complete as possible to be effected by a single person, at one season of the year. The number of plants he observed amounted to above five hundred and fifty."

Tragically, almost all record of those labours has been lost. The list would presumably have appeared as an appendix to Pennant's intended book and it may have been among the mass of notes accumulated for this that Pennant later confessed he had "unaccountably" mislaid. All that have come down to us are three records included in Turner & Dillwyn's *Botanist's Guide through England and Wales* (1805) – maybe the only ones that Davies could by then recollect – a sheet and a half of sketchy jottings on the natural history as a whole (now among the Pennant papers in Warwickshire County Record Office) and a handwritten note by Lightfoot in MS Sherard 456, now in the Botany School, Oxford, subsequently published in *Flora Scotica* (1777), that Davies had found Whorled Caraway "abundantly" in the Island. A specimen of this last, undated and localised no further than "Mann", is now in the British Museum, seemingly the solitary memento kept by Davies of his visits.

The period from which most English counties are able to trace a continuous history of recording, with all the advantages that this brings, is thus for Man virtually a blank; and over the next fifty years, what is more, this virtual blank persisted. In 1809 a Cork physician, Thomas Wood (c. 1775–1857), is known to have come over and procured the Maidenhair Fern for his herbarium. Sometime between 1811 and 1818 Dr John Macculloch (1773–1835), the pioneer of British mineralogy, made the visit that enabled him to state in his classic *Description of the Western Islands of Scotland including the Isle of Man* (Vol. 2, 1819, p. 521) that "except for *Lycopodium alpinum* and *selaginoides* the elevated region produces no Alpine plants"; but, to judge from a list he made for Guernsey, his botany was not to be relied on. The same cannot be said of another primarily geological visitor, the Rev. John Stevens Henslow (1796–1861), who came over with a party of his students from Cambridge in the 1819 long vacation; but his opportunities for botanising were only incidental and all he seems to have managed to snatch were a pondweed at Laxey Mines and an Eyebright on Granite Mountain.

In that same summer the first scheduled steamer service came in. The next year there were two boats weekly and the greater flow of visitors that this encouraged eventually allowed the service to become daily (in 1831).

But even then the Liverpool crossing took usually at a minimum eight hours: it was still an ordeal for the faint-hearted and no light undertaking even for the determined.

Those who came, therefore, were at first mainly the young and the venturesome. And this is reflected in the ages of those who left records from these years. For example, William Wilson (1799–1871), later a bryologist of international renown, came from Warrington when an articled clerk of twenty-three. Thomas Jowett (1801–1832), a Nottingham surgeon, came when twenty-six. The few specimens these brought back, now at Cambridge and Kew respectively, are just what one would expect a holidaying botanist to have gathered: the characteristic Western plants unfamiliar to the English – but, alas, mostly too widespread for their records to be of interest – and more particularly those that were small enough to be slipped between the pages of a book, without incurring the stares or grins of bystanders and without requiring the humping of equipment. The places where they were taken from were never noted, either, confirming that they were collected 'blind'.

This heedlessness of the local geography so eternally characteristic of the first-time visitor was also displayed by another young man, James McNab (1810–1878), an Edinburgh gardener, who came in August 1830 and again in 1832 and proved more assiduous than most. The sizeable list that he made, which H. C. Watson had the use of for his *Outlines of the Geographical Distribution of British Plants*, includes several records of great interest, two of them, Yellow Mountain Saxifrage and Sea Wormwood, backed up by specimens in his herbarium, now at Dublin. Yet not even the latter are localised any less vaguely than 'Isle of Man', which robs them of most of their value.

Yet perhaps it was not altogether unfortunate that the efforts of this long series of visitors had repeatedly come almost to nothing. For had any extensive account of the Island's plants found its way into print, the necessary challenge would have been lacking to the man that the Island itself now at last called forth to try to make good the deficiency. This was Edward Forbes (1815–1854), famous in later years as one of the founding figures of marine biology and eventually, if all too briefly, Professor of Natural History at Edinburgh. One of nine children of a merchant and banker in Douglas, Forbes had the luck to be exiled by a sickly childhood to the countryside round his grandmother's home in Ballaugh. There he was encouraged in an early-displayed bent for natural history, of which a small, neat album of pressed flowers now in the British Museum survives as witness. His serious botanising he himself dated from May 1831, just after leaving school, with further work in the late summers of 1832 and 1834, while on vacation as a medical student from Edinburgh. The outcome was a respectable list of 348 species which he was able to pass to H. C. Watson for publication in his *New Botanist's Guide*. This was sophisticated in indicating for each species not only its frequency but also the geological formations on which it had been observed; but, frustratingly, again it was a list without localities. These Forbes was clearly reserving for the more thoroughgoing Flora of the Island which we know (from a letter of his to C. C. Babington in 1840, now at Cambridge) he definitely had in preparation. It was his developing draft for this which he apparently allowed the authors of various guides to draw on for their sections on botany at this period and, luckily, through these the cream of his localised records has substantially leaked down to us. But what became of the Flora draft itself – or, for that matter, his herbarium (which we know he took with him to King's College London in 1843) – is now an irritating mystery. Nevertheless this is one loss that can hardly be considered all that serious: most of what he achieved we probably have in print and it is doubtful if it was ever much more than a Flora of the parish of Ballaugh and the immediate environs of Douglas.

It was not until the 'Fifties that the next major advance occurred – and for the second time this came from within the Island itself. In 1858 Hugh Ashworth Stowell (1830–1886), an all-round naturalist of Manx descent, arrived from Kent to become Chaplain of The Dhoon, Maughold. Though his stay was to prove short, a mere five years, his impact was considerable. Getting down at once to working the Maughold area, he was soon ready with a paper for the *Phytologist* and a list for Thwaites' *Directory*, the two together amounting to the first fresh contribution for thirty years. At the same time he helped to stoke the ardour of two other young residents, both fellow clerics, Theophilus Talbot (c. 1825–1908) and Richard Paget Murray (1842–1908).

The late William Cubbon as a young man knew Talbot well and in 1953, shortly before his death, I had the good fortune to hear recollections of that *pastor pugnax* from his lips. In turn a Wesleyan and Anglican minister, Talbot retired in middle life after a wealthy marriage. A reveller in the power of the pen, he henceforward dedicated his days to ridding the published histories of the Island of their accretions of inaccuracy. Freed from all constraints of deference, he was merciless towards one and all, from the spokesmen of his own church up to the Governor himself. Manx scholarship was very much the gainer as a result.

Talbot's botanical period unfortunately appears to have been fleeting. In August 1865, on the occasion of a visit by the Cambrian Archaeological Association, Professor Babington of Cambridge managed to arouse his intellectual curiosity by demonstrating the microspecies he recognised among the Brambles. This led Talbot to make his own collection of these the following year and that in turn to his forming a more general herbarium. The resulting specimens – perhaps only a part of the whole – are now in the Manx Museum and constitute, incredible to say, the earliest set anywhere reasonably representative of the Island's vascular flora. All date from 1866–7 and despite many erroneous names they provide a useful indication of what then occurred.

Murray, likewise, was lost to Manx botany all too quickly – though in his case not through losing interest. A keen entomologist as well, like Stowell, his work is much the least known of the three. Indeed that we know at all that he was active in these early years we owe to a short note that he sent to the *Journal of Botany* late in life, in 1897. Amongst other things this reveals that the solitary specimen of that extreme Manx rarity, the Oyster Plant, which forms the pride of Talbot's collection, was seen by him as well, on the beach at Poyllvaaish, perhaps in the other's company. Despite his transfer to a series of English livings and authorship of the *Flora of Somerset* he never entirely cut away from his roots (helped no doubt by his relationship to the Dukes of Atholl, the former owners of the Island) and in the early 'Eighties he returned at least twice, attested by specimens gathered then, now in the British Museum.

Around this time there was someone else hard at work whose identity remains a tantalising mystery. In 1858 a shortish list with localities appeared as an appendix to the second edition of Backwell's Isle of Man guide. The records in this are quite different, in character and quality, from any that had been published before and bear the hallmark of considerable field ability. All we are told is that "the list of plants of Professor Forbes has been verified and much enlarged, by a skilful botanist, who may be said to have searched the Island in its every part to learn the particulars of its Flora." While obviously a great exaggeration, these last words point up what is undoubtedly the most remarkable feature: many of the localities cited are very out-of-the-way (the two or more for the rare Golden Dock, for example, could only have been discovered through examining the many northern ponds) and confirm that whoever it was who was responsible had been working at least parts of the Island systematically. Clearly this was no casual holiday collector nor even another Stowell, walking his parish: he could only have been someone actively preparing a Flora.

With the single possible exception of the Rev. Samuel Simpson (1802?–1881), who before coming to Douglas in 1851 as Chaplain of St. Thomas' had been a well-known Lancaster botanist – but who appears to have dropped botany on entering the ministry, on the evidence of the lack of Manx specimens in his herbarium at Oxford – there was no resident at this period capable of fieldwork of such a standard. Presumably therefore the author was a visitor – and a frequent visitor at that, to judge from the wide range of the localities given. That seems to point in turn to someone from Lancashire or Cheshire. And it so happens that there was someone living in that region at that time who was later to reveal that he had been working on a Flora of the Island. This was James Frodsham Robinson (1838–1884), a druggist of Frodsham, who was long active in

Merseyside botany and recorded extensively in North Wales. In 1873 it was reported in the *Journal of Botany* that he had circulated a prospectus for a volume expected to cost not more than half-a-crown; this was to include an introductory section on botanical rambles and "a very interesting botanico-geological map of the island, drawn and coloured by Professor Forbes when quite a youth." Not long afterwards he expanded on these intentions in the magazine *Science Gossip*, disclosing that he had "worked very hard" at the Manx flora "for several years". He expressed the hope that the volume would very shortly be out – but it never did appear.

In Robinson's preparatory work for that it is tempting to see the solution to the mystery. Unfortunately, this will not do. Robinson's manuscript has recently come to light in the archives of the Royal Botanic Garden, Edinburgh, and there is no resemblance between the list of additions he has appended to Forbes's original handwritten sheets of the 1830s and the one in Backwell's Guide. The latter was clearly unknown to him; moreover, his own new finds are revealed as so meagre that he can hardly have been contemplating a genuine Flora. His object, rather, as he states in a covering letter dated December 1881, was merely to update the Manx list for the benefit of H. C. Watson, then preparing his final, great compendium on British plant distribution, *Topographical Botany* (1873–4).

Meanwhile the trickle of botanical holidaymakers continued. In 1859 and 1860 Charles Pressick Hobkirk (1837–1902), from Huddersfield, was responsible for a few specimens, mainly from the south coast, that eventually passed to the British Museum. 1867 similarly brought Frederick Morgan Webb (1841–1880), from Birkenhead. His visit we know of through records he sent to H. C. Watson for *Topographical Botany*.

A much more auspicious visitor, on three separate occasions, was the veteran Staffordshire naturalist, Robert Garner (1808–1890). The first of these visits, possibly as early as 1854, was written up in print in his *Holiday Excursions of a Naturalist*, published anonymously in 1867. Spring Sandwort, Cowbane and Pillwort are three plants he mentions having come across – with typical beginner's luck – apparently unaware of their great rarity. In 1869 and 1878 he came again, on this last occasion noting Lyme Grass and the Spooyt-vane hawkweed (now known to be *Hieracium perpropinquum*) with almost equal nonchalance. It is painful to think how much more he might have recorded had there only been a published Flora to give direction to his efforts.

On the last of his visits Garner was accompanied in the field by the young son of his hosts (who were connections of his by marriage). This was Philip Moore Callow Kermode (1855–1932), who was subsequently to become the outstanding Manx scholar of his generation. Though best known for his work on antiquities, Kermode had a working knowledge as well of most branches of natural history. A manuscript record-book of his, entitled 'Flora Monensis', has only recently come to light in the Manx Museum (of which he was the effective founder and first Curator). This logs many interesting finds from the Ramsey area. Other members of the Kermode family contributed – just as they jointly seemed to have formed a large album of local and Staffordshire plants which the Museum also possesses.

Garner's influence on Kermode had an outcome that was important more than just botanically. Back in North Staffordshire he was the architect of what had proved to be a most successful field club and, predictably, he broached the idea of a similar body for the Island. Kermode seized on this with enthusiasm and in December 1879 the Isle of Man Natural History and Antiquarian Society was born. From then until recent years (when the Manx Field Club was founded and flourished for a period) this was to constitute the main focus of work in these subjects in the Island and through its publications served as a regular catchment for records that were previously all too often lost to knowledge.

Typical of the otherwise lone workers who were now usefully brought within the shafts of the new Society was George Alfred Holt (1852–1921). Brought up and apprenticed in Douglas, this was another home-grown recruit whose advent made the 'Seventies a time of promising resurgence. When still only twenty-two he had been engaged to write the section on botany for Jenkinson's new *Guide* and in this displayed a wide acquaintance with the plants of the Douglas area. '*Viola canina* var. *stagnina*', recorded from cliffs near Groudle, was doubtless the Pale Heath Violet, a later Groudle specimen of which in his herbarium constitutes the sole Manx record. By coincidence in that same year, 1874, a King William's schoolboy, Charles Bethune Moffat (1859–1945), subsequently a Dublin journalist and prominent in Irish natural history, made two separate finds of the Deptford Pink, a species similarly yet to be seen again.

Like Murray before him and Paton after him, Holt was fated to spend most of his life outside the Island and to assume the role of nostalgically returning native. Exiled as a pharmacist in Manchester, he never failed to pay an annual botanising visit, to begin with specialising in the mosses and hepatics, till then little touched. The outcome was a lengthy paper in 1888 in the Society's *Transactions*. Soon his standing as a bryologist was international; but at the same time it became apparent that the continual work with the microscope had dangerously strained his eyes. Perforce he therefore shifted to the sedges and grasses, over the years building up collections of these then virtually unworked groups which were in due course donated to the Manx Museum. The ablest botanist who had studied the Island's flora up till then, his contribution to our knowledge of the higher plants was particularly important while remaining the least well-known.

Hardly any better appreciated has been the largely-hidden work, from

1887 onwards, of the Island's long-foremost ornithologist, Pilcher George Ralfe (1861–1936). Employed in the Isle of Man Bank and resident in Castletown, Ralfe made a practice of entering in a notebook (now also in the Manx Museum) every new locality he came across for the less common plants he was familiar with. He was not a 'critical' botanist and, in his ultra-modest way, probably attached slight value to this sideline record of the years; yet it is just the kind of unusually full and reliable store of data that subsequent researchers into distribution find invaluable. His wanderings after birds, moreover, took him on to very unbotanical terrain, best exemplified by his finding of the Yellow Vetch among Herring Gulls' nests below the Chasms, so perilous a spot that no one has dared to go looking for it since.

Also outside the mainstream were the labours of the Rev. Samuel Gasking (1852–1925), the Chaplain of St. Luke's, Baldwin for some years in the 'Eighties. Gasking's story is McNab's all afresh: a lengthy list compiled with much trouble, yet rendered almost useless by an absence of localities. This appeared in 1889–90 in an obscure journal called *Research* – so obscure that Ralfe alone of his contemporaries ever had a sight of it. Yet, ironically, it embodies the results of much the most thorough searching of the literature ever carried out until recent years. Gasking alone, for example, spotted the Backwell's list. Unfortunately, though, he performed his task quite uncritically, recklessly admitting items (such as the obvious absurdities perpetrated by Black's guide of 1883) that he must surely have recognised as errors. Through Ralfe these passed down to perplex or mislead Paton. Yet Gasking's field knowledge was certainly quite good, at any rate in his later years when he rose to botanical prominence in Lancashire, and of the many interesting additions that the list includes most were said by him to be of his own making (others he took from unnamed friends). It is possible indeed that we have in its bare bones the skeleton of yet one more Flora of the Island that never came to pass. If so, fear of prejudicing the commercial chances of the eventual work could explain the otherwise puzzling withholding of localities. All the more reason to regret, therefore, that his herbarium has not survived.

Besides this marked upsurge within the Island the 'Eighties witnessed a sharp rise in the number of botanical visitors. These included Stuart Oliver Ridley, then on the zoological staff of the British Museum, in 1881; the North Staffordshire Field Club in 1885; William Botting Hemsley from Kew and Dr Peter Quinn Keegan from Patterdale in 1887; Christopher Robert Billups, probably from Manchester as a medical student, in 1888 (twice), 1891 and 1895; the Wesley Scientific Society, led by G. Swainson, also in 1888; Arthur George Gregor, later a prominent Sussex botanist but then a curate in the Forest of Dean, in 1893. Several of these visits are attested merely by specimens but three were briefly written up.

In September 1896 a much more weighty visit took place. Under the auspices of the British Association for the Advancement of Science, as a follow-up to its meeting in Liverpool that year, a party including several eminent Continental botanists and led by Professor F. E. Weiss of Manchester University came over for a four-day tour. The weather was very poor and the trip was uncomfortably hurried; nevertheless William Philip Hiern (1839–1925), a Barnstaple landowner who spasmodically turned professional, was able to come up with a very respectable list, published the next year in the *Journal of Botany*. But maddeningly, yet again, this lacked any localities – on the ludicrous plea that "all the plants seen were very common". That this was far from true is shown by the presence in Hiern's herbarium at Exeter of at least one outstanding rarity in the shape of Heath Cudweed.

The publication of this list was taken as an affront by the man who then regarded himself as the Island's resident authority. This was Sidney Alfred Pizey Kermode (1862–1925), a half-brother of P. M. C. Kermode and then vicar of Onchan. Usefully connected, confident and energetic, this younger Kermode had quickly come to dominate the Botanical Section of the local Society after returning in 1890 from a spell in England. As a result, apparently taking his botanical capabilities at his own estimate, the Society entrusted to him the preparation of an up-to-date flowering plant handlist, to which end Talbot, Murray, Ralfe, Gasking and his brother all made available their records (though the greater part of these he seems to have chosen to ignore). Evidently written in 1897, his effort eventually appeared in March 1901 in the Society's journal, from which a large number of copies were run off for sale. Subsequently they continued on sale till only recently. Yet the list was a disgrace: glaringly incomplete and pervaded with errors. Its official status nevertheless led it to be taken seriously and for all too long it stood unchallenged as the supposedly standard work.

It is necessary to write thus harshly, not merely because the issue of this publication did Manx botany such an irritatingly persistent disfavour, but also because Kermode's botanical contributions more generally have a distinctly arrogant ring. He obviously felt that he had mastered the flora of the Island and that any additions thenceforward reflected on him personally. His attempt to discount the British Association list suggests that he was prepared to take this attitude to the point of active discouragement of new workers. It was just as well, therefore, that in 1904 his career took him back to England and his involvement came to an end.

Fortunately, Ralfe was on hand to organise the garnering-in of the local records in Kermode's stead. Through his charm and tact the reports of the Botanical Section were soon giving evidence of a sizeable network of collaborators, among them Harry Percival Hannay, one of the Castletown G.P.s; Miss Moore-Lane, another Castletown neighbour; and W. R.

Teare, the Master of Arbory school – to name only those who feature as responsible for important finds. Concurrently Charles Roeder (1848–1911), owner of a warehousing business in Manchester, was studying the folklore of the plants of the Cregneish district, of which he formed a usefully comprehensive collection now in the Manx Museum; and two Huddersfield naturalists, Charles Mosley and W. E. L. Wattam, were publishing lists (sadly, with more optimism than accuracy) made on a series of holiday visits.

These were great days in fact for Manx natural history as a whole, for apart from Ralfe's authoritative coverage of the birds H. Shortridge Clarke, J. H. Bailey and R. T. Cassal were at last making intensive collections of the insects. Even better, following up the promise of the British Association visit, the Island was beginning to attract specialists in certain difficult groups which without such outside help stood little chance of being investigated. A visit to Laxey in 1903 by the Rev. Cosslett Herbert Waddell (1858–1919), Rector of Saintfield, Co. Down, reinaugurated work on the Brambles, for instance. More far-reachingly, in 1900 James Alfred Wheldon (1862–1924), Pharmacist at Liverpool Gaol and the best all-round botanist in the North of England, began coming over to monograph the lichens, an undertaking that he was eventually to carry into print in 1927. In the course of this he sporadically took time off to do some much-needed collecting of 'critical' flowering plants; more strikingly, he also published some first, tentative analyses of the vegetation of certain of the more characteristic habitats. In the course of the latter, unwittingly, he added to the flora Small Bladderwort and the easily-overlooked Fenugreek. In all of this J. W. Hartley, a Cheshire botanist who had a house in Ballasalla and acted as his host, was associated with him, if largely nominally. Further windfalls that Wheldon brought were a start on the fungi (by his son) and a visit from his cryptogamic confrère, Albert Wilson, a Bradford pharmacist, along with a second British Association party in 1923.

By this time another, very different person had begun making regular visits too. This was Cyril Ingram Paton (1874–1949), a schoolmaster in South London who had numerous family connections with Man. Though a botanist and entomologist from boyhood and making notes on his trips as early as 1892, his interests at first were predominantly antiquarian and it was not for another twenty years that he collected his first herbarium specimens. His discovery of the Field Rose, near Balladoole in Arbory, is borne out by one of these. Sometime later, in the 1920s, he was invited to revise Kermode's handlist for a new Museum edition and from that point on botany became his central commitment. Up till then he had been content to paddle after plants: now he waded in, conscientiously collecting in the difficult groups and sending up specimens to the national experts. In this way almost by accident he turned into the long-term serious specialist for want of whom the properly comprehensive investigation of the flowering plants had for so long languished. In recognition, A. J. Wilmott of the British Museum, in an unlikely partnership, gave him much help and encouragement, no doubt hoping that Man would yield some geographically interesting rarities or even a plant or two all its own (just as he fostered the fuller exploring of the Hebrides). In return Paton donated numerous Manx specimens, so that at least one of the national herbaria had a representative collection.

The new handlist duly came out in 1933, as a supplement to the *North Western Naturalist*. Like its predecessor, it was then put on sale as a separate booklet. Unlike its predecessor, however, it evinced Paton's almost pedantic care and took extensive account of the past literature. At the same time it had one serious weakness: Paton then really only knew the North of the Island and his statements on frequency reflected this; consequently they were in many cases most misleading. Although in after years he amassed many more records, with a view to another edition, his meticulously kept notebooks betray little sign that on this particular score he subsequently found cause to modify his judgements. The reason for this was colourful, if curious. Convinced that the internal combustion engine was an out-and-out evil, he refused on principle ever to travel in a vehicle powered by one. This meant that every part of the Island not accessible by train or tram was closed to him except in so far as he could penetrate it on foot. And formidable walker though he was, and continued to be till the end of his days, the inevitable result was that great areas went barely if ever visited by him. Had he not made his home in Castletown during the years of his retirement, his ultimate coverage would scarcely have improved upon that of Forbes.

Even so Manx botany owes Paton a very great debt. Through his doggedness and scrupulous regard for accuracy a solid groundwork was laid which greatly eased the task of those of us who came after in the post-war years. His large herbarium, bequeathed to the Manx Museum along with all his manuscripts, has served as an indispensable core around which a steadily ever more complete collection has since been able to accumulate.

Paton's self-inflicted handicap, moreover, was in some degree offset by the efforts of several helpers. Foremost among these were George Clementson (1882–1958), William Stanley Cowin (1908–1958), George Graves and Ralph Howarth (1889–1954) – all with a general interest in natural history and all at one time or another of Peel – though Cowin, a replica of Ralfe in combining employment in the Isle of Man Bank with being the Island's leading ornithologist, spent most of his life in Douglas.

In parallel, as usual, these years had their quota as well of fly-by-nights, who came and botanised and crept home again all-unnoticed. In 1923 Andrew Templeman, of the Geological Museum in London, discovered the dwarf Willow on Snaefell. The Botanical Exchange Club was told, but no one thought to tell Paton (who indeed never did come to hear of it). In August 1930 Miss M. Everton, a Wild Flower Society member, stayed at Port St. Mary and returned claiming Common Wintergreen near Spanish Head. Similarly A. A. Slack, on a visit to Port Erin, may well have seen the long-lost Mountain Everlasting in much the same area. In 1937 Donald Peter Young, of Sanderstead, while on a family holiday at Peel, unwittingly collected the Southern Polypody in Glen Maye. In that same year and again just after the War J. A. Whellan, then of Liverpool, brought a sharp eye to bear on the district round Laxey and was rewarded with Wood Fescue in Dhoon Glen, still unseen by anyone since.

This prolonged disconnection between resident and visiting effort was brought to an end at last in 1950. In June of that year the Island was chosen as the venue for a week-long field meeting by the Botanical Society of the British Isles. Those were days when private motoring was still difficult and such meetings consequently attracted many of the field elite. E. Milne-Redhead and V. S. Summerhayes of Kew, N. Douglas Simpson of Bournemouth, P. S. Green of Birmingham University and Miss C. W. Muirhead of Carlisle Museum were among those who made the party of sixteen who came over outstanding in its weightiness. None had been before, so Howarth was called in to act as local Leader. As a schoolboy of eighteen I also had the privilege of taking part and was entrusted with the registering of the records. Never before or since has the Island's flora received such massive, concentrated scrutiny and many gaps, particularly in the more difficult groups, were filled as a result. Some of these were the product of extra, unofficial forays which the two Kew botanists made in the evenings and for two or three further days after the meeting ended. The combined work was eventually written up in the BSBI *Proceedings* in 1954.

Thereafter, throughout the 1950s and 1960s, I continued to return almost annually, mostly for either two or three weeks and with a focus on a different part of the Island each time. In these early years I received much help from Howarth and Cowin in particular. G. E. Quayle, then of Narradale, Miss M. Quayle, of Sulby, J. T. Williams, then of Cheadle and C. Bucke, then on the staff of the Douglas High School for Boys, were among those who also contributed valuable records.

In 1954 the BSBI launched their historic Distribution Maps Scheme, which pioneered computer-mapping in Britain and was to culminate in the great *Atlas of the British Flora*. For this purpose Man was recognised as covering part or all of twelve 10-kilometre squares, and for the next few years compiling lists for these took precedence over other work. Miss M. B. Bing, then of Andreas, did a great deal in this direction in the North of the Island; and visits in 1955 and 1956 by Walter Henry Hardaker

(1877–1970), of Birmingham, were outstandingly productive as well. The result was some 5000 records for the Scheme by the end of 1958.

At my instance the BSBI paid a second week's visit in July 1960. A smaller, less star-studded party than ten years before, their most important achievement was the clinching of the identity of O'Kelly's Orchid, dispatched fresh to Kew from the Eairy 'deads'. Exactly two years later three of Britain's most experienced field botanists, D. McClintock from Kent, Mrs B. H. S. Russell from Essex, and the late Miss C. M. Rob of Thirsk, came over in the name of the Wild Flower Society for an all-too-brief weekend and several startling additions were the predictable result.

Dr L. S. Garrad, then of Castletown and shortly to join the staff of the Manx Museum, now appeared on the scene and with Miss M. Devereau of Douglas and a lengthening string of helpers soon brought about a resurgence in the resident effort. These last two decades have in consequence seen the Island worked ever more intensively, till few areas now can have been left unsearched. An avalanche of new discoveries has been the reward.

In these same, last few years our knowledge of the bryophytes has been brought up to date by Mrs J. A. Paton, while P. Earland Bennett and Mr and Mrs J. E. Milne have revived interest in the lichens and larger fungi respectively. Even work in the most difficult groups has flourished: concurrently with my own combing of the Brambles E. F. and B. D. Greenwood, of Merseyside Museums, have done extensive collecting of the Dandelions and R. W. David, of Cambridge, has begun overhauling the Sedges.

After so much by so many – can there possibly remain now more still to do? It is an obvious question and yet an absurd one: for no flora is ever static and if species decrease or disappear, assuredly others will spread or arrive to take their place. There will continue to be plenty for those who come after to look for and record. But never, sad to say, will such work have that very special savour reserved for those who have had the good fortune through these past four centuries to find the Island still substantially untouched.

SYSTEMATIC LIST

The list is drawn up on the following plan:–

SEQUENCE AND NAMES

The sequence and scientific names are those of the standard *List of British Vascular Plants* (Ed. J. E. Dandy, 1958) except where work since then has caused the general adoption of changes. In these cases the previous name is added in brackets, unless it is solely the name of the genus that has changed.

To avoid confusion, the English names have been repeated from my Manx Museum handlist. As far as possible they are those of D. McClintock and R. S. R. Fitter's *Pocket Guide to Wild Flowers* (1956), the handbook most used by visitors – though unfortunately these may not be the ones most familiar in Man. Mere trade names appear in inverted commas.

Manx names are given where these are believed to have been reliably identified with a particular species. The spelling has been checked afresh by members of the Manx Language Society.

STATUS

In the case of an island flora it is more than usually important to be able to identify the aboriginal element, present before the severance from the mainland. Special care has therefore been taken in assigning the species to a series of categories of decreasing 'wildness', as indicated by the following letters:

N *Native*: at least partly in non-artificial habitats and consistently associated in these with certain other species (though not necessarily aboriginal: possibly brought over by birds or wind subsequently to the severance, maybe only recently).

C *Colonist*: an invader allowed in unintentionally as a result of human activities (typically as a weed of cultivation) and now normally present only in open or artificial habitats.

D *Denizen*: growing wild but known, or suspected, to have been introduced originally as a crop or herb.

H *Hortal*: an ornamental either deliberately planted or escaped into the wilds from gardens.

This classification is a modified version of the one devised by H. C. Watson over a century ago and traditionally employed in county Floras ever since. It has been customary to apply the Watson categories in an oddly procrustean fashion, insisting that a species be referred to just the one category only. In reality, of course, many species are of dual or even multiple status and failure to give recognition to their additional categories results in much useful information being suppressed. In this list a comprehensive picture of status has been aimed at and more than one letter may therefore appear.

HABITATS

The habitats are those in which the species occurs in Man. They frequently differ from those favoured by it elsewhere.

FREQUENCY

In descending order the categories employed are: common (or abundant); frequent; occasional or local (depending on the degree of cluster in the distribution); rare. These may be qualified by 'very' or 'locally', as appropriate. The categories are applied on no more precise basis than an assessment in the light of my own and others' field experience within the last twenty-five years or, for the less common species, of the pattern of recorded occurrences. For the benefit of those unfamiliar with the Island's place-names a summary of the broad geographical trend of the distribution is provided in many cases as well. Because of the special interest of the flora of the Calf of Man, the word 'Calf' follows the general statement on frequency if the species is recorded thence.

RECORDS

Where a species seems sufficiently uncommon for individual records to merit listing, these are given in chronological order within each Botanical District. As these Districts have been delineated to coincide as far as possible with natural ecogeographical divisions and their identifying letters are similarly, by deliberate design, geographical (**N**–, **SW**–, etc.), a glance will show the broad pattern of distribution within the Island.

No attempt has been made to follow the common practice of citing the earliest known record for each species. As many of the commonest Manx plants passed unrecorded till late in the last century, the result would have been even more scientifically meaningless than usual. An exception has, however, been made in the case of rapidly-spreading species, the earliest observing of which is clearly of some moment.

For reasons of space localities have had to be kept brief. In many cases fuller details are noted in my record-books eventually to be deposited in the Manx Museum. For certain rarities even the little that could be printed has been made deliberately imprecise, in the interests of conservation. On the other hand in obviously unendangerable groups such as Brambles and Roses six-figure grid references (all within the 100-km square SC) have been added for the future guidance of specialists. Place-names (and their spellings) have been brought into conformity with the current edition of the Ordnance Survey map as far as possible.

The names or initials of recorders follow the locality *in italics*. A name indicates a pre-1950 record, initials alone one made subsequently – thereby enabling the age pattern of the records, too, to be discerned at a glance. A key to both is given below. Where the locality has been noted by several recorders in succession, normally no more than the first two are indicated (in chronological order) and 'etc.' used to cover the rest. Records made jointly are indicated by '&' linking the names or initials. Where no recorder's name appears the record is my own – or made by me in the company of other workers. By time-honoured botanical convention, '!' after a recorder's name indicates that the author too has seen it there himself. As this sign is commonly misunderstood by readers of local Floras, it would be as well to stress that it implies no disrespect to the persons whose records it comes after: rather, as one Victorian author has nicely put it, it is to be taken as 'a mark of approbation'.

HERBARIA

An asterisk after a recorder's name or initials indicates that a specimen collected by that person from the locality in question is in the herbarium of the Manx Museum. This comprises the collections of Talbot, Holt and Paton together with numerous voucher specimens deposited by myself and others since 1950. In addition, there are separate albums containing the collections of Mrs A. W. Brearey and Mrs W. Kermode. Now far and away the largest repository of Manx material, with almost all the recorded species represented, this is recommended as the recipient, except in special cases, of all specimens supporting finds of additional species that may be made in future. Other herbaria are indicated by 'hb' followed by their respective international code letters:–

BIRM Birmingham University (mainly a few specimens collected by P. S. Green in 1950).

BM British Museum (Natural History), London (including a boyhood album of Forbes, the herbarium of Murray and many specimens donated by Paton. With the commendable aim of duplicating in this main national collection the representative set of the Isle of Man material he was building up concurrently in the Manx Museum, Paton sent batches of sheets here periodically over many years and scrupulously notified in his list and its supplements the species represented in them. Unfortunately, unbeknown to him, much of this material was not of acceptable quality and only a smallish portion is in fact now to be found there).

CGE Cambridge University (mainly species of my own collecting).

DBN National Botanic Gardens, Glasnevin, Dublin (hb McNab).

K Royal Botanic Gardens, Kew (including the specimens supplied by Forbes and others in support of the records accepted for H. C.

Watson's *Topographical Botany*, and material collected in 1950 by E. Milne-Redhead and V. S. Summerhayes).

LIV Merseyside County Museums, Liverpool.

LIVU Liverpool University.

LSR Leicestershire Museums, Leicester.

NMW National Museum of Wales, Cardiff (hb Wheldon).

OXF Oxford University.

RAMM Royal Albert Memorial Museum, Exeter (containing the material collected by Hiern in 1896).

It has not been practicable for any of these, other than the fully-indexed Wheldon herbarium at Cardiff, to be combed exhaustively for Manx material. That there are any further substantial Isle of Man collections still undiscovered elsewhere, however, seems unlikely.

References

Sources in the bibliography at the back of this book are referred to thus: (Gasking, 1890) or Gasking (1890). Certain periodicals cited in the text are abbreviated, as follows:–

ASNH	*Annals of Scottish Natural History*
BEC	*Report of the Botanical (Society and) Exchange Club of the British Isles*
Brit Nat	*British Naturalist*
JB	*Journal of Botany*
Mag Nat Hist	*Magazine of Natural History*
Nat	*The Naturalist*
New Phyt	*New Phytologist*
NW Nat	*North Western Naturalist*
Phyt	*The Phytologist*
Proc	*Proceedings of the I.O.M. Natural History & Antiquarian Society*
Proc BSBI	*Proceedings of the Botanical Society of the British Isles*
Proc LBS	*Proceedings of the Liverpool Botanical Society*
Sci Goss	*Science Gossip*
WBEC	*Report of the Watson Botanical Exchange Club*
W F Mag	*Wild Flower Magazine*
YLM	*Yn Lioar Manninagh* (the predecessor of Proc)

In the case of BEC and WBEC, by long convention, the year cited is that to which the report relates, not the year of publication.

Other Abbreviations Used

agg.	aggregate ('lumped') species
The *Atlas*	*Atlas of the British Flora*, ed. F. H. Perring & S. M. Walters (1962) jointly with the *Critical Supplement* to this, ed. F. H. Perring & P. D. Sell (1968).
c (before a date)	around
conf.	confirmed by

corr.	record in MS correspondence
det.	determined by
et al.	and others (where two or more recorders were in company)
fide	in the belief of (but specimen not necessarily seen by)
incl.	including
NHAS	IOM Natural History & Antiquarian Society
per	record communicated through

Key to Recorders

Non-residents are indicated by their then location in brackets following their name. *NHAS, uniquely, is used for both pre- and post-1950 records irrespectively.*

(i) PRE-1950

Dates indicate the known period of fieldwork in Man.

Allchin, Dr W. H. (London) 1846/59
Backwell's – anonymous list in *Backwell's Illustrated Guide*, Ed. 2 c 1855–7
Bailey, Dr J. H. c 1900–10
Bersu, Mrs M. 1945
Billups, Dr C. R. (East Grinstead) 1888, 1891, 1895
Bilton, E. and Bostock, E. 1885
Black's – anonymous list in *Black's Guide* c 1880
Brearey, Mrs A. W. 1866
Br Ass[1] British Assoc. for the Advancement of Science Sept 1896
Br Ass[2] British Assoc. for the Advancement of Science Sept 1923
Br Ass[3] British Assoc. for the Advancement of Science Sept 1936
Clark, Rev. F. F. (Newcastle-under-Lyme) 1835, 1840
Clementson, G. c 1939–58
Conolly, Miss A. P. (Leicester) Mar 1946
Cowin, W. S. c 1914–58
Craine, F. 1939
Davies, Rev. H. (Anglesey) Aug 1774, June 1775
Dickson, Dr H. H. 1918–22
Forbes, E. 1827–37
Garner, R. (Stoke-on-Trent) c 1854, 1869, 1878
Gasking, Rev. S. c 1885–99
Graves, F. S. c 1900–30
Graves, T. H. c 1900–30
Hannay, Dr H. P. 1906
Hardaker, W. H. 1900–2
Holt, G. A. (Sale) 1874–1918
Hoyle, A. C. 1920s
Hunter, J. 1913–18
Jeffcott, Miss c 1880
Jowett, Dr T. (Nottingham) 1827
Keegan, Dr P. Q. (Patterdale) 1887
Keig, J. B. 1895–6
Kermode, P. M. C. c 1895–6
Kermode, Rev. S. A. P. 1884, 1890–1904
Kermode, Mrs W. c 1880
McNab, J. Aug 1830, 1832
Megaw, Mrs E. M. c 1943–55
Moffat, C. B. 1874
Moore, E. J. (Birmingham) 1929
Moore-Lane, Miss 1902–6
Mosley, C. (Huddersfield) 1899, 1903
Murray, Rev. R. P. (Glastonbury) 1860s, 1881–2
Osvald, H. (Sweden) 1940s
Paton, C. I. (Streatham; Sutton) 1892–1949
Quayle, G. E. c 1920–
Ralfe, P. G. 1887–1936
Ray, Rev. J. (Cambridge) July 1660
Roeder, C. (Manchester) 1897

Rylands, T. G. (Warrington) 1841
Savage, Rev. S. 1880s
Spanton, J. 1880–86
Stowell, Rev. H. A. c 1858–63
Talbot, Rev. T. 1865–7, 1880
Teare, W. R. 1902–3
Templeman, A. (London) June 1923
Thomson, W. (Manchester) c 1829
Wagstaffe, R. (Liverpool) 1942–5
Webb, F. M. (Birkenhead) 1899–1903
Wesley Scientific Society 1888
Wheldon, J. A. (Liverpool) 1900–23
Whellan, J. A. (Liverpool) 1937, 1945–6
Williamson, K. 1940s
Wilson, A. 1923
Wood, Rev. R. P. 1881–98
Young, Dr D. P. (Sanderstead) Aug 1937

(ii) 1950 AND SINCE

AB	Miss A. Birch
AC	A. Crellin
ACK	Miss A. C. Kaighin
ADW	A. D. Walker
AH	A. Hitchon (Accrington)
AJP	A. J. Pritchard (Liverpool)
AMH	Miss A. M. Harrison
AMS	A. McG. Stirling (Whitchurch, Salop)
AP	Mrs A. Pickthall
AQR	A. Q. Russell
BSBI[1] BSBI[2] BSBI[3]	Botanical Society of the British Isles, 1950, 1960, 1979 field meetings respectively
BW	Mrs B. Wilson
CB	C. Bucke
D&G	Miss M. Devereau & Dr L. S. Garrad
DJ	Mrs D. Jeavons
DJS	D. J. Slinn
EH	E. Huyton
EMK	Miss E. M. Kelly
EMM	Mrs E. M. Megaw
ETL	Mrs E. T. Ladds
FBG	Dr F. B. Goldsmith (London)
FC	Mrs F. Cain
FHT	Dr F. H. Tyrer (Birmingham)
FR	F. Radcliffe
G&G	E. F. & B. D. Greenwood (Liverpool)
GDR	Dr G. D. Rowley (Bayfordbury)
GEQ	G. E. Quayle
GLQ	G. L. Quilliam
GSM	G. S. Marvin (Droitwich)
HSP	Mrs H. S. Proctor
HSQ	H. S. Quayle
IDA	I. D. Allison
IMK	Miss I. M. Killip
JAP	Mrs J. A. Paton (Truro)
JAR	Dr J. A. Rutter (Liverpool)
JBD	J. B. Devonshire
JC	J. Curphey
JCo	J. Collister
JCC	J. C. Crellin
JEL	J. E. Lousley (London)
JG	J. Green
JH	J. Harris
JK	J. Killey
JR	J. Roscoe
JRB	J. R. Bruce
JS	Mrs J. Sayle
JTW	J. T. Williams (Cheadle)
JWD	J. W. Dawson
KB	K. Bond
KG	Miss K. Guyler
LSG	Dr L. S. Garrad
LVC	L. V. Crellin
M&S	E. Milne-Redhead & V. S. Summerhayes (Kew)
MBB	Miss M. B. Bing
MC	Mrs M. Caine
MD	Miss M. Devereau
MQ	Miss M. Quayle
MWK	Mrs M. W. Kenyon (Woking)
NHAS	IOM Natural History &

	Antiquarian Society: field excursions
NK	N. Kermode
NQ	Mrs N. Quayle
PJ	P. Jennings
PRF-R	P. R. Foulkes-Roberts
RH	R. Howarth
RM	Miss R. Macdonald
RWD	R. W. David (Cambridge)
SCM	S. C. Madge
VLW	Miss V. L. Wilson
VR	Miss V. Roach
VSS	V. S. Summerhayes (Kew)
WFS	Wild Flower Society, 1962 field meeting
WHH	W. H. Hardaker (Birmingham)
WSC	W. S. Cowin

PTERIDOPHYTA

LYCOPSIDA

Lycopodiaceae

Huperzia selago (L.) Bernh. ex Schrank & Mart. Fir Clubmoss
N Moors, bogs, wet rocks. Rare.

C — Snaefell, on and near summit, *Davies, Conolly* etc: mt NNE of Injebreck, *Holt**: Slieau Freoaghane and Carn Gerjoil, 1927, *Anon**: Beinn y Phott, *JS, MC & RM*: North Barrule, *JAP, D & G*: Upper Cornaa old mines, *LSG*. **SW** — Boggy patch below Kionslieu, *MWK, JAP*: South Barrule quarries, *LSG & KB*!: Crosby quarry, one clump, *D & G*.

Also unlocalised records by Forbes and Backwell's. The recent flurry of finds, mostly in localities searched previously, suggests a spread.

Lycopodium clavatum L. Stagshorn Clubmoss
N Moors, usually among heather — but on a wet ledge at the Cluggid falls. Occasional, but unknown on the southern hills. Generally between 600 and 900 ft., *Hoyle*. Apparently much diminished in recent years.

Diphasiastrum alpinum (L.) Holub Alpine Clubmoss
N High moors. Very rare.

C — Snaefell, *Davies*: Carraghan, *Talbot**: mt NNE of Injebreck, *Holt**: between North Barrule and Snaefell, *Savage*: top of Ravensdale, *Mosley & Wattam*: Carn Gerjoil, north slope, 1927, *Anon.**

Also unlocalised records by Macculloch, Forbes and Backwell's.

'***Lycopodia***', in an aggregate sense, have also been reported on moors above Glen Dhoo, *Garner* (1878), in the Dalby Mt–Eairy Cushlin area, *Br Ass*[2] (Proc 2,354), and above Glen Mona, *ADW*.

Selaginellaceae

Selaginella selaginoides (L.) Link Lesser Clubmoss
N Base-rich mires. Very rare.

N — 'Scarce', *Robinson* (1882): The Pollies, Jurby: Rhendhoo Curragh, *D & G*! [**C** — "Except for ***Lycopodium alpinum*** and ***selaginoides*** the elevated region produces no Alpine plants", *Macculloch* (1819,521). Error?]

A specimen from an unstated locality was sent by Holt to Arthur Bennett in 1891 (JB(1896) 449).

S. kraussiana (G. Kunze) A. Braun (Moss Clubmoss), an escape from greenhouses, is naturalised by the Nunnery footpath, Douglas, where it was first noticed in 1971, *D & G* hb BM.

SPHENOPSIDA

Equisetaceae

Equisetum variegatum Schleich. ex Weber & Mohr
Variegated Horsetail

N Moist dune-hollows. Almost certainly extinct.

N — Ramsey, *Backwell's*. There is no reason to doubt this 1850s record; but the habitat — a very likely one — has been largely destroyed by subsequent development. The species ought to occur on the Ayres, but repeated searching has failed to disclose it. The dune plant is a distinct ecotype, var. ***arenarium*** Newm.

E. fluviatile L. Water Horsetail

N Ponds, ditches, curraghs. Frequent.

Abundant in sphagnum bogs at top of Glen Rushen, at 700 ft.

E. palustre L. Marsh Horsetail

N Wet places, railway tracks. Common in the north, frequent elsewhere.

E. sylvaticum L. Wood Horsetail

N Glens, swamps, boggy fields. Local: mainly in the east central area, often in great quantity.

E. arvense L. Common Horsetail

NC Hedgebanks, roadsides, waste places, landslips. Common.

E. arvense × fluviatile (***E. × litorale*** Kuhlew. ex Rupr.) is probably frequent by ditches and on roadsides, as in west Wales. P. G. Taylor, the specialist in the genus at Kew, on a brief visit in 1953 found it in the only likely-looking locality he had time to search (by the stream in Molly Quirk's Glen, Onchan, hb K). It can be spotted by its decumbent stems, with dense branches below and none above, so that it appears long and whip-like.

E. telmateia Ehrh. Giant Horsetail

N Shady, oozy ground and wet grassy slopes, preferably on clay and seldom far from the sea. Very local, but often in great quantity.

W — Boulder clay cliffs between Kirk Michael and Peel, *Hoyle*: Ballanayre Glen, Knocksharry, *Hoyle**, *MD*!: mouth of Glen Wyllin, *RH*, *MD*!: Cooil Darry Glen, *D & G*: mouth of Ballelby Gill, Dalby; railway bank by Peel golf course. **C** — Port Mooar, *RH*!: Port e Vullen, *WHH*, *MBB*!: Upper Glen Wyllin by Ballalonna, *MD*. **SE** — Olympia grounds, *Holt**: Douglas prison grounds and wood nearby, *MD*: foot of Calvary Glen, by Derby Castle. These three Douglas stations all lie close together and are probably inter-related.

It is strange that so conspicuous a plant was not recorded until 1888. Can it have increased?

PTEROPSIDA

Osmundaceae

Osmunda regalis L. Royal Fern; Rhennagh y Reeh

N Bogs, streamsides, wet cliff faces. Local, much rarer than formerly. Calf.

Statements such as 'it grows very plentifully on the rocks about the Isle of Man' (Ray in 1660) and 'the prevailing fern of the glens throughout the Isle' (Clarke 1841) show how abundant this must once have been. At the height of the Victorian fern craze, in the 1850s and 1860s, it is said to have been carried off the Island by the cartload and by the end of the century had become noticeably scarce. Nevertheless it is still abundant in the main curraghs in the north and more widespread in the rest of the Island than generally suspected, particularly on the coast. Extensive re-colonisation may well be in progress. In this connection its recent appearance in two dune slacks on the Ayres is suggestive.

Hymenophyllaceae

Hymenophyllum wilsonii Hook. Scottish Filmy Fern

N Boulders in moist upland glens. Very rare.

C — Injebreck, *Holt**, *JAP* etc!: wet rocks in Sulby Glen near Tholt y Will, *Whellan*, BEC (1946-7) 322. Also unlocalised reports late last century by P. M. C. Kermode (fide Ralfe) and Miss Jeffcott.

Dennstaedtiaceae

Pteridium aquilinum (L.) Kuhn Bracken; Rhennagh Vooar

N Hedgebanks, hillsides, glens. Very common. Calf.

Formerly extensively used for packing the fresh-caught herring forwarded daily by steamboat to the Liverpool markets (Cooke 1867, 3). It was also cut and burnt in Ballaugh parish for the alkali in its ashes, with which linen was then boiled as part of the bleaching process (Shimmin 1915) — a practice also recorded from Worcestershire.

Adiantaceae

Cryptogramma crispa (L.) R. Br. ex Hook. Parsley Fern

N Slate quarries, acid mountain rocks. Very rare.

C — West Baldwin, *Holt*: North Barrule, one clump, 1887, *P. Kermode* per *Paton*. **SW** — South Barrule quarries, abundant, *Backwell's*, *Talbot* etc!: top of Gob ny clee, Slieau Whallian, *Ralfe*: Glen Rushen quarries, one clump, *JS*, *MC & RM*.

'Occurs freely on some of the mountains', *Bailey*, Proc L & C Ent Soc (1908) 18. Also other unlocalised records by Ralfe and by Allchin (Moore 1859a).

Adiantum capillus-veneris L. Maidenhair Fern; Folt ny Moidyn

NH Moist, shaded rock faces, normally by the sea. Rare and very local: virtually confined to the south-west coast.

C — Ruins of St Trinian's, Greeba, 'famous for the quantities . . . growing in and about it', 1774, *Grose* (6, 215), *Woods* (1811) etc., but extinct by 1854, *Garner*. Perhaps introduced. **SE** — Caves at Santon, *Forbes*: rocks of railway cutting near Douglas, perhaps derived from garden-based spores, *MD*. **SW** — Recorded, since *Forbes*, from numerous cliff and cave stations between Peel and Fleshwick Bay. Most of these are difficult of access and in some of them the plant still abounds. 'Still found in one of the nobler glens not far from Glen Maye', *J. F. Robinson*, Sci Goss (1875) 232: South Barrule, 'stronger and stiffer than the normal Manx form', *Miss A. M. Crellin*, YLM I, 227: 'said to grow in caves near the Calf', *Paton* (1927). **S** — Langness, *Forbes*.

var. ***rotundum*** (T. Moore) auct. hort. Long in cultivation, this variety was first collected in 1841 by Rylands from sea cliffs at Glen Maye and given to his Warrington neighbour, W. Wilson, who brought its distinctiveness to public notice in Phyt (1851) 70. Wilson thought it perhaps a new species, by reason of its narrower, oblong fronds, pinnules without the normal cuneiform base, wider-spreading branches and greater hardiness. It was subsequently discovered that an almost identical form occurs on the south-west coast of England. Though neglected by taxonomists in later years, it may in fact be a good geographical race.

Blechnaceae

Blechnum spicant (L.) Roth Hard Fern; Craueyn Skeddan
N Hedgebanks, glens, moors. Common. Calf.

Aspleniaceae

Asplenium scolopendrium L. Hartstongue; Chengey Feeaihee
NH Walls, rocks, damp shady places. Frequent in the south and east, local elsewhere. Calf.

Sometimes on rocks by the sea: Banks Howe and near Port Soderick, *Ralfe*: Port Soldrick, *LSG*: Port Garwick; Ballure. Much reduced by fern-collectors last century and decidedly scarce by 1900. Extensive recolonisation appears to be in progress, doubtless boosted by spores from garden stocks.

A. adiantum-nigrum L. subsp. ***adiantum-nigrum*** Black Spleenwort
NC Walls, rocks (including sea-cliffs), hedgebanks. Frequent. Calf.

[***A. billotii*** F. W. Schultz (*A. lanceolatum* Huds., non Forsk.) Lanceolate Spleenwort
'Once found (1855) between Ramsey and Laxey', *Backwell's*. Though the author of this record appears to have been a careful and capable field botanist, it would be unsafe to accept it in the absence of a specimen. Even so this is a characteristic western species, which might well occur. It commonly grows among ***A. adiantum-nigrum***, some forms of which it closely resembles, and could easily be overlooked.]

A. marinum L. Sea Spleenwort
N Cliff-faces, sea-caves. Frequent along the rocky stretches of the coast. Calf.

In well at Castle Rushen, *LSG*.

A. trichomanes L. Maidenhair Spleenwort
NC Walls, rocks. Common. Calf.

On inland shingle in Kimmeragh gravel-pit, Bride, *D & G*.

Apparently more plentiful than formerly, due to the spread of mortared walls. This is the habitat favoured by the calcicolous subsp. ***quadrivalens*** D. E. Meyer, one of two recently-discriminated cytogeographical races. In west Wales this greatly outnumbers the race of moderately acid shady banks and overgrown dry stone walls, subsp. ***trichomanes***. The latter has as yet been detected in Man only on wet rocks by the Dhoon waterfall*; but other records of the species on rocks — e.g., on the Calf (Leavett 1971) — are doubtless referable to this.

A. ruta-muraria L. Wall-rue

C Walls. Very rare a century ago, now common over much of the lowlands — reflecting the spread of mortared walls. Calf.

A. ceterach L. (*Ceterach officinarum* DC.) Rusty-back

C Walls. Local but spreading. Calf.

First recorded in 1874, this is yet another mildly calcicolous fern that has prospered with the advent of mortared walls. It has only once been noted in Man on coastal cliffs or other rocks, on which it frequently grows in south Wales. Doubtless reflecting its non-indigenous status, the form prevailing in Ireland, var. ***crenatum*** T. Moore, apparently does not occur.

Athyriaceae

Athyrium filix-femina (L.) Roth Lady Fern

N Shady places. Very common. Calf.

var. ***marinum*** T. Moore ('Dickie's Lady Fern'), originally found in a sea-cave near Aberdeen, was collected in Man by Allchin (Moore 1859b). It is distinguished by an elliptic-lanceolate blade, spreading or subdecumbent in habit and rigid, the whole plant being small and very neat. It is doubtless an ecotype at best, without geographical significance.

[***Cystopteris fragilis*** (L.) Bernh. Brittle Bladder Fern

'Old bridge near Castletown', *J. H. Davies*, Phyt (1857) 110. This is a colonist of mortared walls in Wales and so, despite being a calcicole, a species that might occur. However, sterile forms of ***Athyrium filix-femina*** can simulate it closely and two other records, originally accepted (Allen 1954), have since been authoritatively redetermined as that. Davies was concentrating on mosses on this, his only visit, and may have failed to examine his plant with care. The species is also marked in the *Atlas of Ferns of the British Isles* (1978) but on the strength of a specimen in hb LIV from a Derbyshire locality misidentified as Ravensdale in Ballaugh.]

Aspidiaceae

Dryopteris filix-mas (L.) Schott Male Fern

N Shady places. Common. Calf.

D. affinis (Lowe) Fraser-Jenkins Golden-scaled Male Fern
subsp. ***borreri*** (Newm.) Fraser-Jenkins

N Glens, hedgebanks. Frequent, but mainly on the damper east side of the Island. Calf.

This species is apogamous, so that variants produced by mutation or hybridisation can persist and colonise extensive areas. Like the Brambles these could provide useful clues to the relationship between neighbouring florulas, but their study in the British Isles has scarcely begun. Most British plants are known to be triploid, but extensive diploid populations (with larger spores) have been detected in the Lake District and several places further west and might also occur in Man.

D. carthusiana (Vill.) H. P. Fuchs (*D. spinulosa* Watt)
Narrow Buckler Fern

N Damp woods. Very rare; confined to glens along the west coast.

W — Near Glen Maye, *Paton**, conf. A. H. G. Alston: Spooyt Vane bridge, hb CGE, conf. A. C. Jermy.

An unlocalised record by Robinson (1882) — 'rare', on the Peat only — may be reliable. It suggests one find in the northern curraghs, which is more the type of ground in which it chiefly occurs in Ireland.

D. dilatata (Hoffm.) A. Gray Common Buckler Fern

N Shady places. Common. Calf.

A distinctive-looking plant collected from a rocky crevice at 1,750 ft on Snaefell in 1951, hb CGE, is referable to this species and not ***D. dilatata*** var. ***alpina*** T. Moore (i.e. ***D. assimilis*** S. Walker), as originally supposed (Allen 1954).

A solitary specimen of a buckler fern collected from a crevice in Block Eary ravine, at the north-west foot of Snaefell, by *MD** in 1969, has been determined by A. C. Jermy as a probably new, as yet undescribed taxon, intermediate between ***D. carthusiana*** and ***D. dilatata.*** It has the concolorous scales of the former but differs in its very narrow frond. It is not a hybrid between them but an allotetraploid of parallel phylogeny. Already known from several localities in central Scotland, it may turn out to be widespread.

D. aemula (Ait.) Kuntze Hay-scented Buckler Fern

N Glens, shady banks. Rare, and virtually confined to the east.

C — Ballure Glen, etc, *Backwell's*: St. Trinian's, per *P. Kermode*: glen of the Onchan, Sulby; near Mount Rule paper mill, *Ralfe*: Dhoon Glen; Glen Mona: Skinscoe, *D & G*. **SE** — Kirk Braddan plantation; near Oakhill, *Talbot*: roadside at Mount Murray, *Ralfe*.

Polystichum setiferum (Forsk.) Woynar Soft Shield Fern

NH Sheltered lanes, banks, glens. Occasional; plentiful round Glen Maye but otherwise widely and thinly scattered over the lowlands. Noted in twenty localities since 1950, as against a mere three known previously: presumably therefore increasing. It is grown in Manx gardens and doubtless there has been some colonisation from that source, as illustrated by a patently spore-spread colony of the cultivar 'Divisilobum' in Glenbooie, near Knocksharry, *D & G*, det. J. W. Dyce. A more warmth-demanding species than the next, it may also have benefited by a recent mellowing of the Island's climate.

P. aculeatum (L.) Roth Hard Shield Fern
(*P. lobatum* (Huds.) Chevall.)
N Hedgebanks, glens, especially in wetter districts. Rare and very scattered.

C — Ballure Glen, *Backwell's*: near Port Cornaa, *WHH*, *MD*: Garwick Glen, *MB*: Baldhoon road N of Glen Roy mill. **W** — Spooyt Vane, *WHH*! **SW** — Quarry wall, Foxdale, *BSBI*[1]. **SE** — Pulrose; Castletown road near Douglas*, *Holt*: Mount Murray, *MD*. **S** — Hedgebank W of Arragon Veg: N of Monks' Bridge, Ballasalla, *MD*.

Thelypteridaceae

Oreopteris limbosperma (All.) Holub Lemon-scented Fern
(*Dryopteris oreopteris* (Ehrh.) Maxon)
N Glens, stream-sides. Common in the hills.

[***Thelypteris thelypteroides*** (Michx.) Holub Marsh Fern
'Boggy places. Ballure Glen etc', *Stowell*. One of several species recorded only by Stowell. Presumably a misidentification.]

Phegopteris connectilis (Michx). Watt Beech Fern
(*Thelypteris phegopteris* (L.) Slosson)
N Glens and damp, shady rocks in hill areas. Rare.

C — One (deliberately unspecified) glen in the north, *Backwell's*: glen behind Ash-hill, Lezayre, *P. Kermode*: Paris Gill, *Ralfe*: Glen Mona, *P. Kermode*, *Holt* ('abundant') etc!*: Glen Roy, *S. Kermode, Ralfe, C. C. Dadd*: Lhergyrhenny, large patch, *JS, MC & RM*.

[***Gymnocarpium dryopteris*** (L.) Newm. Oak Fern
'In many places', *Forbes* (1848). 'Mountains and glens, frequent', *Stowell* (1860). In both cases attributable to a nomenclatural mix-up, ***O. limbosperma*** clearly being intended.]

Polypodiaceae

† det. A. C. Jermy

Polypodium vulgare L. Common Polypody
N Dry-stone walls. Local; apparently mainly in the moister districts.

P. interjectum Shivas Western Polypody
NC Walls, rocks, trees, dunes. Very common. Calf.

This is more of a lime-lover than ***P. vulgare*** and so has extensively colonised the modern mortared walls (although it grows on the dry-stone ones as well). It also occurs on rocks near or on the sea at several places on the central east coast, on fore-dunes at Rue Point and as an epiphyte on a variety of trees: Ash (most often), Wych Elm, Elder, Oak, Crack Willow, Beech.

P. interjectum × ***vulgare*** (***P*** × ***mantoniae*** (Rothm.) Shivas)
Hedgebank E of Ellerslie*†; turfy wall-top by Santon war memorial†. This hybrid is probably common, as in west Wales — where it sometimes occurs in the absence of either parent.

P. australe Fée Southern Polypody
C Mortared walls. Very rare.

SE — Near Douglas, c 1866, *Talbot**†. **SW** — Old bridge, bottom of Glen Maye, 1937, *Young* hb BM!† A single tuft survives.

A native primarily of limestone rocks, this demands a sheltered situation, well-drained neutral soil and — above all — freedom from frost. It has recently been found to be widespread in north Wales, north-east Ireland and south-west Scotland, tending to hug the coast.

Marsileaceae

Pilularia globulifera L. Pillwort
N Peaty pools, usually submerged. Very rare, perhaps extinct: not recorded for over a century.

N — Andreas, *Backwell's*: Curraghs, *Garner* (1867)

This plant is notorious for a tendency to die out in its known stations after a period of years. Garner's locality seems to have been in the Jurby curraghs.

Azollaceae

Azolla filiculoides Lam. (Water Fern) is grown as a garden aquatic but has yet to be found truly naturalised.

Ophioglossaceae

Botrychium lunaria (L.) Sw. Moonwort; Lus Luna
N Hill pastures, lead mine 'deads', dune heath. Occasional.

Although earlier workers implied this was widespread, there were few records after 1860 until very recently. Rabbits are fond of the fronds and, like so many of the Manx orchids, it has evidently been a leading beneficiary of the myxomatosis epidemics. On the Ayres a marked build-up culminated in 1967 in an explosive increase.

Ophioglossum vulgatum L. subsp. ***vulgatum*** Adder's Tongue
N Damp grassland, flushes, dune hollows. Local in the north, rare elsewhere. Calf.
Markedly few early records and a rush of recent ones suggest an increase.

SPERMATOPHYTA

GYMNOSPERMAE

Pinaceae

The following conifers have been widely planted, especially in the Forestry Board plantations: ***Pseudotsuga menziesii*** (Mirb.) Franco (Douglas Fir), ***Picea abies*** (L.) Karst. (Norway Spruce), ***P. sitchensis*** (Bong.) Carrière (Sitka Spruce), ***Abies alba*** Mill. (Silver Fir), ***Larix decidua*** Mill. (European Larch), ***L. leptolepis*** (Sieb. & Zucc.) Murr. (Japanese Larch), ***L. decidua × leptolepis***, ***Pinus sylvestris*** L. (Scots Pine), ***P. nigra*** Arnold var. ***calabrica*** (Loud.) Schneid. (Corsican Pine), ***P. contorta*** Dougl. ex Loud. (Beach Pine) and its var. ***latifolia*** S. Wats. (Lodgepole Pine). Certain of these regenerate spontaneously and are more or less naturalised in places. ***P. sylvestris*** was formerly a native but has been extinct for some centuries. Sub-fossil examples have frequently been unearthed from the lower layers of the northern curraghs and occur also under hill peat (up to 1,000ft on Mount Karrin).

Cupressaceae

Juniperus communis L. Juniper
N Moors. Very rare, apparently extinct.

C — A solitary male bush on a heathy moorland, Dreem Gill, Glen Auldyn, 1947, *GEQ**; transplanted for protection to a nearby enclosure, where it subsequently died. The fact that there is also a queried 1880s record for Sky Hill (roughly the same locality) in P. M. C. Kermode's notebook strengthens the likelihood that this was no mere bird-sown casual from some planted stock. There is a native population, moreover, on the cliffs of the Mull of Galloway, only about twenty miles distant.

Taxus baccata L. (Yew) is occasional as a planted tree, but scarcely naturalised.

ANGIOSPERMAE

Dicotyledones

Ranunculaceae

Caltha palustris L. Marsh Marigold; Bullught etc
N Marshes, wet fields, curraghs, ditches. Frequent in the north, local elsewhere; mainly in the lowlands. Calf. Forbes termed this 'very common', but it is hard to believe that this was correct even early last century or even just in those northern parts with which he was mainly familiar.

Aconitum compactum Reichb. (Monkshood; Croan Reisht) has been noted as an escape on four occasions. It is common in old gardens. ***Consolida ambigua*** (L.) P. W. Ball and Heywood (Larkspur) occurred as a weed in Castletown, 1968, and on a verge near Richmond Hill, 1968-73, *LSG*.

Anemone nemorosa L. Wood Anemone; Lus ny Geayee
NH Glens, plantations, stream-banks. Locally abundant in the northern and eastern glens, rare or absent elsewhere. Its remarkable absence from the south (it has been introduced into lower Colby Glen and possibly also Silverdale) was first noted by Ralfe. Oddly, too, it only seldom occurs in open hill pastures in Man, though so commonly elsewhere. A form with the corolla completely pink on both sides, var. ***carnea*** auct., grows on the banks of the Neb by Tynwald Mills, *MD*. Another form, with flowers 4cm in diameter and broader leaflets, agreeing in most respects with E. J. Salisbury's description of his var. ***robusta***, occurs sparsely with the type in Summerhill Glen, Douglas; it has doubtless been introduced.

A. apennina L. (Blue Anemone) is naturalised on a shady stream-bank by Greeba Bridge, *MD*. ***Clematis vitalba*** L. (Traveller's Joy) is also naturalised in hedges in several places.

Ranunculus acris L. Meadow Buttercup
N Grassy places. Very common. Calf.

R. repens L. Creeping Buttercup
NC Cultivated ground, ditches, shady places. Very common. Calf.

R. bulbosus L. Bulbous Buttercup
NC Dry banks, close turf, railway tracks. Locally common on the coast, occasional inland.

R. arvensis L. Corn Buttercup
C Cornfields. Very rare and doubtless extinct.
S — Malew, 1902, *Moore-Lane*, Proc 5, 25.

R. parviflorus L. Small-flowered Buttercup

C Bare, dry ground. Very rare.

S — Langness, abundant in a ploughed field, 1899, *Gasking* hb BM, BEC (1901)4; 1942, *Paton**.

A decreasing species in the British Isles, now confined mainly to the coastal parts of the South-west. At Langness at almost its Britannic northern limit.

[***R. auricomus*** L. Goldilocks

Listed by Gasking without details. A lime-loving rarity in the west, so rather unlikely to occur.]

R. lingua L. Greater Spearwort

NH Ditches, margins of pools and lakes. Rare, and confined to the north (as a native).

N — The Lhen, *Backwell's*, *Talbot* etc (now gone): Curraghs, *Garner* (probably same locality as next): pool W of Sandygate, abundant, *BSBI*[1]!: stream by Ballacrebbin, Andreas, *MBB*.

Also introduced as an ornamental at Ballasalla House and St. John's Forestry Board nursery, *LSG*.

R. Flammula L. subsp. ***flammula*** Lesser Spearwort; Lus y Steep

N Wet places. Common. Calf.

Formerly used in Man for curdling milk, combined with rennet.

R. sceleratus L. Celery-leaved Buttercup

NC Muddy, mineral-rich soil, usually by the sea. Very local: now confined to the extreme south-east corner.

C — The Rhaa, Lonan, *Talbot*. [**SW** — Listed from the Calf by an anonymous worker ("V.B.") in 1938. Error?]. **S** — Abundant in marshes along W shore of Langness, reproducing profusely and spreading along the tideline, *Paton*, *MD*! Presumably from this source carried to marshes, pools, river shingle and waste ground in numerous recorded localities between Poyllvaish and Ronaldsway and elsewhere on Langness.

R. hederaceus L. Ivy-leaved Crowfoot

N Marshes, muddy pools. Local, with a coastal tendency and avoiding the moister districts. Particularly widespread in Bride.

R. omiophyllus Ten. (*R. lenormandii* F. W. Schultz)

N Peaty pools, curragh drains and muddy places, especially in the hills. Common. Occurs up to 1100ft on Snaefell, *R. H. Goode*, WBEC (1914-15) 480.

Oddly, although so widespread and plentiful in Man, absent from the northern half of Ireland.

[***R. fluitans*** Lam. Claimed by the unreliable Robinson (1882) from an unspecified, apparently solitary locality in the central lowlands. In Ireland known from just one stream.]

R. trichophyllus Chaix (incl. subsp. ***drouetii*** (Godr.) Clapham)
N Brackish water near the sea. Very local: virtually restricted to the extreme north and south coasts. (†conf. C. D. K. Cook)

N — 'Scarce', *Robinson* (1882): pond near Lhaggagh, Andreas, 1936, *Paton** (now gone): Ballakinnag Dub, Smeale†; pond NE of Braust†: pond on Ayres NE of Knock-e-Dooney; old gravel-pit W of Point of Ayre, *D & G*. **C** — Saltmarsh, Port Cornaa, *LSG*. **S** — Pond, Scarlett, *S. Kermode, Br. Ass.*[1] hb RAMM: stream, Strandhall, *Teare, Paton*: mouth of Colby stream.

R. aquatilis L. (*R. heterophyllus* Weber) Water Crowfoot; Cass Feagh
N Ponds. Local; mainly in the north.

R. peltatus Schrank Water Crowfoot; Cass Feagh
N Ponds, reservoirs. Frequent in the north, rare or absent elsewhere. Calf.

[***R. baudotii*** Godr.
Listed by Gasking without details. Paton described it as 'common', but four gatherings labelled as this in his herbarium show that he misapplied the name to forms of ***R. aquatilis*** and ***R. peltatus***. Nevertheless a likely species to occur.]

R. ficaria L. Lesser Celandine; Lus ny Mlainyn
subsp. ***ficaria***
N Shady places, banks, hillsides. Very common. Calf.

subsp. ***bulbifer*** (Albert) Lawalrée
C Banks, usually near gardens. Local.
The production of bulbils is now regarded as the only reliable external character distinguishing this tetraploid race. Unlike the diploid, subsp. ***ficaria***, it is usually largely sterile, which additionally tells against a native status. The association with gardens is general throughout the west of the British Isles and suggests either accidental introduction in imported soil or some special folk use antedating the ornamental era. Presumably because of the bulbils the plant was formerly much valued as a remedy for piles, and in the Faeroes its presence today exclusively in churchyards is attributed to one-time cultivation on this account. In Silesia the bulbils are also known to have been eaten as an alternative to peas.

Aquilegia vulgaris L. (Columbine) is locally abundant in the Ballaugh Curraghs and, being characteristic of fen peat as a native and accepted as indigenous in areas bordering the Irish Sea, might well be supposed to be of the same status here. However, the fact that it seems to be increasing is suspicious; it has also been reported from this much explored area only in the last thirty years. Forbes (who knew the Curraghs well) firmly marked the species in his catalogue as introduced — and presumably knew of it solely as an obvious stray from cottage gardens. There have been several such records of it since, including several from glens.

Myosurus minimus L. Mousetail
C Sandy cornfields, bare ground flooded in winter. Very rare, apparently long extinct.

S — Near Castletown, 1816, *Anon* hb LIV. This most interesting record came to light only in 1979. The sheet was in a collection purchased from E. B. Woodruff in 1937 but the identity of the collector cannot be guessed at.

[***Thalictrum flavum*** L. Common Meadow-rue
'Scarce', *Robinson* (1882). The context implies more than one find in the central lowlands. A likely species geographically, but an unreliable recorder.]

BERBERIDACEAE

Mahonia aquifolia (Pursh) Nutt. × ***M. repens*** G. Don (Oregon Grape) is naturalised in one or two plantations and on roadsides.

NYMPHAEACEAE

Nymphaea alba L. White Water-Lily; Duillag Vaiht
N Shallow peaty pools. Very local: confined to the north.

N — The Lhen, *Backwell's*, *Talbot*, etc (now gone): Gat-y-Whing, *S. Kermode*, YLM (1899) 501, *Paton*!; Curragh-y-Cowle, *Paton*!: pool W of Sandygate, *BSBI*[1]!: pool behind Sandygate post office: dub, St. Jude's, *MD*.

Other white-flowered water-lilies have been planted in the Nunnery grounds and in the mill-pool on the Calf. These are presumably ***N. odorata*** Dryand. or one of the horticultural derivatives of its cross with ***N. alba***. A pink-flowered plant in Ballaleigh quarry pool, Michael, *MD*, may be ***N. alba*** var. ***rosea*** C. Hartm., a water-garden variety which might have been brought there by waterfowl; but it is too inaccessible to be examined.

Nuphar lutea (L.) Sm. Yellow Water Lily; Duillag Lheenagh
N Shallow pools, wide ditches. Very local: confined to the north.

In much the same localities as the last species, but more widespread. Unexpectedly, neither was recorded by Forbes.

Papaveraceae

Papaver rhoeas L. Corn Poppy

C Cultivated and waste ground. Frequent in the south, rare or absent elsewhere.

Var. ***strigosum*** Boenn., produced by a dominant gene and more southerly in Europe, was noted on a tip in Billown quarries in 1962, *WFS*.

P. dubium L. Long-headed Poppy

C Cultivated ground. Frequent, except in the east.

P. lecoqii Lam. Yellow-sapped Poppy

C Gardens. Rare.

W — Outside Glen Wyllin, 1962, *WFS**: Mitre Hotel, Kirk Michael, 1971, *D & G*. **S** — Strandhall, 1971, *MD*.

Perhaps overlooked previously. Quite widespread in parts of Ireland, including old gardens.

P. hybridum L. Bristly Poppy

C Cultivated ground. Very local.

N — Near Smeale, *Ralfe*: Jurby, *MB*. **W** — Ballaleigh, Michael, *GLQ*. **S** — Scarlett, *Backwell's*: Port St. Mary, *Ralfe*: near Castletown Claddagh, *Paton*: S of Kirk Malew, *Paton*: Langness, *BSBI*[1]: Castletown, *M & S*: by Silverburn S of Ballasalla, *LSG*.

A lime-lover, this southerly species is very rare in Ireland.

P. argemone *L.* Pale Poppy

C Sandy cultivated fields, railway tracks. Local; mainly in the far north and far south.

This is confined exclusively to railway tracks over a large part of west Wales. In Man, however, it has been noted only in two places on the Castletown-Port Erin stretch.

P. somniferum L. (Opium Poppy) occurs frequently on tips and waste ground. As early as 1860 Stowell complained of it as a troublesome weed in gardens. ***Meconopsis cambrica*** (L.) Vig. (Welsh Poppy) is naturalised in various places, including on rocks and (at Port Soderick) at the foot of sea-cliffs. Though accepted as native in north-east Ireland and North Wales, the rocks on which it grows there are more basic than any in Man and the habitats altogether wilder.

Glaucium flavum Crantz Yellow Horned Poppy; Barrag Vuigh
N Sandy and stony beaches, cliff ledges. Local: south-west and north coasts.

Sometimes wanders a little inland: on a hedgebank at the neck of Langness and several plants in hollows of gravel (simulating a shingle beach) in Kimmeragh gravel pits, Bride. RH noted a great increase during the 1940's at Dalby, one of its traditional localities, suggesting substantial fluctuations.

Chelidonium majus L. (Greater Celandine; Lus ny gollan geayee) occurs in hedges near houses, in widely scattered localities. Introduced into Britain by the Romans (on the evidence of the post-glacial deposits), its orange latex was widely used for warts and eye troubles.

FUMARIACEAE

†det. H. W. Pugsley ‡det. N. Y. Sandwith

[***Corydalis claviculata*** (L.) DC. Climbing Corydalis
'Hedges and bushy places', *Stowell* (1863). In this, his later list Stowell makes no mention of ***Fumaria capreolata***, which alone of the two featured in his first one (1860); probably therefore he had become confused about them in the meantime. Alternatively, he may have been deceived by cleistogamous-flowered plants of ***Fumaria*** growing in shade, which sometimes closely simulate ***C. claviculata***. Although the latter is characteristic of oceanic deciduous woodland and common in west Wales and Galloway, it is decidedly rare in Ireland.]

C. lutea (L.) DC. (Yellow Corydalis) is occasionally naturalised on walls and waste ground.

Fumaria capreolata L. White Ramping Fumitory
N?C Cultivated ground, tips, railway tracks, hedgebanks. Local.

In Ireland and south-west England this occurs in various natural habitats (such as cliffs and coastal sands) and is widely accepted as indigenous. In Man, however, its behaviour in this direction does not appear to extend beyond hedgebanks (for example, near Dalby and in Malew) and its status is thus more problematic.

F. purpurea Pugsl. Purple Ramping Fumitory
N?C Cultivated fields, beaches. Local.

N — Base of clay cliffs N of Ramsey, appearing indigenous, *Whellan*†, BEC (1946-7) 282: Ramsey, *M & S* hb K‡: NW of Ballaugh; Orrisdale, *WHH*. **S** — Turnip field, Port Erin, 1888, *F. C. King* hb NMW: Port Erin, *Br. Ass.*[1] hb RAMM!.

Whellan's suggestion that this might be native in Man is particularly interesting. It has also been recorded in coastal habitats just across the sea in Galloway.

F. bastardii Bor. — Tall Ramping Fumitory

NC Cultivated and waste places, sea-cliffs. Frequent.

Another predominantly western species which occurs both as a weed and in natural habitats — and in this case with even stronger claims to native status. In one part of Somerset it grows *only* on banks and in hedgerows, especially near the sea. In Man, however, it has only once been found in a seemingly indigenous situation: on cliffs at Laxey, again by Whellan (BEC (1946-7) 282). This was var. ***hibernica*** Pugsl., a rather slight variety that is equally as widespread as the type in Ireland and occurs in plenty on the Wigtownshire coast.

F. muralis Sond. ex Koch — Common Ramping Fumitory; Booa Ghone
subsp. ***boraei*** (Jord.) Pugsl.

NC Cultivated ground, cliffs, hedgebanks. Frequent.

Of all Manx Fumitories the most widespread in native-looking habitats — eg dry heathy ground at Glen Wyllin mouth and cliff-path above Perwick Bay.

F. officinalis L. — Common Fumitory

C Cultivated ground. Local; mainly in the south-east.

An obviously latecoming immigrant from the south and, unlike the other species, nowhere appearing native in Man.

Cruciferae

Brassica napus L. (Rape) has occurred once or twice as a relic of, or escape from, cultivation.

B. rapa L. — Field Cabbage; Napin Feie

C Cultivated and waste ground. Local; mainly in the north.

Especially frequent in the Kirk Michael district, where (as so commonly in northern England) it also occurs naturalised on a stream-bank.

B. nigra (L.) Koch — Black Mustard

N?D Beaches, waste ground. Rare. Calf.

> **W** — Tip near Ballacross, Peel: Ballaleigh, Michael, *LSG et al.* **SW** — Calf, *Ralfe*, *LSG*. **S** — Knock Rushen, abundant among the shingle at high-water-mark, *Holt*, *Paton*!: Ballasalla.

Although well-established at Knock Rushen for over sixty years and claimed as indigenous on beaches in the Clyde area, this appears more convincingly native on the sea-cliffs of southern Wales and south-west England. Unfortunately, as the main mustard of commerce the species has such a long history of cultivation that its occurrences on beaches cannot be above suspicion.

Erucastrum gallicum (Willd.) O.E. Schulz occurred on Ramsey tip in 1978, *D & G*, det. E. J. Clement.

Rhynchosinapis monensis (L.) Dandy — Isle of Man Cabbage

N Coastal sands. Local; now virtually restricted to the north.

N — 'Plentifully, going from the landing-place at Ramsey to the Town', 1660, *Ray* (*Catalogus*, 103). The Island's earliest localised plant record. It still grows intermittently on the foreshore at Ramsey Mooragh as well as in between the houses there and has been frequent till very recently northwards as far as the Dog Mills. It reappears at Cranstal Point and thence, often in some abundance, westwards along the Ayres to beyond Blue Point, reappearing afresh on the brows just south of the Lhen (where Forbes knew it 'in great plenty'). **W** — Near Peel, *Davies*. Long extinct. **SE** — Douglas sandhills, *Forbes*, *Jowett* hb K: grounds of Castle Mona, *Forbes*, *Holt**. Long extinct. **S** — Poyllvaaish, two plants, 1961, *LSG*.

Despite its English name — a mere translation of the Latin one which John Ray first bestowed on it (still the only British flowering plant which commemorates the Island) — this also occurs around the shores of the Firth of Clyde and along the east side of the Irish Sea, with outlying stations in Iona and in Glamorgan. In Cornwall and Devon it is thought to be an introduction. As it is known nowhere else — not even, very curiously, on the coasts of Ireland — it is a reasonable presumption that it originated somewhere within this present-day area, quite possibly in the Isle of Man itself. A closely-related species, also diploid (or an ancient tetraploid), is found only on Lundy Island. For Manx botanists the plant is thus of major phytogeographical no less than historical interest.

Sinapis arvensis L. — Charlock; Brashlagh

C Cultivated ground, tips. Common. Calf.

S. alba L. — White Mustard

C Cultivated ground, tips. Local; mainly in the south-east.

Diplotaxis muralis (L.) DC. (Stinkweed) is an increasing casual on tips and elsewhere. First noted at Peel* in 1951, it has since occurred at Ramsey (four times) and Derbyhaven. ***D. tenuifolia*** (L.) DC. (Wall Rocket), which has also increased greatly in southern England in recent years, accompanied ***Papaver lecoqii*** as a flower-bed weed in Kirk Michael, 1968, *D & G*. In 1981 one plant also on Peel brick-works site, *D & G*.

Raphanus raphanistrum L. Wild Radish; Rahghyl Feie

C Arable fields. Occasional; mainly in the driest districts. Calf.

Ralfe also called this 'common', which, if correct, identifies another victim of increased agricultural efficiency. A characteristic follower of rye crops, it was apparently first brought to Britain by the Romans. Today it occurs across Europe in three main colour forms, which succeed one another geographically, the single genes responsible for them presumably being selected for different intensities of light. The southernmost, with white flowers, var. ***raphanistrum*** is rare in Man: near The Cronk; Union Mills; Kentraugh, *LSG*. The middle one, the pale yellow var. ***ochroleucus*** (Stokes) Peterm., is the prevalent form in England except in the south and east; it appears to be rare in Man too, with only five records. Instead, the northern form with golden yellow flowers, var. ***luteus*** L. (var. *aureus* Wilmott) is the principal one with us.

R. maritimus Sm. Sea Radish

N On the drift-line of shores. Very local but increasing.

N — Kirk Michael, *S. Kermode*: Ayres N of Rue Point, *BSBI*[1], *MBB*!: S of Point of Ayre, *D & G*. **S** — NW Langness, *Paton* etc! (abundant by 1964): Derbyhaven, *Paton*, *BSBI*[1]!: Kentraugh, *Paton*, *D & G*: Poyllvaaish, *WFS*!

First recorded in 1897, this appears to be a comparatively recent addition to the native flora — even though it occurs on many of the coasts opposite. So conspicuous a plant is unlikely to have been overlooked in the Castletown area had it been present earlier.

Crambe maritima L. Sea Kale; Cabbag Hraie

N On the drift-line of shores. Local and rather sporadic.

Traie Cabbag, by Knockaloe, takes its name from this plant, which has long been esteemed as a vegetable. In the last century carts used to be sent over for it from Dalby (yet it still grows there in plenty). Although decreasing on the Irish and most neighbouring coasts, the rather numerous recent records for it in Man suggest the contrary here.

Rapistrum rugosum (L.) All. (Bastard Cabbage) has occurred once as a casual: between the Eairy and Granite Mt., *BSBI*[1] hb BM, K.

Cakile maritima Scop. Sea Rocket

N On the drift-line of shores. Common in the north, occasional and rather sporadic elsewhere.

Conringia orientalis (L.) Dumort. (Hare's-ear Cabbage) has occurred in gardens in Ramsey, Sandygate and Castletown and elsewhere since 1947, as an ingredient of bird seed or hen food.

Lepidium sativum L. (Garden Cress) sometimes appears on tips.

[***L. campestre*** (L.) R. Br. Common Pepperwort
Roadside near Jurby, *Wheldon* (1909-10): 'specially abundant on waysides but less common than ***L. heterophyllum***', *S. Kermode* (1911): Dog Mills, *BSBI*[1] (Allen, 1954). This last record is now known to have been an error. Kermode clearly had an erroneous conception of the species, while Wheldon, unaware that this was not known as a Manx plant, failed to take a voucher specimen. Superlative field botanist though he was, it seems probable that for once he was careless or mistaken. Earlier records, by Forbes and Stowell, were made in an aggregate sense and are certainly referable to the next.]

L. heterophyllum Benth. (*L. smithii* Hook.) Smith's Cress
NC Dry banks, roadsides, slaty trackways, shingle. Common. Calf.
Especially plentiful along the railway and tramway tracks.

L. ruderale L. (Narrow-leaved Pepperwort) has occurred once as a casual: near Richmond Hill, 1874, *T. Entwistle**.

Coronopus squamatus (Forsk.) Aschers. Common Wart-cress
N?C Stony beaches, pond-margins, trampled places, waste ground. Local; mainly in the far south and near the sea, but on the increase in the north-west. Calf.

So readily disseminated on hooves and footwear (it is characteristic of farmyards) that it is difficult to be sure of its native status. However, it has been recorded on beaches, especially just above high-water mark, at Niarbyl, Fleshwick, Poyllvaaish (since the 1850s) and Knock Rushen; and is also known by two ponds in Jurby. In such habitats it is normally accepted as native in county Floras. Against this must be set its non-discovery in British post-glacial deposits earlier than Roman times.

C. didymus (L.) Sm. Slender Wart-cress
C Waste ground. Rare; a recent arrival, first noted in 1950.

N — Farmyard, The Cronk, *BSBI*[2]!: Ramsey tip; Kirk Michael tip, *D & G*: Larivane housing estate, Andreas; Vollan promenade, Ramsey; Ballakinnag Ayres; Close William, Andreas, *MD*. **SE** — Factory premises at Kirk Braddan*. **S** — Tip on Langness, *BSBI*[1] hb K.

Cardaria draba (L.) Desv. Hoary Cress
C Waste ground, roadsides. Rare, but slowly spreading.

N — Waste heaps, Ramsey Mooragh, 1918, *Wheldon*: Kimmeragh gravel pits, Bride, 1957. **W** — Garden weed between Glenfaba and Patrick, 1972, *D & G*. **SE** — Belmont Hill, S Douglas, since 1962!; Douglas tip, 1970; Ballabrooie housing estate, S Douglas, 1974, *MD*. **S** — NW Langness, 1939; Knock Rushen, since 1942! *Paton*.

Reputedly first introduced in Britain with army bedding-straw during the Napoleonic Wars, this vicious weed has since spread very widely, transported in manure.

Thlaspi arvense L. Common Pennycress
C Cultivated ground, roadsides, tips. Local; mainly in the north as a field weed. Calf.

Though absent from most of Ireland, this long seems to have been a speciality of sandy fields in Ballaugh, Jurby and Andreas. There is a specimen, labelled merely 'in ye Isle of Man', in Willoughby's herbarium at Nottingham (vol. 3, facing p. 831) which must have been collected on his visit with Ray in 1660. It was also one of the few plants that Davies recalled from his visits in 1774–5: 'Isle of Man, but I do not recollect the spot' (in Turner & Dillwyn 1805).

Teesdalia nudicaulis (L.) R. Br. Shepherd's Cress
N Sandy heathland. Very rare.

N — Near The Cronk, locally plentiful, in two places, *WHH**, *MQ* etc.

Very rare in Ireland and confined there mainly to sandy lake-shores.

Capsella bursa-pastoris (L.) Medic.
Shepherd's Purse: Sporran y Vochilley
C Cultivated and waste ground. Very common.

Cochlearia officinalis L. Common Scurvy Grass; Guilley Bing
N Rocks and banks near the sea, salt-marshes. Common. Calf.

Up to ¼ mile inland at Keristal, in a runnel beside the railway.

[***C. scotica*** Druce Scottish Scurvy Grass
Cliffs near Peel, *Forbes*: Port Soderick and Cass-ny-Hawin, *Stowell*: Langness, *Talbot**, det. A. J. Wilmott: 'Common', *Paton* (but he also applied this name to ***C. anglica*** in his herbarium). Recent research suggests this is a mere northern race of ***C. officinalis***. Many of the characters traditionally relied on have been shown to be unworkable, the most consistent being the dwarf habit, clasping stem leaves and the usually truncate basal ones. It remains to be seen whether this entity, as thus redefined, occurs at all in the Island. Apart from records from the Irish east coast, which equally now need checking, it appears to have the kind of West Irish-Hebridean distribution that regularly excludes the Isle of Man.]

C. danica L. Early Scurvy Grass
N Dry, bare places near the sea. Common. Calf.

C. anglica L. Long-leaved Scurvy Grass
N Saltmarshes. Very local.

N — Ramsey, *Paton**. **C** — Port Cornaa. **S** — Knock Rushen, abundant, *Paton**: mouth of Silverburn, Castletown. Also recorded from 'seashores' by *S. Kermode* (1900).

This often accompanies ***C. officinalis*** and both Dutch and Irish botanists have concluded that extensive hybridisation occurs to the point of introgression. At least some of the Manx populations display variability suggestive of this but more intensive study is needed.

[***Subularia aquatica*** L. Awlwort
Listed for vice-county 71 in ASNH (1898) 46. An obvious misprint, as the paper in question was expressly concerned with Scottish records exclusively.]

Lobularia maritima (L.) Desv. (Sweet Alison) is an occasional escape on waste ground.

Erophila verna (L.) Chevall. subsp. ***verna*** Whitlow Grass
NC Short, dry turf and walls. Locally abundant on the north coast, from The Cronk up to Blue Point; otherwise very local, confined to round Peel and the far south — all areas with a mean annual rainfall of under 35 in.

No hygrophilous forms have been noted, but it occurs along the upper tideline between Strandhall and Poyllvaaish, *LSG*.

Armoracia rusticana Gaertn., Mey. & Scherb. (Horse Radish) is occasional near houses.

Cardamine pratensis L. Lady's Smock; Losserey ny Boaldyn
NCH Bogs, marshes, dune-slacks, damp grassy places. Very common. Calf.

A polyploid complex still inadequately understood. In Man, as in much of the rest of the British Isles, virtually all plants encountered appear to be of hybrid origin, the result of wholesale crossing between different chromosome races consequent upon the breakdown of previously isolating ecological barriers. The two races involved in Man are those prevailing in Ireland and upland Britain: a dwarf, white-flowered plant of bogs, which appears to be subsp. ***polemonioides*** Rouy (*C. nymanii* Gand.) and an octoploid with 2n = 64; and a tall, robust plant of reedswamp, which falls within subsp. ***palustris*** (Wimm. & Grab.) Janchen and is evidently responsible for the somatic number of 72 counted on north-east Ireland material. It is the latter plant to which I have given the MS name 'subsp. ***atlantica***' or 'subsp. ***palustris*** var. ***atlantica***' in herbarium determinations — for populations like this, with ovate-oblong, petiolulate leaflets to the lower stem leaves and numerous, approximate ones to the basal leaves, are characteristic of the west of the British Isles. Further study may well show, however, that they are not separable from similar taxa known on the continent.

Individuals, or whole populations, with double flowers sometimes occur spontaneously, seemingly as a by-product of crossing. In Man these have been recorded from: Near the Slock; old Staarvey road S of Kirkmichael, *Paton*: roadside, Rhendhoo, Jurby, *MD*. A double form of the tetraploid with 2n = 30, subsp. ***pratensis*** (*C. dentata* Schultes?), is also widely cultivated as 'Bachelor's Button' and is prone to escape. A colony of over 500 plants on a grassy bank by the Strang crossroads, *MD*, is referable to this.

C. flexuosa With. Wavy Bittercress
NC Damp, often shady places, gardens, beaches. Common. Calf.

On sea shingle at Port Garwick and between Scarlett and Poyllvaaish. Abundant under bracken on the treeless Calf, by Cow Harbour.

C. hirsuta L. Hairy Bittercress
C Bare ground, wall-tops, railway tracks, gardens. Common. Calf.

Barbarea vulgaris R. Br. Wintercress; Burley Loughlinagh
C Stream banks, roadsides, waste ground. Occasional, but fugitive and often only singly; mainly in the north.

Most of the older records doubtless refer to the next (the presence of which in the Island went unrecognised till 1962).

B. intermedia Bor. Early Wintercress
D River banks, waysides, disturbed bare ground. Local; mainly in the north and south-east.

Originally sown in clover leys. Tastes unpleasantly bitter so, unlike the next, not likely to have been cultivated as a salad plant.

B. verna (Mill.) Aschers. (American Land-cress) is an increasing casual, recorded four times since 1967, at Ramsey, Sulby Bridge and Douglas.

Rorippa nasturtium-aquaticum (L.) Hayek Watercress; Burley
N Marshes, streams, ditches, especially near the sea. Local; mainly in the extreme north and south. Calf.

R. microphylla (Boenn.) Hyland. Brown-leaved Watercress
N Streams, ponds. Rare or overlooked.

N — Pond by Kimmeragh, Bride. **C** — Stream, Port Lewaigue, hb BM, **S** — Stream, Atholl Park, Port Erin*.

In Hertfordshire this has been found to replace the preceding species in streams with clay bottoms. The Manx records are too few to yield any ecological generalisation.

R* × *sterilis Airy Shaw
Though sterile, the hybrid is more widespread in Man than its parents and usually unaccompanied by either. This is explained by the fact that, with its greater vegetative luxuriance, this is the Watercress most favoured for cultivating. Reflecting this, it typically occurs in old mill dams and farmyard ponds. Unlike ***R. nasturtium-aquaticum***, it shuns brackish water and its distribution is altogether less coastal. The numerous recorded localities, however, all lie in the south and the central valley.

R. sylvestris (L.) Bess. Creeping Yellow Cress
NC Lake-shores; gardens. Rare, but liable to increase.

N — Garey House, Lezayre, 1962: cottage, N Andreas, 1971, *MD*. **W** — Forestry Board nursery, St. John's, 1972, *MD*. Brought in with garden plants from England, where in recent years new, non-paludal biotypes have become pernicious weeds. **C** — Margins of The Clypse and Kerrowdhoo Reservoirs, *Cowin*!*. First noticed c1946. Likely to be genetically distinct from the weed plants and introduced by waterfowl from indigenous populations across the sea.

R. islandica (Oeder ex Murray) Borbás Marsh Yellow Cress
N Muddy ponds. Rare and very local.

N — Point of Ayre, *Backwell's*: dried-up pond towards Smeale, 1933, *Paton** hb BM: Lhaggagh, abundant in large, permanent pool and sparsely in small one nearest Smeale corner (Paton's locality?); pond in old gravel-pits W of Point of Ayre, *D & G*.

Unexpectedly, Paton's Smeale gathering was recently found by Dr B. Jonsell of the University of Lund to belong to the true plant so called and not to the species which has hitherto usually passed under this name in Ireland and Britain, ***R. palustris*** (L.) Bess. The former has half as many chromosomes, is typically arctic-alpine in its world range and closely related to taxa in western North America. The very few, scattered stations in the north and west of the British Isles in which it has so far been detected point to random, long-distance dispersal by migrant geese. The Lhaggagh plants are this same species and so too probably was that from the Point of Ayre. Nevertheless ***R. palustris*** ought to occur, especially in view of its commonness as a weed on the mainland opposite.

Hesperis matronalis (L.) (Dame's Violet) is well naturalised in various places.

Erysimum cheiranthoides L. Treacle Mustard
D Roadsides, railway tracks. Rare; confined to the north.

N — Roadside, Ballaugh, *Forbes*; still there, 1929, *Paton**: roadside, Jurby, *Stowell*: Lhen Bridge, one plant, 1919, *Ralfe*: railway opposite Gob y Volley, 1962, *WFS*!. **C** — Maughold, *WHH*.

Its absence as a weed of cultivated fields (its normal habitat) suggests this owes its presence in Man solely to its one-time popularity as a vermifuge, when it formed a principal ingredient in the famous Venice treacle.

Cheiranthus cheiri L. (Wallflower; Blaa Voalley) has been naturalised for at least a century on the ruins of Rushen Abbey. It has also been long established on rocks in a quarry nearby and has been noted on old walls in Ballasalla, Castletown, Port St. Mary, Peel and Ramsey.

Alliaria petiolata (Bieb.) Cavara & Grande Garlic Mustard
D Shady places near houses. Rare.

Though so common a hedgebank plant in England, in Ireland this becomes a pronounced calcicole and rare over large areas. It nowhere has a native look in Man and its anomalous distribution is additionally suspicious. It was formerly in herbal use, for sauces and as a salad plant.

Sisymbrium officinale (L.) Scop. Hedge Mustard; Burley Cleiee
C Roadsides, farmyards, waste ground. Common.

In Man this was once used herbally, for coughs and hoarseness (Quayle 1973, 70) — though it is uncertain whether it was actually cultivated. The glabrous form, var. ***leiocarpum*** DC., is frequent, especially in farmyards and around hen runs. This is the prevalent form in the Mediterranean region and North America and is probably a common impurity in grain imported thence. Other characters have been claimed to be associated with the glabrosity and possibly it merits subspecific rank.

S. orientale L. Eastern Rocket
C Waste ground, tips, gardens. Rare.

N — Jurby, 1914, *Wheldon* hb NMW: Andreas Rectory, 1930; The Lhen, 1932*; brow near Killane mouth, Jurby, 1932, *Paton* hb BM: tips etc., Ramsey, since 1962. **W** — Peel, 1937, *DPY*. **SE** — Douglas tip, 1960.

An increasingly frequent weed in the Irish Sea area, introduced with 'screenings' from foreign grain used as poultry food.

Arabidopsis thaliana (L.) Heynh. Thale Cress
C Walls, dry banks, cultivated ground, railway tracks. Frequent, varying much in quantity from year to year.

Camelina sativa (Gold of Pleasure) has begun appearing on tips at Douglas and Ramsey* since 1960, probably as a derivative of bird-seed. The plants belong to var. ***pilosa*** DC.

RESEDACEAE

Reseda luteola L. Weld; Wullee Wuss
D Waste ground, dry banks, field borders. Local; mainly in the north. Formerly grown as a crop for its dye and still betraying this origin in certain of its present-day locations. Fluctuates in quantity: particularly prolific in 1970.

R. alba L. (White Mignonette) was naturalised last century on hedge-banks in Ballaugh. It turned up again in 1974 on Ramsey tip, *D & G*.

VIOLACEAE

Viola odorata L. Sweet Violet; Blaa Villish
N?H Hedges, shady banks. Local; mainly in the north.
Although a common escape, this is accepted as native in England as far north as Westmorland and in central Ireland — provided it grows on the limestone to which it appears compelled to cling towards the limits of its natural range. A colony growing in Billown lime quarries, along the north edge under thorny scrub with ***Arum maculatum***, *LSG*, might conceivably therefore be a relic of a once more extensive indigenous population in that rather limy area — the more so as all these plants are purple-flowered (var. ***odorata***) and at the northern end of its British range the proportion of purple to white flowers apparently increases. On the other hand purple flowers seem to be the rule in the gardens in that south-east corner of the Island. In the north, by contrast, the plants widely naturalised in hedges are almost always white-flowered. These are normally var. ***leucantha*** Gaud. (var. *dumetorum* (Jord.) Rouy & Fouc.), the form so abundant in the West of England; but specimens answering tolerably well to the more lime-demanding var. ***imberbis*** (Leight.) Hensl. occur in one locality remote from houses near Ballachurry, Andreas, *MD**. Examples of the former have the petals flecked with violet on the back, suggestive of past crossing with the type.

V. riviniana Reichb. Common Dog Violet
N Glens, hedgebanks, dry heaths, cliff turf, railway tracks. Common. Calf.
Often flowers in the autumn in Man, as in other westerly areas.

[***V. reichenbachiana*** Jord. ex Bor. Wood Dog Violet
Claimed by the unreliable Robinson (1882) from an unspecified, apparently solitary central lowlands locality. Paton's (1933) Colby record

rests on a poor specimen* so det. E. Drabble but which D. H. Valentine finds indeterminable. Another Paton gathering, also det. Drabble, he considers ***V. riviniana.*** Recent material, however, from the Dhoon (*MBB* 1959) and Ballacuberagh, at Sulby Glen mouth (*MD* 1970) Valentine is inclined to pass, but further collecting is needed for certainty. A disliker of acid soils and barely Scottish, it is not a species necessarily to be expected.]

V. canina L. subsp. ***canina*** Heath Dog Violet

N Dunes, heathy turf by the sea. Locally common in the north, rare elsewhere. Calf.

The prevailing form, of sandy ground, is var. ***sabulosa*** Reichb. (var. *dunensis* Becker). This is presumably a separate ecotype from the smaller, more diffuse heath and moorland form, var. ***pumila*** S. F. Gray (var. *ericetorum* (Hayne) Reichb.). The latter grows in at least two places on the Calf, but has not otherwise been recorded. Forbes knew this species as '***V. montana***', Stowell as '***V. lactea***' and S. Kermode as '***V. canina*** var. ***pumila***'. The cross with ***V. riviniana*** is not infrequent in neighbouring counties and should be looked out for, especially on the Ayres (where both species are common); it can readily be spotted by its very much larger tussocks, showy mass of blossom and undeveloped capsules.

V. lactea Sm. Pale Heath Violet

N Dry lowland heaths. Very rare, perhaps extinct.

SE — Groudle, 1883, Holt*. Presumably the basis of the record credited to Holt in JB (1905) suppl. 15. Well before this Holt (1874) had recorded '***V. canina*** var. ***stagnina***' from cliffs near Groudle, which sounds like the same plant. The post-1930 record marked in the *Atlas* is the result of a confusion.

There is ample suitable ground in the Groudle area for this strongly Atlantic species. In many of its former localities in the South of England it has been submerged by ***V. riviniana***, with which it is interfertile and crosses very freely. It is not known in Scotland and in Ireland only in the south, so in Man it is at the limit of its range and perhaps only hung on here precariously (though it still grows in several localities in Anglesey). It is very intolerant of competition and demands full exposure to sun, so any crowding in of vegetation could easily prove fatal.

V. palustris L. subsp. ***palustris*** Marsh Violet

N Bogs, lake shores, wet glens. Frequent, especially in hilly districts.

The western race, subsp. ***juressi*** (Link ex K. Wein) Coutinho, ought to occur as well and has been assiduously sought. A plant abundant in Glen Roy answers to its description to the extent of having acute summer leaves and larger (12-13·5 mm) flowers, but lacks the hairy petioles and bracteoles around the middle of the pedicel which are additional, though not invariable, characters claimed to be associated with these. Plants at Eary Cushlin and in a plantation N of Kionslieu, *LSG**, on the other hand, combine slightly hairy petioles with subacute summer leaves. Non-flowering specimens exhibiting merely this last character, together with more prominent veins and crenation, have been seen N of Cronk-y-Voddy, above Glen Auldyn and below Block Eary — in this last case also with sparse hairiness on the upper surface and margin of the leaves but not at all on the petioles. The taxon needs more study, if possible biometrically.

V. lutea Huds. Mountain Pansy

N Upland grassland, especially on base-rich soils. Very rare, apparently extinct.

C — 'On the mountains', *Forbes*: North Barrule, *Stowell*: Snaefell, *Black's*. Also listed, without details, by McNab (Watson 1832).

Not recorded since 1883. In Ireland only known in the southern half.

V. tricolor L. subsp. ***tricolor*** (incl. *V. lepida* auct., *V. pesneaui* auct., etc) Heartease; Braag ny Cooaig

NC Dry grassland, cultivated fields. Local.

N — 'Fields', *Forbes* hb BM: 'sandy ground of the north', *S. Kermode* (1911): Ramsey; Jurby; Andreas, *Paton*: abundant on sandy heathland from Orrisdale to Broughjairg Beg, *Paton** (det. E. Drabble as ***V. pesneaui***), *RH* etc! **C** — Above Glen Mona: above Narradale, *MD*. **W** — Peel golf links and adjacent railway bank among bracken, *Ralfe** (det. E. Drabble as ***V. lepida***), *RH* etc hb K: railway track S of Glen Wyllin. **S** — Fields at Creggans, Malew, *Stowell* (as ***V. curtisii***): Colby, *Brearey**.

Seemingly native in the Orrisdale locality and possibly in the Peel one too. Both populations are wholly mauve-flowered, though with the former are particoloured crosses with subsp. ***curtisii.***

subsp. ***curtisii*** (E Forst.) Syme Seaside Pansy

N Sandy ground by the sea. Very local.

N — Near the sea, Kirk Michael, *Forbes*: between Orrisdale and The Cronk, here and there, *Holt**, *J. S. Rouse*, det. E. Drabble, BEC (1926) 304, etc!: Ramsey, *Paton**, det. E. Drabble.

Much confused with maritime forms of subsp. ***tricolor*** (which are also common on dunes) and wrongly described in the books in consequence. The true plant is never other than yellow-flowered and apparently unknown outside the British Isles.

V. arvensis Murr. Field Pansy

C Cultivated and waste ground, railway tracks. Locally frequent. ***V. arvensis*** × ***tricolor*** appears to be quite widespread.

Polygalaceae

Polygala vulgaris L. (incl. ***P. oxyptera*** Reichb.) Common Milkwort
N Bare ground, roadsides, coastal turf, dunes. Frequent. Calf.

Blue flowers predominate, pink ones also occur, while the apparently ecotypically distinct populations along the sandy northern coast, var. ***dunensis*** (Dumort.), are very largely white. Where these colour forms meet, as on the lead-mine deads by The Eairy, a welter of intermediates may be found. Like those of ***Anthyllis vulneraria***, however, their distribution appears to be random, undetermined by any selective influences.

P. serpyllifolia Hose Heath Milkwort; Lus y Vainney
N Heaths, especially in the hills. Common. Calf.

Pink, deep blue and pale blue forms occur, patches of all three sometimes growing on one and the same hillside.

Hypericaceae

Hypericum androsaemum L. Tutsan
N Damp places in light shade, wet rocks. Frequent, sometimes locally abundant in the moister districts, virtually absent from the north and far south (including the Calf).

H. × ***inodorum*** Mill. (*H. elatum* Ait.) (Tall Tutsan) has escaped in Foxdale and on the W outskirts of Ramsey. ***H. calycinum*** L. (Rose of Sharon) is naturalised in a few places, including on the Calf. It was planted alongside the Manx Electric Railway track and still survives here and there.

H. perforatum L. Common St. John's Wort
C Dry banks, waysides. Very local; mainly round Laxey and St. John's.

C — Laxey Glen Gardens, in two places, *Ralfe*, *JEL*!: below Laxey bus station. **W** — Sandhouse, German, *Ralfe*!: old sandpit by St. John's station, *Ralfe*!: Peel, 1917, *Paton*; abundant in railway cutting ¾ mile S of Peel station, *Clementson*! **SE** — Cliffs near Derby Castle, 1916, *Holt**. **S** — Port Erin, *Roeder*, *LSG* (on brooghs above swimming pool).

Unknown to S. Kermode and all earlier workers and unrecorded till the 1890s, this looks suspicious in all its present-day localities. Able to reproduce itself freely by vegetative shoots, it was doubtless imported accidentally, then spread around and has obstinately persisted. In Ireland it is decidedly a lime-lover.

H. maculatum Crantz subsp. ***obtusiusculum*** (Tourlet) Hayek (*H. quadrangulum* auct.) Imperforate St. John's Wort
C Open woodland. Very rare.

N — Patch in long grass in conifer nursery, Bishopscourt, first noticed 1977, *MD**, det. N. K. B. Robson.

This species was listed by S. Kermode (1900) as in 'hedges etc' — but certainly in error.

H. tetrapterum Fr. Square St. John's Wort

N Marshes, bogs, ditches, especially near the sea. Frequent, but absent from the whole of the centre. Calf.

H. humifusum L. Trailing St. John's Wort

NC Dry fields and banks, bare ground, gardens. Occasional, often occurring singly. Calf.

Paton termed this 'common' and Stowell 'abundant' (and certainly, as Ralfe noted, it is especially plentiful in the area nearest Stowell's home) but it is hard to believe that these were not exaggerations and that the plant has since decreased greatly.

H. pulchrum L. Elegant St. John's Wort; Lus y Chiolg

N Hedgebanks, dry grassy places. Very common. Much used as a tonic in Man.

H. elodes L. Bog St. John's Wort

N Bogs, wet fields. Formerly common, now very local. Calf.

A strongly Atlantic species, evidently highly sensitive to changes in humidity. In Forbes's day it was 'very abundant on moorlands, both on the mountains and near the sea' and Stowell knew it 'in profusion' in certain fields in Maughold where there is not a sign of it now. Only in ultra-oceanic spots, such as the Calf and Clay Head, does it still survive in its erstwhile plenty. The same marked decrease has been noted in northern Ireland and north-west England.

Cistaceae

[***Tuberaria guttata*** (L.) Fourr. Annual Rock-rose

'*In pratis . . . in Insula Mona*', intended by Hudson (1762) for the other Mona, Anglesey, the *locus classicus* of this species, was misattributed by subsequent eighteenth-century authors to Man. One, James Dickson, distributed specimens labelled 'In sandy fields, Isle of Man' in his *Hortus Siccus Britannicus* in 1797, but they are not the British race and must have been raised from foreign seed by that notoriously inaccurate (or unscrupulous) nurseryman. Unfortunately, tempted by a record for a species so geographically appealing, I admitted it for the *Atlas* before recognising its spuriousness.]

Tamaricaceae

Tamarix gallica L. (French Tamarisk) was recorded by Garner (1878) from the sands N of Ramsey and (as ***T. anglica*** Webb) by Keegan (1888) from an unstated locality. Doubtless planted in both cases as a windbreak.

Caryophyllaceae

Silene vulgaris (Moench) Garcke Bladder Campion; Lus y Lhemeen
C Roadsides, waste ground, dry banks, railway tracks. Frequent in the north and south-east, elsewhere widely scattered and often singly.

S. maritima With. Sea Campion; Lus ny Brooinyn Hraie
N Beaches, cliffs. Common. Calf.

S. gallica L. Small-flowered Catchfly
var. ***anglica*** (L.) Mert. & Koch
C Sandy arable fields near the coast. Formerly widespread in the north, now rare and confined to one small area in the south.

N — Jurby, *Forbes*, *Stowell* etc: Ballaugh, *Stowell*, *Holt**: Andreas, Jurby and Bride, *Backwell's*: road through (Jurby?) Curraghs, *Garner*: N Ramsey brooghs, *P. Kermode*; N of Jurby, *Wheldon* hb NMW: Kionlough, Bride, *Ralfe*. **S** — Scarlett; Poyllvaaish, *Ralfe*: several cornfields along W bank of Silverburn N of Castletown, *LSG*.

Last seen in the north in 1920, this was rediscovered in the south in 1967. Var. ***gallica*** appeared in a St. John's lawn, 1978, apparently introduced with grass seed, *ACK*, det. E. J. Clement. Var. ***quinquevulnera*** (L.) Boiss., formerly cultivated for its attractively spotted flowers, was recorded outside a garden at The Lhen by S. Kermode, det. Kew, YLM, 3, 611.

[***S. acaulis*** (L.) Jacq. Moss Campion
'In cliff crevices and on the turf above . . . ***Sedum anglicum***, ***Silene acaulis***, ***maritima and coronopus***, ***Scilla verna***', *Black's*. Some maritime species, not this alpine, obviously intended. Even Gasking (1890) scoffed at this as one of the 'evident errors inseparable from guide books'. Nevertheless it qualified for inclusion in his list as a species that had been recorded, however ludicrously — and unfortunately Paton, who never saw Gasking's original paper, was thereby deceived into treating the record seriously.]

S. noctiflora L. (Night-scented Catchfly) occurred as a casual at Little Ness, near Port Soderick, c 1885, *Ralfe*.

S. dioica (L.) Clairv. Red Campion; Blaa ny Ferrishyn
N Hedges, glens. Common. Calf.
Albino specimens have been noted since 1950 in nine places. Four of these

are on the west coast between Peel and Jurby and include a whole patch in Bishopscourt Glen. It is highly unusual, in my experience, for albinoes to exhibit a detectable pattern in their distribution.

S. pratensis (Rafn) Godr. & Gren. (*S. alba* (Mill.) Krause)
White Campion
C Waste ground, roadsides, cornfields. Frequent and spreading. Still mainly on the lighter soils of the north and far south, but starting to colonise the Douglas area. Significantly, never recorded by Forbes; apparently widespread by 1900, however. The hybrid with ***S. dioica*** is not uncommon and, being fertile, can occur in the absence of the parents — hence its occurrence on the Calf in 1965.

Lychnis flos-cuculi L. Ragged Robin; Lus ny Cooag
N Marshes, swamps, wet fields. Local, especially in the south. Calf. An albino specimen at Hillberry, *WSC*.

Agrostemma githago L. Corn-cockle
C Cornfields. Formerly 'very common' (Forbes), now extinct except as an alien casual: with Cornflowers at Ballaterson, Maughold, 1966, introduced with seed from the Continent, *GEQ*.

Brought into Britain by the Romans with their rye crops, this has been a conspicuous victim of more efficient cleaning of seed in the last half-century.

[***Cucubalus baccifer*** L. Berry Catchfly
'In hedges in the Isle of Man', *Robson* (1777). Another instance of mis-translation of 'Mona', intended for Anglesey — the original record for which is in any case dubious.]

Dianthus armeria L. Deptford Pink
N or C Dry grassland, especially on sandy soil. Very rare and doubtless long extinct.

S — Near Ballasalla; site of King William's College chapel, 1874, *Moffat*, Nat (1886) 370 and Sci Goss (1886) 69.

D. deltoides L. (Maiden Pink) was found by Peel Road Station 'years ago', *LVC* — doubtless introduced with grass seed — and there is an unlocalised specimen in Talbot's herbarium presumably collected in the Island c 1866. A ***Dianthus*** of undetermined species was also recorded by Spanton, c 1880, in a field at The Dog Mills.

Vaccaria hispanica (Mill.) Räusch. (Cow Basil), a casual at Ramsey in 1900, has begun to occur increasingly frequently in the last fifteen years as an introduction with bird seed. ***Saponaria officinalis*** L. (Soapwort) is well established in many places but always near houses. The mucilaginous juice will lather with hot water and was used for cleaning woollen fabrics of their grease. From this it earned the name in Man of 'Fuller's Herb'. The underground parts were also used as a tonic and for purifying the blood (Quayle 1973, 69). The fact that it is usually double-flowered with us suggests that it may have been grown as an ornamental as well.

Cerastium arvense L. Field Mouse-ear

N Sandy fields, dry turf, usually by the sea. Very local.

N — Ballaugh, etc, *Stowell*: Ballaugh, *S. Kermode*, *Paton*: road to Ballaghennie Ayres, *D & G*. **W** — Peel, *Paton*. **S** — Derbyhaven, *Forbes*, *Ralfe*, etc!; Gansey Point, *Ralfe*, *D & G*: Balladoole!; Hango Hill!; Poyllvaaish, abundant!, *Ralfe*: Port St. Mary, *OEB*, New Phyt (1955) 141, *MD*: St. Michael's Island: Chapel Hill, Balladoole, abundant. 'Isle of Man', 1822, *Wilson* hb CGE: 'in sandy fields in several localities', *Forbes*.

On slightly calcareous ground along the south coast and on acid sand in the north — just like ***Astragalus danicus.*** Like the latter, too, it is proportionately much more plentiful in Man than in Ireland, where it is very rare away from the Galway Bay and Dublin neighbourhoods. Dr O. E. Brett counted the chromosomes of a Port St. Mary specimen and found 2n = 72, the usual number in Britain.

C. fontanum Baumg. (*C. holosteoides* auct.; *C. vulgatum* auct.) subsp. ***triviale*** (Murb.) Jalas var. ***triviale*** Common Mouse-ear

NC Grassland, dunes, waste places, coast rocks. Common. Calf.

A neat, strict form with leaves very congested below grows on wet maritime rocks at Onchan Harbour (hb BM) and a form with bright green, shining, subglabrous leaves on Snaefell summit. The species is very variable and prone to produce such distinctive local ecotypes, which scarcely merit names. An exception is the large-flowered var. ***holosteoides*** (Fr.) Jalas, which is characteristic of the banks of tidal rivers and dune slacks, more particularly in northern Britain; this ought to occur in Man but a careful look-out has failed to disclose it.

C. glomeratum Thuill. (*C. viscosum* auct.) Sticky Mouse-ear

NC Dry turf, walls, paths, railway tracks, short marshes. Local. Calf.

As this is customarily looked upon as a xerophyte, its presence in marshes is distinctly startling — and to the best of my knowledge hitherto unknown. ***Myosotis discolor*** presents an interesting parallel. Its associates in this habitat include ***Gnaphalium uliginosum***, ***Potentilla anserina***, ***Plantago major***, ***Juncus articulatus***, ***Stellaria alsine*** and ***Veronica serpyllifolia.*** I have seen it growing thus by Ballagawne in Rushen and in abundance near The Rhaa, in Lonan.

C. diffusum Pers. (*C. atrovirens* Bab.; *C. tetrandrum* Curt.) Dark Green Mouse-ear
NC Maritime sands, rocks and turf, cliff-tops, walls. Frequent. Calf.
Also in sand- and gravel-pits up to two miles inland. Though abundant in Ramsey station-yard, however, only one inland railway track occurrence has been noted (contrary to its widespread practice in England): on the Neb bridge near St. John's.

C. semidecandrum L. Little Mouse-ear
N Dunes. Very local; confined to the north.
Stowell's mystifying description of it on 'walls, everywhere' is an obvious error.

[***Stellaria nemorum*** L. Wood Chickweed
Ballure Glen; Ballaglass waterfall, *Stowell*. This is a distinctive plant and occurs in glens as close as Wigtownshire. On the other hand it is unknown in Ireland. Other Stowell records are manifestly wrong and both localities have been searched to no avail several times. But it is hard to suggest what might have been mistaken for it: although the sole Caernarvonshire record is assumed to have been an error for ***S. neglecta*** Weihe, there is no evidence for that species in Man either.]

S. media (L.) Vill. Common Chickweed; Fleih
C Cultivated and waste ground. Very common. Calf.

S. holostea L. Greater Stitchwort; Lieen ny Ferrishyn
N Hedges, glens. Common. Calf.
Grows under the shade of stands of ***Phalaris arundinacea*** in The Congary, near Peel. Ascends to 1100ft above Keppel Gate, *LSG*.

S. graminea L. Lesser Stitchwort
NC Dry grassland, railway tracks, roadsides; river banks, curraghs, tall marshes. Common in the north, local round Douglas and Peel, largely absent elsewhere.
Occurs in two distinct classes of habitat in Man, one wet and the other dry (cf. ***Cerastium glomeratum*** and ***Myosotis discolor***). In the former it is presumably native, in the latter doubtless adventive. Two separate ecotypes seem likely to be involved.

S. alsine Grimm Bog Stitchwort
N Marshes, flushes, wet tracks. Common. Calf.

Sagina apetala Ard.
subsp. ***apetala*** (*S. ciliata* Fr.) Fringed Pearlwort
NC Dunes, dry bare ground near the sea, walls, railway tracks. Local; mainly in the north. Calf.

subsp. ***erecta*** (Hornem.) F. Hermann (*S. apetala* auct.)
Annual Pearlwort

NC Dry bare ground near the sea, waysides, walls, railway tracks, quarries, pavement cracks. Frequent.

S. maritima G. Don — Sea Pearlwort

N Sandy and rocky places by the sea, driftlines, saltmarshes. Frequent. Calf.

S. procumbens L. — Mossy Pearlwort

NC Marshes, streamsides, walls, paths, lawns. Common. Calf.

A fleshy form grows in damp places on Snaefell summit. Also a form on the Ayres closely simulating ***S. subulata***, *CES*, det. F. N. Hepper.

S. subulata (Sw.) C.Presl. — Heath Pearlwort

N Dry bare ground near the sea. Very local. Calf.

N — Point of Ayre, in plenty, *BSBI*[1] hb BM: central Ayres, thinly scattered, *D & G*! **SE** — Port Groudle; Douglas Head. **SW** — The Chasms*; Calf, path between farm and Sound: Bradda Head, *MB*.

'Rare', *Forbes*. Unlocalised specimen collected by Jowett in 1827 (Watson 1837) in hb K.

At Port Groudle this grows in very sparse, gravelly soil in shallow crevices on the upper side of rocks by the shore — exactly the habitat in which it grows most typically in Norway.

S. nodosa (L.) Fenzl — Knotted Pearlwort

N Base-rich mires, formerly also in dune slacks. Very rare.

N — Ramsey, 1877, *Holt** (presumably the '***Minuartia verna***' recorded from Ramsey Mooragh by Spanton in 1886): near Ballaghaie, Jurby, *Paton*, *MD*: Rhendhoo curragh, Jurby, in plenty: midway between Cranstal and Ballaghennie, *D & G*. Listed by Gasking without details.

Minuartia verna (L.) Hiern — Spring Sandwort

N Old copper and lead workings. Very rare.

SW — Abundant on a headland near the sea, in ***Armeria*** sward, *D & G*!* Discovered in 1971.

Garner definitely visited this very spot in or around 1854 and, assuming the plant was there by then, must assuredly have seen it. His subsequent, cryptic statement (1867), 'occurs on the débris of mines', appears from its context to refer to the hills but may merely have been a deliberate deception.

Honkenya peploides (L.) Ehrh. — Sea Sandwort

N Fore dunes, sandy shingle. Common. Calf.

Moehringia trinervia (L.) Clairv. Three-veined Sandwort
N Shady banks by streams. Very rare; in one small area only.

C — E bank of Sulby River by Ballakerka and W bank by Ballacuberagh, Sulby, both in good quantity*; also with ***Veronica montana*** in grounds of Ballamanaugh, Sulby, *D & G*!

Listed by Gasking without details.

Arenaria serpyllifolia L. Thyme-leaved Sandwort
subsp. ***serpyllifolia***
NC Walls, dry banks, maritime turf, shingle. Local; mainly in the south-east. Calf.

subsp. ***leptoclados*** (Reichb.) Nym.
C Walls, dry banks, quarries. Very local; confined to the north and far south-east.

N — Near Ellanbane; Ballaugh village. **S** — Kentraugh*; Balladoole House; Scarlett; near Hango Hill; Derbyhaven; about Castletown; Billown and Ballahot quarries.

The above two subspecies frequently occur together.

subsp. ***macrocarpa*** (Lloyd) Perring & Sell
N Fixed dunes. Common along the coast from Kirk Michael northwards. A record for the species on Ramsey Mooragh (1880, *Spanton*) also doubtless relates to this.

A. balearica L. (Balearic Pearlwort), a common rock-garden species, is well naturalised on a wall in Castletown, *ACK*, and as a widespread weed in the grounds of Ballamanaugh, Sulby, *D & G*.

Spergula arvensis L. Corn Spurrey; Lus y Chorran
C Cultivated and waste ground, river and lake shingle. Very common. Calf.

The form with a non-papillose seed-coat, var. ***sativa*** (Boenn.) Mert. & Koch, is much commoner than the type, as elsewhere in the north and west of the British Isles. The character is due to a single gene without dominance, and plants exhibiting it enjoy the selective advantage of germinating more readily at low temperatures; hence they gradually increase in ratio towards the colder parts of the specific range. B. Millard Griffiths, JB (1922) 229, studied the two forms in a field near Kewaigue and found var. ***sativa*** predominated 4:1.

Spergularia rubra (L.) J. & C. Presl Sand Spurrey
NC Sandy heathland, paths, railway tracks, waste ground. Locally common near the coast in Ballaugh, elsewhere scarce and widely scattered, often occurring singly. Calf.

Characteristic of slaty paths by the sea (cf ***Trifolium arvense***). Stowell knew it only in cornfields (in Maughold and Lezayre), but it has been seen in nothing nearer than a ploughed field at Scarlett in recent years. There are very few pre-1950 records and it would appear to have increased. Surprisingly, a great rarity in Ireland.

S. rupicola Lebel ex Le Jolis — Cliff Spurrey; Corran Traie

N Maritime rocks and cliffs. Common. Calf.

S. media (L.) C. Presl — Greater Sea Spurrey

N Saltmarshes. Very local.

N — Ramsey Harbour. **S** — NW Langness; Scarlett, *Paton**: mouth of Silverburn, Castletown; Ronaldsway; Balladoole.

Though unrecorded until 1938, presumably overlooked rather than a recent immigrant.

S. marina (L.) Griseb. (*S. salina* J. & C. Presl) — Sea Spurrey

N Drier zones of saltmarshes. Local.

The form with a papillose seed-coat, var. **neglecta** (Kindb.), appears to be the prevailing one in Man, as in Ireland.

Illecebraceae

Scleranthus annuus L. subsp. ***annuus*** — Knawel

C Cultivated fields, railway tracks. Local, but often abundant where it occurs; mainly on the sandy soils of the north. Proportionately more plentiful than in Ireland.

Portulacaceae

Montia fontana L. — Blinks

N Marshes, bogs, streamsides, lake-shores, pools, trickles. Common. Calf.

Three geographical races occur:-

subsp. ***chondrosperma*** (Fenzl) Walters (*M. verna* auct.)

SE — Douglas, 1888, *Billups* hb LSR†

The commonest in south-east England. Predominantly coastal in the south-west and Wales, but widely scattered (perhaps by birds) northward from there. Only one Irish record known. Generally in drier places than the others.

subsp. ***amporitana*** Sennen (subsp. *intermedia* (Beeby) Walters)

SW — Cringle Reservoir, *Paton**†

The commonest in south-west England and widespread in Wales.

subsp. ***variabilis*** Walters
Evidently common. Material from at least nineteen localities (including Calf) has proved to be this†. It is also represented in both the gatherings in which the preceding subspecies have been detected. The commonest in North Wales, north England and (seemingly) Ireland. Apparently a largely stabilised hybrid between subsp. ***amporitana*** and the mainly northern race, subsp. ***fontana***. A fruit of the latter has been found in a Late-Glacial deposit near Ballaugh† (Mitchell, 1958), but it now seems to be extinct in Man — though a specimen of subsp. ***variabilis*** from the R. Glass near Quarter Bridge, Douglas, comes close to it†.

†det. S. M. Walters

M. perfoliata (Donn ex Willd.) Howell — Spring Beauty
C Sandy cultivated and waste ground. Local; confined to the north.
First noticed in 1902, this North American species had become widespread, according to Paton, by 1930. Recent records have been rather few and mainly from Bride. It has arrived in Ireland only in the last few years and is still very rare there. Particularly associated with market gardens and nurseries, like the ***Galinsoga*** species it seems to have been extensively dispersed through horticultural commerce.

M. sibirica (L.) Howell (Pink Purslane) is a rapidly increasing escape, first noted only in 1955 — the entry for vice-county 71 in Druce (1932) is probably a misprint — and already in almost every glen and ramping along the gravel exposed in stream beds. The spread was particularly explosive from about 1970 onwards. The white-flowered form accompanies the type in Molly Quirk's Glen, Onchan, *MD* and Bradda Glen, *D & G*. Oddly, the species is still rare in Ireland.

Aizoaceae

Carpobrotus edulis (L.) N.E. Br. (Kaffir Fig) has recently become established in Ramsey shipyard, *D & G*. Profusely naturalised in south-west England, it is a species liable to spread.

Amaranthaceae

Amaranthus hybridus L. subsp. ***hybridus*** (Green Pigweed) occurred as a casual at Grenaby, 1959, *VLW**, det. J. P. M. Brenan. The specimen is referable to the type variety, which has become especially common in recent years as an introduction in wool manure.

Chenopodiaceae

Chenopodium bonus-henricus L. (Good King Henry; Orragh Feie) has been recorded from various places in the north and from the more inland villages in the far south, generally near cottages. It used to be grown as a vegetable and cooked like spinach.

[***C. vulvaria*** L. Stinking Goosefoot
Ballaugh shore, *S. Kermode* (1900). Because of the distinctive character of this species and its occurrences as a casual on nearby coasts, I was originally inclined to give Kermode the benefit of the doubt and this record was therefore included in the *Atlas*. On further reflection, though, his namings were too erratic for any otherwise unrecorded species to be accepted on his authority in the absence of a specimen.]

C. album L. Fat Hen; Coll Mea, Cabbag y Volley
CD Cultivated and waste ground. Very common. Calf.
The second of the Manx names points to one-time use of its leaves as a vegetable (as in Lincolnshire this century). The seeds also have a high protein and fat content and in Denmark have been found to be an important ingredient in an Early Iron Age gruel. Some authors have considered the species native in coastal habitats and along tidal rivers, but I have never seen it growing convincingly in such situations in Man.

[***C. viride*** L. (*C. suecicum* J. Murr)
Castletown, *Ralfe*. Doubtless, like most British plants so named, merely the f. ***cymigerum*** (Koch) Schinz & Thell. of ***C. album***.]

[***C. ficifolium*** Sm.
Listed by *Wattam* (1901), without details. A patently unreliable source.]

C. murale L. Nettle-leaved Goosefoot
C Waste places, dung heaps. Rare.
N — The Garey, Lezayre, 1967, *D & G*; Ramsey tip, 1967. **W** — About Peel castle, *Garner* (1867). **S** — Castle Rushen gate, 1901; plentiful on the shore behind Queen St. Castletown, 1909, 1934, *Ralfe**: roadside, Castletown, 1964.
['On the sand, common', *Forbes*. Queried at the time by Watson and undoubtedly an error.]

[***C. urbicum*** L. Upright Goosefoot
The record in the *Atlas* is based on a specimen of mine collected in Port St Mary in 1958 and determined as this by the British Museum. It was subsequently examined by J. P. M. Brenan, who considered it probably a form of ***C. rubrum***.]

C. rubrum L. Red Goosefoot

N Muddy duckponds, gulleries. Rare. Calf.

N — West Nappin pond, by Jurby church, *RH*!; Ballasalla, Jurby, in a goose-pond and a duck-pond nearby: The Lhaggagh, Andreas, *D & G*: **SW** — Gullery, Caigher Point, Calf, 1957. **S** — Castletown, *Br. Ass.*[1] hb RAMM.

Listed by Gasking without details. A nitrophile, characteristic of waterfowl droppings, with a marked coastal tendency, this is also native on the Irish coast but apparently absent from the whole west of Scotland. It appears abundantly in a Late-Glacial deposit near Ballaugh (Mitchell 1958).

Beta vulgaris L. subsp. ***maritima*** (L.) Arcang. Sea Beet; Beetys Feie

N Sandy, rocky and stony shores. Frequent, but almost absent from the east coast. Calf (abundant).

Still often collected to be eaten, cooked like spinach.

Atriplex littoralis L. Grass-leaved Orache

N Mud and shingle near the sea. Very rare and confined to the Ramsey area.

N — Ramsey Harbour, *Holt**!: bank of Sulby R. by footbridge W of Ramsey. **C** — Port e Vullen, 1958, hb BM.

Recorded by Stowell from 'sandy shores of the North', but clearly only in an aggregate sense. A Germanic species, in Man close to its north-western limit.

A. patula L. Common Orache; Mooyn Goayrey

C Damp, rich cultivated and waste ground. Common. Calf.

A. prostrata Boucher ex DC. (*A. hastata* auct.; *A. deltoidea* Bab.) Halberd-leaved Orache

NC Beaches, saltmarshes; dry waste ground. Frequent. Calf.

The maritime plants are more prostrate and have a higher proportion of large seeds as well as entire and thicker leaves, but they form merely one end of a continuous gradient of variation and are not now thought worthy of taxonomic recognition.

A. glabriuscula Edmondst. Babington's Orache

N Drift-lines. Perhaps frequent. Calf.

This species has just been freshly delimited taxonomically and its distribution in Man needs re-study. Both it and ***A. prostrata*** are extremely variable and many of the characters used in the past are not to be relied upon. Material in Paton's herbarium was determined by A. J. Wilmott in the 1930's as the hybrid between them, but though they are known to be freely interfertile the presence of such crosses in Man requires confirmation. More recently P. M. Taschereau has determined material from the Dhoon* and N of Cranstal* as the hybrid between this species and ***A. longipes*** Drej.

A. laciniata L. Frosted Orache
N Sandy and shingly shores. Local; mainly in the north.

Halimione portulacoides (L.) Aellen Sea Purslane
N Saltmarshes. Very local: now south coast only.
Apparently a re-invader. Recorded from 'L . . ny G . . .' (Ramsey?) by Spanton in 1884 and known to J. R. Bruce in the 1930's in abundance on the S side of Port Erin Bay till extinguished by the building of the present wall. In 1967 two plants were found at the SW tip of Langness, *MD**; the following year it was noticed in some plenty near Poyllvaaish and has subsequently proved to occur at intervals most of the way from Port St. Mary to Ronaldsway, *D & G*. Five plants noted in this last locality in 1973 were undoubtedly new arrivals. It is hard to believe that this species can have been missed by the many capable botanists who worked stretches of this coast a few years previously and it appears that a genuine, and rapid, spread is in progress.

Suaeda maritima (L.) Dumort. Common Seablite
N Saltmarshes, rockpools. Occasional. Calf.

N — Ramsey, *Backwell's*; *Paton*!: Rue Point ternery, one plant, 1977, *MD*. **C** — Port Mooar, *RH*. **SE** — Onchan Harbour, *WHH*. **SW** — South Harbour, Calf, *MB*. **S** — NW Langness, *Ralfe*; *GDR*!: Poyllvaaish, *Ralfe*; *Paton*!: Strandhall; Knock Rushen; Derbyhaven: Port Erin, *MB*: SW and E Langness, *MD*.

Oddly patchy: unrecorded for Scarlett, Peel or the Dalby area. Presumably largely overlooked till recently rather than increasing.

Salsola kali L. Saltwort; Lus y Tollan
N Sandy shores. Local; confined to the north, the west and the Castletown area.

†det. A. J. Wilmott
Salicornia europaea L. agg. Glasswort (Marsh Samphire)
N Saltmarshes. Very local.

N — Ramsey, abundant, *Backwell's*; *Holt* etc.: Ballaugh shore, *Hoyle* (extinct). **C** — Port Cornaa, *LSG*. **S** — NW Langness, *Paton, GDR* etc.: Knock Rushen, *JTW*: Balladoole: SW tip of Langness, *MD*.

A difficult group of microspecies, taxonomically controversial, greatly prone to vary with habitat conditions and necessarily studied fresh on an ample sample of specimens. Many are largely inbreeding and populations not readily assigned to one or other species are not unusual. Material from only three of the Manx localities has ever been examined by specialists:—

S. dolichostachya Moss Mouth of Sulby R., Ramsey, *Paton**†.

Much the most widespread British species, characteristic of open or sandy mud in the lowest saltmarsh zones, apparently requiring frequent submersion.

S. europaea L. (*S. stricta* Dumort.) NW Langness, *Paton**†.

S. ramosissima J. Woods (*S. gracillima* (Towns.) Moss; *S. smithiana* Moss) NW Langness, *Paton** hb BM†: SW tip of Langness, *MD* hb LIVU, det. P. W. Ball ('not identical with the S. England plant' and somewhat intermediate between this and ***S. europaea***). Common in southern Britain but apart from one Galloway locality not known nearer than Merioneth. The Irish populations are distinctive and confined to the south and east. Found in all saltmarsh zones except the lowest.

The only other species at all likely to occur in Man is ***S. fragilis*** P. W. Ball & Tutin, which also comes up the west coast as far as Galloway and occurs in Ireland.

Tiliaceae

Tilia platyphyllos Scop. (Large-leaved Lime) is naturalised and self-sown in Ballure Glen*. It was also listed by Gasking (1890). ***T. cordata*** Mill. (Small-leaved Lime) has been planted, in an impure form, in Claughbane Lane, Ramsey.

T. cordata × ***platyphyllos.*** Trees variously combining the characters of these interfertile species have been noted in several places. The particular form of the cross recognised as ***T.*** × ***vulgaris*** Hayne (Common Lime; Theiley) has been much more extensively planted, particularly in the north.

Malvaceae

Malva moschata L. Musk Mallow

H Fields, roadsides, usually near houses. Occasional; mostly in the north.

An old cottage garden favourite, still grown extensively in the Island. Plants with white or off-white flowers are not unusual. Though Forbes recorded it on sea-cliffs and it has been found in some quite wild-looking stations, I doubt if it has ever been but an escape.

M. sylvestris L. Common Mallow; Lus ny Moyl Mooarey

D Roadsides, waste places, farmyards, upper beaches. Common, especially along the south coast.

Though this shows a fondness for rocky banks and cliffs by the sea and has been claimed as indigenous in such habitats in southern England and

South Wales at least, it also displays a marked association with farmyards and cottages and in the West of Ireland and the Hebrides is still to be seen cultivated in gardens. Equally suspiciously, it makes its first appearance in post-glacial deposits in the Romano-British levels. Like ***Althaea officinalis***, for which it has always done duty both in function and name, its mucilaginous juice led to extensive use formerly for poultices and ointments. In Man the leaves were also used for curing dysentery and the flowers for coughs (Quayle 1973, 69). Here, too, it was specially in demand to counteract the effects of walking or lying on ground 'quick' with magical force (Gill 1963, 318). Its absence from the Calf is additionally suggestive.

M. neglecta Wallr. Dwarf Mallow
D Waste ground. Very rare.

N — Knock-e-Dooney, Andreas, in quantity, *MQ**, *MD* (first noted 1956 but said by the occupants to have been there many years): Smeale corner, outside new bungalow, 1977, *MD*. Also recorded by Gasking (1888-9) and Wattam (1899), without details.

Lavatera arborea L. Tree Mallow; Lus ny Moyl Mooarey Mooar
ND Maritime rocks, beaches, waste places. Very rare as a native; frequent and locally abundant as an escape, especially in the south. Calf.

This is generally accepted as native on guano-rich rocks and cliff-ledges in the west of the British Isles as far as Ailsa Craig and the Giant's Causeway. Forbes recorded it near Spanish Head and on the Calf, which sound like genuinely indigenous localities (though tides might have brought it from the naturalised populations plentiful from Port St. Mary eastwards). In 1968/9 a single plant was refound on the Calf east coast (Leavett 1971).

[***Althaea officinalis*** L. Marsh Mallow
Occasional in grassland near Lough Cranstal (Moore 1931, 131). Also listed by Gregson (1887) and Wattam (1899), without details. All presumably due to mismatches of the English and Latin names, ***Malva sylvestris*** being intended.]

Linaceae

Linum bienne Mill. Pale Flax
ND? Dry grassy banks and hillsides, roadsides, normally within two miles of the sea. Local, but sometimes abundant where it occurs.

Known only from four areas: (1) sandy roadsides and fields in the north, especially in Bride and Andreas (with a record as far inland as Sulby); (2) the hinterland immediately east of Peel; (3) the south coast; (4) clifftops along the central east coast from Groudle to Port Soderick. There had been no records from the last two areas for over sixty years till in 1969 I found it in abundance in a railway cutting near The Arragon, roughly midway between.

Man is easily the farthest north in the British Isles this plant reaches as a native. It is strongly Atlanto-Mediterranean and no doubt the Manx climate suits it particularly. All the same it is surprising that it should occur in such quantity at the extreme of its range and I cannot suppress a suspicion that at least some of its occurrences in the north are the relics of one-time cultivation. It is believed to have been the progenitor of ***L. usitatissimum***, for which possibly it substituted in those western areas where it was plentiful.

L. usitatissimum L. (Cultivated Flax; Lieen) is nowadays a rare casual, but must once have been a frequent stray. Feltham (1798, 57) wrote that 'the growth and manufacture of flax is very general through the island; almost every farmer and cottager growing a little, both for the use of their families and for exportation'. On some of the larger farms, he recorded, it was grown by the acre.

L. catharticum L. Fairy Flax; Lus ny Dew etc.

N Dry grassland, heaths, dunes. Locally common, especially in the north. Calf.

Surprisingly, like ***Myosotis discolor*** and ***Cerastium glomeratum***, also in damp habitats: common in ***Succisa-Molinia*** grassland in Jurby Curraghs; marsh by The Guilcagh, Andreas; The Creggans, Knockaloe; etc.

Radiola linoides Roth Flax-seed; Lus y Ryptar

N Damp, bare sandy or peaty ground. Rare except on the Calf; apparently much decreased.

N — 'Wet places in the northern parts', *Backwell's*: Andreas area, *S. Kermode*, YLM 4, 191: hollows on the Ayres, at Sartfield, Ballaghennie, and inland of Rue Point: footpath near Ballavarry, Andreas, one clump, 1969, *D & G*. **C** — Sulby Glen, *Stowell, S. Kermode*. **W** — Hill S of Peel, 1922, *Wheldon* hb NMW. **SE** — Douglas Head; Banks Howe, *Stowell*. **SW** — Near Cregneish, *Holt**: abundant over much of the Calf, *WSC, Leavett*!: bog above The Chasms, at 450ft, hb CGE: track to Bradda Head, *MB*. **S** — Port St Mary, *Holt**: central Langness, *WHH, MD*.

Surprisingly, never found by Ralfe or Paton. Forbes termed it 'common' and as late as the 1850s it was evidently widespread in areas from which it has vanished. A similar decrease has occurred in north-east Ireland and is presumably attributable to the same climatic change that has also greatly reduced ***Hypericum elodes*** and ***Wahlenbergia hederacea*** (Allen 1953). The highly humid atmosphere it prefers survives now only on the Calf and its environs; elsewhere it lingers on just in spots where water has stood in winter.

Geraniaceae

Geranium pratense L. (Meadow Cranesbill) is well established on a grassy laneside by Ballacooiley, Ballaugh*; in a hedge by The Lhen chapel; and in a rough field at Riversdale, Ramsey. There is also an old record for Malew. Although held to be native in some of the counties opposite, the occurrences in Man suggest merely a garden escape.

G. versicolor L. (Pencilled Cranesbill), a frequent escape in parts of Britain with mild winters, has been recorded on four occasions. It has long been established in a lane near West Craig, Andreas*.

G. ibericum Cav. (Iberian Cranesbill), commonly grown in Manx gardens and sometimes escaping, is well-naturalised at Cronk ny Maghlane, near Crosby, *D & G*.

G. phaeum L. (Dusky Cranesbill) is well-naturalised along a farm lane near Ballamooar, Ballaugh, *MD*.

G. sanguineum L. (Bloody Cranesbill) is grown in Manx gardens and an occurrence in a sandpit on Ballaghennie Ayres, 1969, *D & G*, was clearly an escape. A 1913 record for Ramsey Mooragh, *Miss Gale* fide *P. Kermode*, is more problematic; the dune flora here was formerly rich and the species is native on all the coasts opposite other than the Irish.

[***G. pyrenaicum*** Burm.f. Pyrenean Cranesbill
Ballaugh, 1925, *A. C. Holt* fide *Paton*: Ramsey tip, 1967, *LSG*. In the absence of specimens these records must be doubted. Large-flowered forms of **G. molle** are often taken for this.]

G. columbinum L. Long-stalked Cranesbill
N Dry open grassland, margins of copses. Very rare.
N — Ballaugh, 1946, *Paton*: edge of dunes etc, Lhen, *Paton**! **SE** — Edge of Crogga Glen N of Balnahow, *BSBI*[2]. **S** — Near Ballasalla, 1878, *Holt*.

G. dissectum L. Cut-leaved Cranesbill
C Roadsides, cultivated and waste ground. Frequent, especially in the south, usually singly. Calf.
Semi-casual in Man and nowhere looks in the slightest indigenous.

G. molle L. Dovesfoot Cranesbill; Lus ny Freenaghyn Mooarey
NC Dry grassland, dunes, beaches, waste ground. Frequent. Calf.
Albino at Port Erin, 1912, *Holt*: Ballaghennie Ayres, 1976, *D & G*. Used herbally for mouth and eye sores (Moore 1898).

G. pusillum L. Small-flowered Cranesbill
NC Dry grassland, beaches; roadsides, waste ground. Local.

G. lucidum L. Shining Cranesbill
C or H Walls, roadsides and as a weed in gardens. Rare.
N — Ramsey tip, 1979, *MD*. **C** — Churchtown, Lezayre, *MBB**!: Glen Tramman; bottom of Ballaugh Glen, in three places, *D & G*. **S** — Bagnio House, Castletown; Great Meadow, *LSG*.

G. robertianum L. Herb Robert; Crouw Yiarg, Lus yn Rose, etc.
N Hedgebanks, glens. Common.
Also on shingle (var. ***maritimum*** Bab.): Point of Ayre and along east central and south coasts.

Erodium maritimum (L.) L'Hérit. Sea Storksbill
N Dunes, bare ground near the sea. Frequent, except on the east coast.
Albino on Langness, *S. Kermode*, YLM 4, 79, and Peel Hill (a colony). Very small-flowered plants at the Point of Ayre. Rarely strays inland: on a wall near Ballagawne, Rushen.

E. moschatum (L.) L'Hérit Musk Storksbill
D Roadsides, waste ground. Very rare; not recorded since 1902.
S — Port Erin, *Bailey*, *Br Ass*[1] hb RAMM, etc: Colby village*; roadside near Ballabeg, *Teare*.
Once grown in cottage gardens for its musky scent as well as medicinally.

E. cicutarium (L.) L'Hérit. Common Storksbill; Lus yn Ashlish
NC Dunes, sandy heathland; roadsides, waste places. Frequent, mainly in the north.
A very variable species, the more glandular forms of which have been unsatisfactorily distinguished as 'subsp. ***dunense*** Andreas'.

E. glutinosum Dumort. Sticky Storksbill
N Dunes. Confined to the north coast and frequent there from Sartfield to the Point of Ayre.
Also variable and by no means as densely glandular and small-flowered as stated in the books. The almost sterile hybrid with ***E. cicutarium*** doubtless also occurs and should be looked for.

Oxalidaceae

Oxalis acetosella L. Wood-sorrel; Bee Cooag
N Glens, hedgebanks. Common, locally abundant.
On Snaefell at over 2000 ft, *Ralfe, GDK*.

Plants with flowers blue ('var. ***coerulea*** Pers.'), rose-purple ('var. ***subpurpurascens*** DC.') or pure pink ('var. ***rosea*** Peterm.') have been reported, but interestingly only from the north half of the central district.

O. corniculata L. (Sleeping Beauty), ***O. exilis*** A. Cunn., ***O. incarnata*** L., ***O. corymbosa*** DC., ***O. latifolia*** Kunth and — in particular — ***O. articulata*** Savigny (*O. floribunda* Lehm.) occur as garden weeds and spill over on to waste ground. An unusual species widespread and long-established as a weed on Douglas Promenade is ***O. cf. lasiandra*** Fucc., det. E. J. Clement.

Balsaminaceae

Impatiens glandulifera Royle (Himalayan Balsam) has escaped here and there but only recently been noted along streams: Laxey River, near mills, 1966, *IMK*, by 1973 abundant from there to the sea, *MD*, and all up tributary N of Minorca, 1972: R. Neb, near Peel power station, 1970, and abundant along the river by 1974, *D & G*. Likely to spread rapidly in this habitat, in which it has become so abundant in Britain.

Aceraceae

Acer pseudoplatanus L. (Sycamore; Shykey), introduced sometime before 1760, is now common and regenerates very freely. Calf.

A. campestre L. (Maple; Malpys) was recorded by McNab as an introduction. Isolated trees, some clearly old, have been noted in recent years from several localities, mainly along the foot of the northern hills.

Hippocastanaceae

Aesculus hippocastanum L. (Horse Chestnut; Castan) is self-sown in several places.

Aquifoliaceae

Ilex aquifolium L. Holly; Cullyn, Hollin

NH Glens, hedges. Local, absent from large areas.

Appears native in the northern and eastern glens and the northern curraghs. Its especial profusion along the north, east and south fringes of the northern hills is striking and noteworthy, for though no less plentiful in Cumbria it is almost absent from hedges in Galloway and most of the rest of Scotland (see map in Pollard et al. 1974, 242). Presumably it was only in these warmer wet regions that it prevailed as an undershrub in the aboriginal Durmast Oakwood.

Rhamnaceae

[***Rhamnus catharticus*** L. Common Buckthorn
Listed by Wattam (1901) without details. A patently unreliable source.]

Leguminosae

Lupinus arboreus Sims (Tree Lupin) is abundantly naturalised by the railway N from Rhencullen, *D & G*.

Genista tinctoria L. subsp. ***tinctoria***
Dyer's Greenweed; Lus Wuigh Wooar
D? Rough pastures, roadsides. Very local.

N — Recorded in a chain of stations extending right down the centre of Andreas parish*, from near Smeale to Closelake, thence S and E to near The Dhoor. **C** — Heathy roadside by Social Cottage, Lonan, one plant.

This cannot be confidently accepted as a native in Man, for a variety of reasons: its peculiar distribution; its remarkable absence from Ireland; the fact that it was formerly grown and harvested, at any rate in England (as 'Woadwax'), for use as a basis in dyeing wool and linen green; and its suspicious occurrences on roadsides and field borders (cf. ***Reseda luteola***, another old dyer's plant). One must also be mindful of the ease with which it has become naturalised in wild spots in North America. On the other hand it grows on cliffs, a seemingly impeccable habitat, on the Wigtownshire coast just opposite and its presence in Man is consistent geographically with its range in Britain. Oddly, the first record was only by Gasking (1888-9); but its extreme localisation could well have led earlier workers to miss it.

Ulex europaeus L. Gorse; Aittin Frangagh, Conney Frangagh
D Hedges, rough grassy places, to over 1000ft. Common. Calf.

Probably wholly an introduction in origin, as its Manx (and Welsh) name of 'French Gorse' suggests. It was formerly extensively used in farm rotation in the west of the British Isles, together with the next serving as the main source of winter fodder. When the introduction of turnips, c. 1780, began to undermine its value as a crop, it apparently took on a new lease of life as a substitute for hawthorn in hedging. Townley (1791, 1, 36) speaks of the sod fences then 'sometimes covered with a few straggling whins' and Feltham (1798, 52) likewise remarks that this plant 'is seldom seen on the top'. Forty years later, however, we read of it as forming 'most of the fences throughout the Island' (Anon 1836, 118). It does so still today.

***U. europaeus* × *gallii*.** A single bush on the Carnanes, Rushen, *Wheldon* and *A. Wilson*, conf. G. C. Druce & J. Fraser, BEC (1923) 379. The two species are fully interfertile and this cross is probably not uncommon. It is most readily spotted by its autumn and winter flowering.

U. gallii Planch. Western Gorse; Aittin

N Heaths, hill grassland. Common and locally abundant. Calf.

Before the introduction of the stouter and more luxuriant ***U. europaeus*** the Manx peasants depended largely on this for fuel and winter fodder. Special gorse-mills, sometimes with water-power, in which the plant was crushed with mallets in wooden troughs, were at one time frequent, continuing in use down to around 1840. Horses, especially, thrived on the plant, which was highly esteemed medicinally — in particular for ridding animals of worms.

[***U. minor*** Roth Lesser Gorse

Before ***U. gallii*** was separately distinguished, the dwarf species was regularly named as this. After writing that all the Manx records were presumably errors, Bennett (1901) claimed to have been sent 'undoubted' material of this species from Douglas Head by a Glasgow botanist, L. A. Watt. There is no specimen in Bennett's herbarium and he is known to have misnamed as this windswept plants of ***U. gallii*** from Scilly. On geographical grounds it is most unlikely.]

Sarothamnus scoparius (L.) Wimm. ex Koch subsp. ***scoparius***

Broom; Guilckagh (in north), Jucklagh (in south)

NCH Dry grassland, river shingle, roadsides, waste ground. Local.

A characteristic early coloniser of shingle bared by river erosion. Till recently common around Foxdale, where it flourished on the lead-mine 'deads', but on the whole thinly scattered and in part introduced. Along with gorse and heather once the main source of fuel, its former importance is attested in several place names. Seventeenth-century Manx peasants also inhabited huts 'most commonly thatched with broom'.

Ononis repens L. Rest-harrow; Camraasagh etc.

N Roadsides, banks, sandy ground, almost always by the sea. Locally common; mainly in the north and along the south coast.

var. ***maritima*** Gren. & Gdr. **N** — Point of Ayre, *Wheldon* hb NMW, BEC (1917) 216. A distinct dune form, with much larger seeds and leaves more like those of ***O. spinosa*** in shape. Probably widespread on the Ayres. var. ***horrida*** Lge. **N** — Ramsey Mooragh, *Paton*!

[***O. spinosa*** L. Spiny Rest-harrow
'Very rare; borders of peat', *Forbes* (1837b). The wording suggests a single locality. Much more probably, as Paton suggested, the spiny form of ***O. repens*** than this non-Irish species. Perhaps significantly, not in Forbes' subsequent lists.]

Medicago sativa L. (Lucerne) continues to occur round Castletown and in the north — especially round Ramsey — as a relic of cultivation.

M. lupulina L. Black Medick
NCD Maritime turf, stony shores; roadsides, waste places. Common, especially on roadsides in the north.
Looks native on the south coast. Elsewhere largely a robust form once included in clover mixtures, which is doubtless different genetically.

M. arabica (L.) Huds. Spotted Medick
N or C Rough ground, especially near the sea. Rare and very local: Castletown area only.

S — Malew, *Moore-Lane*: Knock Rushen, *Paton**! (two patches): Derbyhaven, *Paton*, *LSG* (one large patch): by Airport entrance, 1955, since built over.

In the two Paton localities, discovered in the 1940s, this grows on the upper part of the storm beach and might possibly be native. It is accepted as indigenous along the coast of Wales.

Melilotus officinalis (L.) Pall. (Common Melilot) is an increasing casual on waste ground and tips. Old records for Castletown and Bradda in the period 1905-9 were not reliably distinguished from ***M. altissima*** Thuill. but were probably also this.

M. alba Medic. (White Melilot) was recorded by Forbes (1837b) as 'occasional and apparently introduced with corn'. It recurred in 1972 at Orrisdale Head, in a rye grass and clover crop, accompanied by ***M. officinalis***, *D & G*.

M. indica (L.) All. (Small-flowered Melilot) has twice been found as a casual: Ramsey Mooragh, 1918, *Wheldon*: sandpit, St. John's, 1952*.

Trifolium ornithopodioides L. Fenugreek
NC Dry sandy turf near the sea. Very local.

N — Ramsey Mooragh, *Wheldon* (1918), *RWD*: Ayres at rare intervals from Point of Ayre to Sartfield*. **C** — Port Mooar, *BSBI*[3]: Maughold Head, *EH*. **SW** — Quarry, Cregneish, 1962 (with other Ayres species, presumably introduced with sand).

A southern species, here almost at its northern limit.

T. pratense L. Red Clover

ND Grassy places generally. Very common.

The cultivated plant, var. ***sativum*** (Crome) Schreb., is altogether more robust with duller flowers and hollow stems. It is doubtless widespread but has not generally been distinguished, so that the range of the native plant remains obscure. Suggestively, the species is unrecorded from the Calf.

T. medium L. Zigzag Clover

D? On a dry hedge-top. Very rare.

S — Near Ballanank, Malew, a single patch, known since 1960*.

Recorded by Gasking, S. Kermode ('fields, etc.') and Ralfe (near Douglas), but probably in error for a form of ***T. pratense*** that closely simulates it. This confusion is so common that records unsupported by a specimen are not acceptable. Though accompanied in the Malew station by ***Brachypodium sylvaticum***, it can hardly be indigenous in view of the artificiality of the habitat. It has been reported on field-borders in England and may once have been sown in clover mixtures. As a native, it is characteristic of lush pastures, open woodland and (in the West) rocky river banks, especially on clay or limestone.

T. incarnatum L. subsp. ***incarnatum*** (Crimson Clover) was known to S. Kermode (1900) on field-borders. It used to be sown in clover leys.

T. arvense L. Haresfoot Clover

N Sandy places along the north coast, at intervals, and on Castletown golf links; cliffs and associated stony rubble along the east central coast, from Groudle to Port Soderick. Very local.

The cliff populations may constitute a distinct ecotype. That at Onchan Harbour, at any rate, is a stiffly erect plant quite different from the form of the sands.

T. striatum L. Soft Clover

NC Dry turf, especially near the sea. Locally common, but mainly in the north and far south.

Material from Derbyhaven and Langness, *M & S* hb K, constitutes an exceptionally woolly form, which N. Y. Sandwith found was approached only by specimens from Cornwall.

T. scabrum L. Rough Clover

N Fixed dunes, maritime turf. Very local.

N — Ramsey Mooragh, *Bruce*, JB (1908) 335, *Wheldon* hb NMW etc: near Ballaghaie, Jurby. **S** — Poyllvaaish, abundant.

In Ireland rare and exclusively south-eastern.

T. hybridum L. (Alsike Clover) is frequent in fields and waste places as a relic of cultivation. Calf.

T. repens L. White Clover; Lus ny tree duillaghyn
NCD Grassy places generally, waste ground. Very common. Calf.
Probably native in exposed maritime turf and on moist, heathy ground in curraghs.

T. fragiferum L. Strawberry Clover
N Damp, saline grassy places near the sea. Very rare.
N — Ballaugh, *Forbes* (1840): near Dog Mills, *Stowell* (1860). Both these localities probably lost through coast erosion. **S** — Scarlett, *Backwell's*, *Paton*! Fluctuates in quantity here: abundant in 1971 after a run of poor years, *LSG*.
'Dry pastures, etc.', *S. Kermode* (1900); perhaps an error. In Ireland very rare outside the south-east corner.

T. campestre Schreb. Hop Trefoil
NCD Sandy maritime turf; dry waste ground, roadsides. Common.
An exceptionally large-flowered form, widespread on field-borders, var. ***majus*** (Koch) Gremli, is reputedly a fodder variety of Continental origin.

T. dubium Sibth. Common Yellow Trefoil
NCD Grassy places generally. Very common. Calf.
Native in dry maritime and calcareous turf; also on wet coast rocks at Onchan Harbour. Single plants occur scattered over the Calf (Madge 1974), which suggests its Manx status is predominantly that of a weed.

T. micranthum Viv. (Slender Yellow Trefoil) occurred singly, as a casual, on the railway track near Greeba in 1957*. Bennett, JB (1896) 449, recorded receiving a Manx specimen from Holt but no more details were made known. Bennett's determinations were not always reliable and, like Gasking (1890), what he passed as this may have been merely depauperate ***T. dubium*** — on which the Whitestrand record in my Manx Museum handlist has since turned out to have been based. The species ought to occur as a native in Man in the short coastal sward, as in County Down and Wales.

Anthyllis vulneraria L. subsp. ***vulneraria*** Kidney Vetch
NCD Dry maritime turf, especially along the cliff-tops; inland along railway tracks and on waste ground. Locally common. Calf.
Oddly, not on the dunes proper. The Manx populations mainly have lemon- or golden-yellow petals and are referable to var. ***langei*** Jalas and var. ***vulneraria***; but intermediates between the latter and var. ***coccinea*** L., with wholly orange-red standards, also occur on the brooghs N of

Ramsey and in Jurby, on the Dalby coast and by Cronk ny Arrey Laa, *D & G*. A gathering from The Dog Mills, N of Ramsey, *BSBI*[1] hb K, is one of the intermediates ('***A. pseudovulneraria*** Sagorski') between subsp. ***vulneraria*** and the Central European subsp. ***carpatica*** (Pant.) Nym. that have been introduced into Britain for fodder and now occur casually, det. J. Cullen.

Lotus corniculatus L. Common Birdsfoot Trefoil; Crow Cheyt
NCD Exposed short turf by the sea; dry banks, roadsides. Common. Calf.

A tall form with slender leaflets, var. ***longicaulis*** Mart.-Don., occurs on waste ground etc; it is evidently a South European race grown for fodder.

L. uliginosus Schkuhr Greater Birdsfoot Trefoil
N Roadsides, damp grassland, marshes, bogs. Common. Calf.

Most Manx plants are referable to subsp. ***vestitus*** (Lange) Hansen, which is densely villous, has the standard on average narrower and flowers of a deep yellow; it is also said to dry a strong green. This is the prevalent race of Oceanic Europe and in its moister climate noticeably tolerant of dry habitats, commonly occurring on roadsides (as I have also seen it in Brittany). By contrast, the more continental subsp. ***uliginosus*** (*L. major* var. *pilosus* Gray), which is never more than ciliate, has a subrotund standard and bright golden-yellow flowers, appears to be confined to wet ground. It has been noted in Man from:—

N — Near Bride, *Wheldon* hb NMW, BEC (1917) 217. **C** — Glen Auldyn; bog, Port Cornaa. **SE** — Santon Burn SW of Arragon Veg.

Flower number and corolla length, additionally used by Larsson and Lawalrée to separate the two, I do not find reliable — though biometric study may disclose some differential clustering on average.

Astragalus danicus Retz. Purple Milk-Vetch
N Dry short turf near the sea. Very local: south and north-west coasts.

N — Kirk Michael, *Holt**: Killane mouth, *Ralfe*, *MQ* etc!: N of Orrisdale. **S** — Dreswick Point, Langness, *Backwell's*, *Talbot* etc: Poyllvaaish, *Holt*, *S. Kermode* etc: Sound opposite Calf, *Roeder*, *Cowin* etc: Scarlett, *S. Kermode*, *Ralfe*, etc: St. Michael's I., *Ralfe*, *Paton*: between Port St. Mary and Perwick, *Ralfe*: Langness near St. Michael's I., *Wheldon*, BEC (1943-4) 714: slopes below Keeil Vael, Balladoole, *JWD*!

One of the Island's most interesting plants, being relatively much more widespread than in Ireland — where it is confined to the limestone of the Aran Islands in Galway Bay. Apart from some localities in Galloway and the Hebrides it is also absent from the entire west coast of Britain. Lime does not appear to be essential to it; rather, it is the freedom from shade ensured by its coastal habitats that is the primary determinant of its occurrence. The Manx populations appear remarkable stable and enduring but closer, year-to-year study of them is needed.

Ornithopus perpusillus L. Common Birdsfoot
NC Sandy and other dry ground, short maritime turf. Frequent in the north, scarce elsewhere.

Coronilla varia L. (Crown Vetch) occurred as a casual in a stubble field by Ballacross, Andreas, 1958, *MBB**.

[***Hippocrepis comosa*** L. (Horseshoe Vetch). Listed by Wattam (1901), without details. An obvious error: a species of chalk and limestone unlikely to occur.]

Vicia hirsuta (L.) Gray Hairy Tare
NC Dry grassy places, railway tracks, tips. Frequent in the north, scarce and scattered elsewhere.
This looks indigenous along the top of shingle beaches at Port Mooar, Knock Rushen and Scarlett and in maritime turf at Poyllvaaish.

V. tetrasperma (L.) Schreb. Smooth Tare
N or C Dry grassy places? Very rare.

S — Three plants in an unrecalled locality (probably Knock Rushen) near Castletown, 1967, *LSG**.

A characteristically eastern species in Britain, merely casual in Ireland but perhaps native in west Wales where its occurrence is mainly coastal.

V. cracca L. Tufted Vetch
NC Roadsides, railway tracks, bogs, swamps. Common. Calf.
Despite its fondness (in Man) for wet ground this is common on railway tracks. Stowell (1860) found it a most persistent garden weed in Maughold. A dwarf form with large flowers (12 × 6·5 mm) grows in saline turf at Port Mooar; similar plants have been reported from maritime habitats in Scotland and may constitute a distinct eco-geographical race.

V. villosa Roth (Lesser Tufted Vetch) appeared in a field at Jurby in 1893, imported with foreign corn-seed, *C. Butler* per *S. Kermode*, det. BM; and on Ramsey tip in 1976, as a bird-seed casual, *D & G**, det. E. J. Clement.

[***V. orobus*** DC (Upright Vetch). Listed for Man in Watson (1873-4). The authority was not published but appears in Watson's MS at Kew as 'Lightfoot appendix'. Reference to Lightfoot's *Flora Scotica* (2, 1129) shows that this relates to Douglas in Lanarkshire.]

V. sylvatica L. Wood Vetch

N Damp, sheltered hollows opening onto the sea. Rare and very local.

W — Glen Maye, locally plentiful on open grassy cliff, *Backwell's*, *Brearey** etc!: Traie ny Volain, S of Contrary Head, *Ralfe*: broogh N of Glen Maye, abundant (some pure white), *ACK*.

V. sepium L. Bush Vetch

N Roadsides, bushy places, sea-cliffs. Common. Calf.

With pure white or cream flowers in a few places.

V. lutea L. Yellow Vetch

N Sea-cliffs, shingle beaches. Very rare.

SW — Rough ground under The Chasms, in considerable abundance among herring gulls' nests, *Ralfe*. Discovered in 1907 but because of the perilous access not searched for since. **S** — Kentraugh beach, one plant, 1902 only, *Ralfe & Teare*.

Native in the south-west of Scotland but not in Ireland. Clearly brought over by gulls.

V. sativa L. (Common Vetch; Pishyr Chabbal) may still continue to occur as a relic of cultivation, but ***V. angustifolia*** var. ***segetalis*** is nowadays usually misdetermined as this.

V. angustifolia L. Narrow-leaved Vetch

var. ***angustifolia***

NC Acid, sandy grassland, maritime turf, bare waste ground. Local. Calf.

This looks convincingly native on the Ayres near Rue Point, as a rare constituent of the dune-heath community, and in short turf by the lighthouses on the Calf. A form with pale pink flowers in a sandpit on the Ballaghennie Ayres, *MD*.

var. ***segetalis*** Koch

D Among coarse grasses on richer, less acid soil. Frequent.

V. lathyroides L. Spring Vetch

N Dry, short turf, mainly by the sea. Very local.

N — Sandy fields of Andreas; S end of Ayres near Ballaugh, *Forbes*: 'with ***Ornithopus***, often abundant', *Stowell*: Ramsey, *Backwell's*, *MD*: Ayres S to The Lhen. **C** — Wall-top near Cornaa, *MD*. **SW** — Dry slope by coast road SE of Dalby, *MD*. **S** — Derbyhaven, *Backwell's*.

Lathyrus aphaca L. (Yellow Vetchling) has occurred since 1975 as a bird-seed casual at Ramsey, a Turkish form with bright lemon-yellow corolla, *D & G*, det. E. J. Clement.

L. pratensis L. Meadow Pea
NC Roadsides, grassy places. Common. Ascends to 1000ft at the Round Table.

L. latifolius L. and ***L. grandiflorus*** Sibth. & Sm. (Garden Everlasting Peas) both occur naturalised, the former rarely, the latter commonly, especially in the north.

L. linifolius (Reichard) Bässler (*L. montanus* Bernh.) Bitter Vetch
N Sea-cliffs, grassy banks, glens (normally within about a mile of the sea). Very local: mainly south-west coast and Douglas Bay area.

In Man this seems to demand a permanently moist atmosphere, resembling ***Osmunda regalis*** in its liking for wet cliff faces. The glen localities may well represent a gradual, bird-assisted spread inland from the cliffs.

Rosaceae

Spiraea douglasii Hook. and ***S.*** × ***billiardii*** Herincq, the usual garden representatives of ***S. salicifolia*** L. agg. (Bridewort), both occur as escapes. ***S. latifolia*** (Ait.) Borkh. is also naturalised in numerous Curraghs periphery localities and in several other places. ***Filipendula vulgaris*** Moench (Dropwort) is naturalised on hedgebanks between Kirk Braddan and Union Mills, *Paton*, *AB*! and in a lane near Kella, Sulby, *HSQ*!

F. ulmaria (L.) Maxim. Meadowsweet
N Wet fields, watersides. Common. Calf.

[***Rubus chamaemorus*** L. Cloudberry
'Mr Gregson states [the Northern Spinach moth, ***Eulithis populata*** L.] occurs on the mountains, and feeds on the whinberry and cloudberry', *H. S. Clarke*, Brit Nat (1892) 24. Presumably Crowberry (***Empetrum nigrum***) intended.]

R. saxatilis L. Stone Bramble
N Shady rocks in hilly districts. Very rare: NW glens only.

C — Sulby Glen, *Forbes*, *Ralfe*: Bishop's Glen, *Forbes*: Glen Helen, *S. Kermode*.

R. idaeus L. Raspberry; Berrish yu Croaw Gharey
ND Glens, curraghs, heathy roadsides; waste ground (as an escape). Local: concentrated in the centre of the Island and around Ramsey.

With white fruits (var. ***albus*** S. F. Gray) on roadside S of Foxdale, *LVC*!

R. spectabilis Pursh (Salmonberry) is profusely naturalised in Port Soderick Glen, *JTW*, *D & G* and also occurs about Laxey, *D & G*.

[***R. caesius*** L. Dewberry
'Glens and mountains', *Stowell* (1860): cliffs in Maughold, *Stowell*, Zoologist (1862) 7898: Ballure Glen, *P. M. C. Kermode*: shore N of Ramsey, *WHH*. Also unlocalised record by Wattam (1901). Probably all errors for members of the section ***Triviales*** of the next (which have Dewberry in their make-up) — as was the Peel record in Allen (1954) — or for other white-flowered brambles. True ***R. caesius*** is a lime-lover and most likely to occur with us on dunes, on which it is abundant on some neighbouring shores.]

R. fruticosus L. agg. Bramble (Blackberry); Dress Smeyr
NCDH Hedges, glens, bushy places, waste ground. Very common. Calf.

The Island's sod hedges form an ideal habitat for brambles, which have colonised them in exceptional profusion accordingly. In the moister climate of the north and west of the British Isles these plants are less shade-demanding and so markedly less characteristic of woods (cf ***Conopodium majus***). Their susceptibility to grazing tends to bar them from pastures and their vigorous tip-rooting well fits them for linear spread. They also favour the moderately acid soils most of Man has to offer.

This is fortunate scientifically, no less than aesthetically, for no other group in the Manx flora can offer such a diversity of indigenous forms, mostly with restricted, and comparatively recently-achieved, Britannic ranges, thereby of maximum value for deducing affinities between smallish geographical areas. This diversity is due to the reliance of brambles on asexual reproduction almost exclusively, resulting in numerous true-breeding minor strains which lend themselves to differentiation as micro-species. Some 350 of these have been distinguished in the British Isles, but the greater number are in the southern half, or otherwise peculiar to one area. Climate and insularity combine to keep the total in Man down to a much more manageable 40. As its commonest forms are luckily unusually distinctive and many of the rest have clear-cut local ranges, the Island is an excellent place in which to begin the study of a group that, while undeniably difficult, is unreasonably shunned.

The Manx brambles were first studied by the foremost mid-Victorian authority, Professor C. C. Babington, who spent a few hours collecting round Douglas in 1865. This seemingly stimulated the then leading resident botanist, Talbot, to make collections of his own during the next two summers. Both sets of specimens survive, at Cambridge and the Manx Museum respectively, but the names on the sheets are long outdated and much of the Talbot material is too ill-gathered for confident redetermination.

In Edwardian years some sporadic further gatherings by Wheldon and by a Co Down enthusiast, the Rev. C. H. Waddell, were submitted to Babington's successor, the Rev. W. Moyle Rogers. Many of these are now in hb NMW and BM respectively and have proved redeterminable.

Annoyingly, however, vouchers for Wheldon's most intriguing records are not among them.

No other significant work on the group took place till 1958, when I embarked on an intensive combing of the whole Island. My 1958-63 collections (now in hb BM) have been examined by both E. S. Edees and the late B. A. Miles independently, subsequent ones (also in hb BM) by either Edees or A. Newton. I am deeply indebted to them for their help and patience. As in other areas a certain proportion of the species have proved unnameable. Some of these may well be peculiar to the Island, the products of autochthonous crosses, others may be detected in the still little-explored neighbouring parts of Ireland and Scotland. Because of the multiplicity of names already existing it is the convention among bramble specialists to describe as new only those species whose range extends to more than one vice-county. For this reason the Manx 'unnameables' are necessarily distinguished merely by their serial numbers in the list that follows.

A by-product of this recent intensive work has been the discovery that the Manx sod hedges can be dated comparatively according to the number of bramble species they harbour. Certain ones, bounding manifestly ancient lanes and trackways, produce revealingly higher totals. The explanation is presumably that the longer a hedge has stood, the progressively greater the statistical probability of additional bramble species being sown by birds or creeping in. For fuller details see Allen (1972a, 1972b, 1978b).

(Section ***Suberecti*** P. J. Muell.)

R. scissus W. R. C. Wats.
N — Ballaugh Curraghs, sparingly near the Ballaugh side, *Wheldon* per Rogers, JB (1915) 139. It is evident from his Record Book that Rogers saw no specimen and there is none in Wheldon's herbarium. Nevertheless this is a most distinct species and there is unlikely to have been a mistake. It is characteristic of open, peaty ground and the prevalent member of the Section in the Pennines.

[***R. bertramii*** G. Braun (*R. opacus* Focke ex Bertram)
SW — Greeba Curraghs NE of Kennaa, one small patch in open fen. Probably this, but only inadequate panicles present. A western species, not yet recorded from Ireland.]

R. plicatus Weihe & Nees
N — Ballaugh Curraghs, *Wheldon*: one bush under gorse, Ballamona Lane, Sulby Curraghs.

R. briggsianus (Rogers) Rogers (*R. holerythros* auct.)
N — Stream-bank (376949) SE of The Rule, Ballaugh Curraghs. A strongly Atlantic species with its main British population in Cornwall.

(Section ***Triviales*** P. J. Muell.)

R. hebridensis Edees
Common and generally distributed. A recently-described species as yet known elsewhere only round the Firth of Clyde and in the Inner and Outer Hebrides. It is the plant that Babington (1869, 90) described as abundant 'near Douglas' — probably Onchan Harbour, where it is exceptionally profuse — and puzzlingly referred to his ***R. incurvatus***. It appears in the Handlist as ***R. monensis*** Bart. & Riddelsd., a North Wales species with which Miles mistakenly identified it. A bush with pure white flowers has been noted in the Ballaugh Curraghs.

M54 'The Maughold Bramble'
Very local: frequent about Ballure, recurring S to the Corrany and Cornaa. Like the above clearly allied to ***R. conjungens*** (Bab.) Warren.

R. sublustris Lees agg.
Local. A plant passing under this name is frequent in carr in the Ballaugh Curraghs and reappears on the old road W of Staarvey (one patch only). Another form, closer to ***R. tuberculatus***, is frequent round Peel and along the south-west coast, favouring open situations and even exposed cliffs. A third form, round Douglas, has the flowers pinkish on first opening and is probably a recent hybrid.

R. tuberculatus Bab. (*R. myriacanthus* auct. angl., non Focke)
'The Douglas Bramble'
Locally common over about two square miles from Ballabeg, Lonan, and Baldwin S to upper Glen Grenaugh and W to the Braaid, with outlying patches near Cooilcam, Malew and beside the railway E of St John's; also in gardens in Ramsey, imported with soil. Characteristic of margins of glens, standing heavyish shade, but also in open situations, including cliff-tops. Though a western species, not certainly native in Man. Clearly the '***R. althaeifolius***' seen round Douglas by Babington.

(Section ***Silvatici*** P. J. Muell.)

M39 'The Marown Bramble'
Local: thinly scattered over the mid-eastern section of the central and south central lowlands, within the quadrilateral Injebreck-St John's-Ballasalla-Douglas, especially up to 700ft on the slopes overlooking the central valley, with a main concentration between the headwaters of the River Dhoo and the Santon Burn. Outlying occurrences as far off as Glen Maye, Spooyt Vane, Kirk Lonan and Ballajora in Maughold reflect its pronounced orientation to bird dispersal. Similar to the Cornish ***R. stanneus*** Bart. & Riddelsd., it is also in Kirkcudbrightshire.

R. laciniatus Willd. (Parsley-leaved Bramble) has occurred as a bird-sown escape: N of Port Groudle, *JTW*: Bishop's Glen, *MD*.

R. lindleianus Lees

N — A single colony on W edge of Ballaugh Curraghs (362952), first discovered by Wheldon in 1909. Also claimed 'near Douglas' by Babington, but probably in error for ***M39***. In view of the frequency, even abundance, of this wood-margin species in the nearby parts of Scotland and Ireland it looks as if it may be a recent, bird-brought immigrant.

R. nemoralis P. J. Muell. (*R. selmeri* Lindeb.)
Very common, as in all the surrounding counties. Frequently grows at the very edge of the sea in the east and ascends to 800ft.

R. amplificatus Lees 'The Laxey Bramble'
Very local: confined to the glens of the Laxey river and its tributaries, where it is frequent and shows a preference for shade. One of the most abundant species of north-east Ireland this, too, is unaccountably scarce.

R. pyramidalis Kalt.
Widely distributed and locally common, especially in the coastal parts of Lonan and Santon, apparently preferring high oceanicity and largely avoiding the west (in keeping with its overall Atlantic distribution). It ascends to 750ft.

R. polyanthemus Lindeb.
Very common, as in all the surrounding counties, ascending to 800ft.

R. cardiophyllus Muell & Lefèv.
Local and bicentric: (i) common along the Sulby and its tributaries as far as the mouth of Sulby Glen, reappearing in the Ballaugh Curraghs, where it is the prevailing bramble of the more open parts of the swampy areas; (ii) along the Glass/Baldwin, upper Santon Burn and Colby River. A southerly species. Some gatherings have been wrongly referred to ***R. dumnoniensis*** Bab.

R. errabundus W. C. R. Wats.
Very common, as elsewhere over the northern half of the Irish Sea area, where this Britannic endemic has its centre. Except perhaps for ***R. ulmifolius*** the most abundant Manx bramble, ascending highest of all, to 1,000ft. This is the '***R. salteri*** var. ***calvatus***' which Babington found very common round Douglas.

R. cumbrensis A. Newton 'The Abbeylands Bramble'
Rare and very local in hedges of old lanes: two colonies near Abbeylands,

at 225 and 440 ft (374792, 368807), recurring as scattered bushes SW to the 250 ft contour round the upper branches of the Silverburn. It was presumably this that Wheldon (per Rogers, JB (1915) 140) noted on his walk up Silverdale in 1909 and correctly identified with a plant known to him in northern Lancashire as ***R. silurum*** (A. Ley) W. C. R. Wats. It is not that mainly Welsh endemic, however, but this allied, recently-described species of the fringes of upland oakwood, apparently otherwise peculiar to the Lake District and the area to the south. Poor Manx material of it has been passed as ***R. lindebergii*** P. J. Muell.

(Section *Discolores* P. J. Muell.)

R. ulmifolius Schott
Very common. More completely a lowland plant than the other generally-distributed species and more tolerant of non-acid soils and exposure to salt-laden winds, thus dominating areas shunned by other brambles. Its near-monopoly of the youngest hedges points to a great increase within the last two hundred years, which its rather southerly British range and marked scarcity in Galloway and the Clyde region make the more remarkable. A bush with pure white flowers has been noted outside Ramsey.

[***R. cornubiensis*** (Rogers & Riddelsd.) Rilst. (*R. bifrons* auct. angl.)
Listed for vice-county 71 by Watson (1948, 619; 1958, 102) on unknown evidence. In 1951 Watson also suggested this name for a Douglas gathering of Talbot's. It is suspected that he had an erroneous conception of the species.]

R. procerus P. J. Muell. (Himalayan Giant), an increasingly common escape in southern England, was noticed on waste ground in Ramsey in 1974, *MD*.

(Section *Sprengeliani* (Focke) W. R. C. Wats.)

R. sprengelii Weihe 'The Lonan Bramble'
Very local: abundant in hedges and heathy pastures N of Kirk Lonan and all down the stream thence to Fairy Cottage beach, with outlying clumps within a one-mile radius (collected here by Waddell in 1903); also two small patches on a south-facing hedgebank NW of Newtown, Santon (318742) — a peculiarly disjunct range almost identical with that of ***R. bartonii.*** A southerly species almost absent from Scotland, scarce in Wales and rare and south-eastern in Ireland.

R. lentiginosus Lees 'The Curraghs Bramble'
Very local: abundant and more or less continuous over about a square mile in the Ballaugh and Sulby Curraghs, with an outlier on the Sulby Claddagh. Clearly spreading aggressively, which suggests a recent immigration. It is otherwise virtually confined to northernmost Wales and the adjoining Marches.

(Section ***Appendiculati*** (Genev.) Sudre.)

R. lanaticaulis Edees & Newton (*R. hebecaulis* sensu W. C. R. Wats., non Sudre) 'The Southern Glen Bramble'
Locally common: an Atlantic species, with a southerly trend, profuse along streams of all sizes throughout the (moister) eastern half of the Island up to Laxey, thinning out northwards and virtually absent from the west. In the wetter and bleaker centre its place is taken by ***R. hylocharis***, which also keeps more exclusively to the shade of the glens.

R. vestitus Weihe & Nees 'The Silverdale Bramble'
Locally common: in plenty up Silverdale and along the major roads in the south-east of the Island, from Ballasalla to Douglas Head. Its dense concentration and absence from the oldest of the lanes give it the appearance of a recent intruder still in process of primary spread. A southern species, intolerant of very acid conditions, it is unlikely to have been able to survive the rigours of the Sub-Atlantic period in an area like Man; it is also the most obvious bramble to arrive and infiltrate in response to a swing to a warmer, drier climate. Even so there is an 1860 gathering from Richmond Hill in Talbot's herbarium. A solitary plant growing on the roadside in Glen Maye (doubtless transported on a tyre) shows that it has a good way to go yet. The Manx population is unusually homogeneous, being wholly var. ***albiflorus*** N. Boul. except for a single rose-flowered bush on the Silverburn bank opposite the Airport.

R. bartonii A. Newton 'The Fairy Cottage Bramble'
Very local: abundant along edges of wooded ravine at Fairy Cottage; and a small colony in a green lane by Ballaveare, Port Soderick (340734). This species is otherwise known mainly in north and central Wales and the Welsh Marches. While not obviously spreading like ***R. lentiginosus*** and ***R. rubristylus***, which share this same extra-Manx distribution, there is reason to suspect that all these three are relatively recent immigrants, probably brought over by thrushes (Allen 1974).

R. criniger (E. F. Linton) Rogers 'The Glen Maye Bramble'
Very rare: a small colony along N edge of oak-hazel scrub on steep slope half-way down Glen Maye. A southerly species unknown in Scotland, Wales or Ireland, though widespread in the southern Pennines and

occurring as far north as Co Durham. Two other southerly rarities, ***Arctium minus*** subsp. ***nemorosum*** and ***Bromus ramosus***, occur in this same small fragment of presumably aboriginal woodland.

R. wirralensis A. Newton 'The Port Soderick Bramble'
Local, preferring light shade: frequent about Port Soderick and thence thinly along the southern east coast S to Port Grenaugh and N to Garwick, recurring up to 1½ miles inland; also scattered bushes at 300-450 ft between Baldwin and Union Mills and a distant outlying patch SW of Greeba Bridge. Such a distribution suggests a strongly Atlantic species — and indeed, in addition to the region bordering the south-east of the Irish Sea from which it was described in 1972, it is proving widespread in Ireland and Wales. Babington collected it as '***R. leucostachys***' and there is an 1866 specimen in hb Talbot queried by Riddelsdell as ***R. mucronulatus*** Bor. (with which this species has been confused hitherto). Wheldon's '***R. mucronatus***' from the head of the Silverburn was doubtless also either this or ***M3***.

M3
Widely distributed and locally common, especially in the south-east; largely absent between Douglas and Ramsey and from the centre but reappearing in the (less humid) west coast glens. An extremely variable plant, with leaves plicate and white beneath in dry, sunny places, becoming remarkably large in shade. The latter state has been passed as ***R. macrophyllus*** Weihe & Nees; ***M38*** of the Handlist has also proved to be merely a version of it.

R. lettii Rogers (***M59*** of the Handlist) 'The Ballure Bramble'
Very local: common on the Ramsey side of Ballure Glen; also a colony in an old plantation near Grenaby (259726). This is the plant from 'Tower Hill Wood' (Lhergy Frissel), Ramsey distributed by Wheldon through the Botanical Exchange Club in 1918. Riddelsdell at first referred it doubtfully to ***R. danicus*** (Focke) Focke, then in JB (1930) 337 pronounced it ***R. griffithianus*** Rogers — a determination later endorsed by both Miles and W. H. Mills. Edees, however, could not accept this name for the plant I rediscovered here in 1958 and eventually, in 1972, Newton found it compared excellently with a good series of this little-known species hitherto supposed to be an Irish endemic. It is abundant in Co Down and was presumably bird-carried thence.

R. hibernicus Rogers (***M67*** of the Handlist) 'The Jurby Bramble'
Very local: abundant in curraghs and adjacent hedges over c ½ sq mile S and W of Jurby East, with an outlier E of Close Taggart (376963); also a colony in Sulby Curraghs by Ballamona (404951). Another supposed Irish endemic at last identified in 1972. Locally very abundant in Co

Down and Armagh, it has since been established as identical with a plant frequent in south Wales.

R. infestus Weihe & Nees (*R. taeniarum* Lindeb.) 'The Santon Bramble'
Very local: scattered over the Santon Burn basin, with outliers to the north as far as the Greeba Curraghs; also an isolated patch in the far south-west, among bracken on the cliffs at the Chasms — a range reflecting its apparently exclusive dependence on bird dispersal. A northern species.

R. radula Weihe ex Boenn. 'The Onchan Harbour Bramble'
Rare: in some plenty on the cliff-top (and -foot) at Onchan Harbour; also isolated patches on modern hedgebanks in the central valley, near Ellerslie (329784) and Greeba Bridge (293813). A Continental species, mainly in east England and Scotland — yet, perplexingly, with a Manx range typical of a strongly Atlantic one.

R. echinatoides (Rogers) Sudre
Very rare: Fairy Cottage cliffs, a small colony just above the sea. Also claimed from Silverdale Glen, in one place, by Wheldon (per Rogers, JB (1915) 143 and Record Book); but though this is a widespread and distinct northern species with which he is likely to have been familiar, it is hard to believe that he found just about the rarest of Manx brambles on his first collecting foray.

R. rubristylus W. C. R. Wats. 'The Foxdale Bramble'
Very local: abundant and continuous along roads and on lead-mine 'deads' for a considerable distance about Foxdale. Spreading aggressively and patently a recent incomer. Mainly a west Midlands species it also occurs in Ireland (possibly widely).

R. adenanthoides A. Newton (*R. pseudadenanthus* W. C. R. Wats. p.max.p.)
Very local: large colonies at (i) plantation opposite the Nunnery, Douglas, (ii) Lower Ballacottier Glen (and nearby hedges) just S of the Clypse, (iii) over ¾ sq mile NE of St Mark's, (iv) plantation S of Knocksharry. Also isolated bushes in Maughold at 483923 and 474899, probably outliers of some further, undiscovered colony. I have been unable to relocate the Onchan Harbour bush erroneously named '***R. wolley-dodii***' by Watson in 1951 (Allen 1954). Although this is a widespread North English and Irish species the density of its few, disjunct populations and their presence mainly in artificial habitats suggests a comparatively recent arrival.

M37 'The Balnahow Bramble'
Very local: abundant in lane to Balnahow, Santon and along the railway banks W to Ballaquiggin, with outliers by the Crogga, at Keristal and in Mount Murray plantation; also three clumps by Ballanank, Malew

(283724). Spreading aggressively and patently either a recent immigrant or of recent origin (***R. hylocharis*** × ***vestitus***?)in situ. A most beautiful bramble strikingly similar to the Dartmoor ***R. orbus*** W. C. R. Wats.

R. micans Gren. & Godr. (*R. anglosaxonicus* Gel.; ***M13*** of the Handlist) 'The Baldrine Bramble'
Very local: abundant about Baldrine and frequent in coastal Lonan below the 500ft contour N to above Minorca, displaying a liking for stream banks and light shade. A mainly south-west England species, unexpected so far north. Notably large-fruited, it is probably a late, bird-brought immigrant, like its neighbour ***R. bartonii***.

(Section ***Glandulosi*** P. J. Muell.)

R. hylocharis W. C. R. Wats. 'The Northern Glen Bramble'
Locally common: the characteristic species of all glens N of the central valley, spilling across to Slieau Whallian plantation and with an outlying patch near Mount Murray. Though preferring shade it occurs in hedges up to a mile from woodland and even in treeless ravines, as an Atlantic species evidently requiring high humidity above all. Presumably Babington's '***R. lejeunii***', for there is a specimen so labelled in Talbot's herbarium, also collected in 1865, perhaps in his company. It is also the plant collected by Waddell in 1903 and Wheldon in 1918 and successively determined by Rogers and Riddelsdell as '***R. pallidus***' (both sheets now in hb BM).

R. dasyphyllus (Rogers) E. S. Marsh.
Locally frequent, with a strange bicentric distribution: widespread, in places common, along the northern foot of the hills, then reappearing in plenty round Union Mills and Douglas (where Babington collected it as '***R. villicaulis*** var. ***derasus***') and scattered thence northwards and south-westwards. In general it appears recent and intrusive (as in many parts of Britain), characteristic of manmade habitats, in particular the edges of plantations. It also has an odd tendency to grow round bridges and waterfalls, as if attracted by the heightened moistness: a native primarily of hilly districts, it may find the lowland areas it has happened to penetrate in Man inadequately humid.

Three further, unidentified species occur in just a solitary patch each: ***M66*** in carr in Ballaugh Curraghs, possibly now extinguished by the Wildlife Park clearance (probably 'North Wales ***villicaulis***'); ***M82***, a white-flowered ***Sylvatici***, in an old lane at the back of Crosby (327799); ***M26*** on the bank of an ancient ridgeway by Spooyt-vane bridge (308887).

Summary of Main Geographical Affinities
(excluding escaped species)

distribution elsewhere not yet known	4
Cumbrian	1
Irish	2
Welsh/West Midland	3
SW England	2
southern	4
northern	6
western	8
eastern	1
British Isles generally	6
	37

Potentilla palustris (L.) Scop. Marsh Cinquefoil; Lus ny curreeyn
N Swamps, peaty pools, bogs. Locally frequent, scarce in the far south.

P. sterilis (L.) Garcke Barren Strawberry
NC Glens, dry banks, walls, shingle (at Port Mooar). Common.

P. anserina L. Silverweed; Duillag argid
NC Marshes, swamps, drift-lines; roadsides, cornfields. Very common. Calf.

P. recta L. (Sulphur Cinquefoil) has occurred as an escape by Ramsey Mooragh, 1959, *EMK**, and is naturalised by Ballasteen Dub, Andreas, *MD*. ***P. hirta*** L. (Hairy Cinquefoil) was recorded by Garner (1878) on a dry bank 'near Jurby' — subsequently specified as Ballamoar (*IOM Times*, 10 Dec 1881). In a paper read to the NHAS he claimed it also occurred near Peel.

P. erecta (L.) Räusch. Tormentil
N Dry acid pastures, heaths. Very common. Calf.

P. × ***mixta*** Nolte (incl. ***P.*** × ***italica*** Lehm.), a sterile cross of uncertain origin, most probably ***P. erecta*** × ***reptans*** with added chromosomes, is common and has spread along roadsides and into pastures over a large part of the Island from which ***P. reptans*** is absent. Much confused with the latter, it differs in its often 4-merous flowers and 3-5-nate cauline leaves. From the very similar ***P. anglica*** it is best told by its empty, infertile anthers.

P. anglica Laichard Trailing Tormentil
N Wet peaty places, swamps, damp pastures. Local.

P. anglica* × *erecta (***P.* × *suberecta*** Zimmet.) is apparently frequent.

P. reptans L. Creeping Cinquefoil
NC Long damp grass near the sea; shingle banks, roadside verges. Very local: abundant along the south coast W to Perwick Bay, typically associated with ***Ononis repens***, thinning out inland (probably as an invader) to the line Ballakilpheric-Ballamodha-Santon Head, with an outlier by Mount Murray Inn. Also claimed by Paton and Leavett (1971) for the Calf, but confirmation needed. Adventive and seemingly only fugitive north of this: Douglas, 1916, *Holt**; once on a building site at Ramsey, *Paton* and a single plant on a hedgebank at Peel. It was formerly used to cure the diarrhoea to which Manx kittens are peculiarly prone. A double form at Ronaldsway farm site, *LSG*.

Fragaria vesca L. Wild Strawberry; Soo halloin
N?D Glens, bushy places, railway banks, hedgebanks, quarries, gardens. Local.

F. moschata Duchesne (Hautbois Strawberry), once popular in cottage gardens, is naturalised in hedgebanks at Mount Murray*, near Kirk Braddan, at Cronk ny Moghlane, Marown, etc. Its modern replacement, ***F.* × *magna*** Thuill. (Garden Strawberry), has become widely established on railway banks and escapes occasionally elsewhere.

Geum urbanum L. Herb Bennet
NC Glens, plantations, shady roadsides, shady cliff-faces. Local.

Forbes (1837b) thought this missing from the flora and Stowell failed to record it. Like ***Circaea lutetiana*** and ***Lapsana communis*** it is typically a shrubbery colonist round Douglas and away from the glens may be largely adventive in origin.

Agrimonia eupatoria L. var. ***sepium*** Bréb. Agrimony
N Grassy cliff-tops. Very rare.

C — The Dhyrnane, E of Port Mooar, *P. Kermode*, *Ralfe* etc!*: Maughold brooghs, *Ralfe*: path to lighthouse, Maughold Head, *AH*.

The sole locality known to Forbes, being on the Slate, was probably one of these. All other records probably relate to the next and are listed thereunder. Both species grow together on sheltered clay cliffs on Arran.

A. procera Wallr. (*A. odorata* auct.) Fragrant Agrimony
D Verges of old lanes. Rare and highly disjunct.

(**N** — Andreas, etc, *Backwell's*: The Lhen, *Ralfe*, *Paton*). **W** — Near Spooyt Vane, *Ralfe*, *Paton**. **SE** — Lane by Meary Vooar, Santon Head, a large colony, *Ralfe*, *NHAS*!*. **S** — (Lane from Ballasalla to Derbyhaven, *Ralfe*: Arbory, in a field near the school, *Dr Clague* per

Paton: Port St Mary, *Cowin*): lane near the Factory, Ballasalla, two plants, 1962, *LSG*. Also an unlocalised specimen of Talbot's*.

Brackets denote records for ***A. eupatoria*** in the aggregate sense. One or both species were once much prized herbally but it was the fragrant plant which was singled out for making a tea taken for chest complaints. In view of this, the ease with which its fruits are dispersed, its anomalous range in Man and suspect proximity to habitations, and its restriction to woods in those areas of Britain where it is unarguably a native, a denizen status seems most likely.

Alchemilla glabra Neygenf. Lady's Mantle

N Streamsides in the hills. Very rare, perhaps extinct.

C — A single plant on a bridge in upper Narradale, 1954 only, GEQ*, det. S. M. Walters. Erroneously marked for two squares in the *Atlas*.

This is common in the mountain areas opposite and ought to be widespread. Presumably intense grazing is the culprit. Even the lowland microspecies of ***A. vulgaris*** L. agg. are virtually absent (Forbes believed totally so), and no specimens having been kept in any of the following cases, their identity remains unknown:—

W — Roadside by Ballaspet, W of St John's, *T. H. Graves*. **SE** — Near Garwick, 1907, *T. H. Graves*. **S** — Among ruins, Grenaby, one plant, 1903, *Teare*: Kallow Point, Port St Mary, one plant, 1950, *JRB*: Colby area, 1951, *GDR*.

The evidently casual nature of most, if not all, of these occurrences tells against a native status. They may have been relics of herbal use or the escaped ornamental, ***A. mollis*** (Buser) Rothm. — as was almost certainly a plant on a roadside at Glen Wyllin, 1953, *MQ*, det. S. M. Walters. Introduction with grass seed is a further possibility.

Aphanes arvensis L. Parsley Piert

C Dry turf, walls, cultivated fields, waste ground. Very local: mainly round Castletown.

N — Cultivated field near Point of Ayre, *D & G*. Marked for the Lhen square in the *Atlas* through a punching error. **SE** — Douglas, tip, *WFS*! **SW** — Wall by South Barrule reservoir, *MD*. **S** — Chapel Hill, Balladoole*; Billown quarries: walls N & W of Airport; Cass-ny-Hawin, *LSG*. Also an unlocalised specimen c 1880 in hb Mrs Kermode.

More of a lime-lover than the next and perhaps native in England on limestone pavement.

A. microcarpa (Boiss. & Reut.) Rothm. Parsley Piert

NC Dry, bare places especially on heaths, fixed dunes; waysides, cultivated fields. Occasional but often abundant where it occurs, with a coastal and particularly a western trend. Calf.

Sanguisorba minor Scop. subsp. ***muricata*** Briq. (*Poterium polygamum* Waldst. & Kit.) Fodder Burnet

D Dry fields and banks. Rare.

N — The Lhen and nearby, 1928-30; near Ramsey station, 1931, *Paton*: Broughjairg, Ballaugh, *D & G*. **SE** — Near Governor's Bridge, 1958, *CB*.

Acaena anserinifolia (J. R. & G. Forst.) Druce (Pirri-pirri Bur) and ***A. inermis*** Hook.f. are plentifully naturalised beside Cringle Reservoir, *MD*, both det. P. F. Yeo.

Rosa arvensis L. Field Rose

H Hedges. Very rare.

S — Lane from near Ballabeg station to Balladoole, 1910, gone by 1924, *Paton**. A southern species, very rare in Scotland. Also recorded by Ralfe from Groudle Glen. An old planting survives in a cottage hedge at Ballahutchin hill, Union Mills, *LSG*.

Rosa pimpinellifolia L. Burnet Rose; Drine Drughaig

N Dry banks, heaths, dunes. Frequent, locally abundant, especially near the sea.

Plants with pink or red flowers occur along the central Ayres, in patches, and have also been reported in Jurby, E of Orrisdale and in Glen Auldyn and Glen Ballyre, Michael; they are characteristic of dunes elsewhere and may be the result of crossing with ***R. villosa.***

R. rugosa Thunb. (Ramanas Rose) is naturalised in several places. A hybrid involving it also forms a large colony on Foxdale 'deads', *GDR*. ***R. virginiana*** J. Herrm. (Virginian Rose) has occurred on rough ground at Onchan. ***R.* × *alba*** L. (White Rose), a one-time cottage garden favourite, is naturalised widely, especially in the north.

R. canina L. agg. Dog Rose

N Hedges, bushy places. Local.

Because of their highly peculiar 'pseudo-sexual' system of reproduction, which permits a 'free-for-all' leading to no two bushes being alike, the plants which constitute this and the succeeding species are not satisfactorily classifiable below the broadest level. Arduous attempts have been made to capture the welter of variation in a network of minor named forms but this does such violence to the actual situation in nature that there seems to be little to be said for their use. They have therefore been omitted in the following account.

The ***R. canina*** aggregate embraces three distinct clusters of forms, probably best treated as subspecies. Their Manx ranges are known as yet imperfectly:—

R. canina L. sens. strict. Locally frequent in the lowlands but usually as isolated bushes. Southern in its Britannic range and unfond of acid soils, it may be a comparatively recent immigrant.

R. dumetorum Thuill. More plentiful than ***R. canina***, especially in the northern curraghs and older lanes.

R. dumalis Bechst. Widespread in the north, with populations on the eastern cliffs (Port Garwick and Onchan Harbour). Largely takes the place of ***R. canina*** in northern Britain and in Man may prove the prevailing one of the three in the wetter areas. All the Manx plants seen have glabrous leaflets.

R. canina × ***pimpinellifolia*** (***R.*** × ***hibernica*** Templeton). Hedgebank between Onchan and Onchan Head, abundant*†.

R. tomentosa Sm. agg. Downy Rose
N Hedges, bushy places. Common. Calf.
The forms of this cluster around three more substantial foci than in ***R. canina*** and are more generally accepted as separate species as a result:—

R. tomentosa Sm. sens. strict. Southern in Britain and so rare in Man.
N — Cronk Sumark, Sulby, *Br Ass*[3], det. E. B. Bishop. **C** — Lane above South Cape, Laxey*†. **S** — Colby area, *GDR*: lane E of Grenaby 268724, *BSBI*[2]!†.

R. sherardii Davies
Common (as in Wales).

R. sherardii × ***tomentosa***
N — Sulby Curraghs*†.

R. villosa L. subsp. ***mollis*** (Sm.) Keller & Gams
Common (as in Scotland).

† det. R. Melville

R. rubiginosa L. Sweetbriar; Drughaig Villish
H Hedge-tops, waste places, usually near houses. Occasional in the north, rare elsewhere. Plentiful in Billown lime quarries, but doubtless only naturalised.

Prunus spinosa L. Blackthorn; Drine Airn
N Hedges, hillsides, river-sides, cliffs, shingle. Frequent on the coast, perhaps more local inland.

P. domestica L. (Plum), in various forms, escapes into hedges and thickets.

P. cerasifera Ehrh. (Cherry-plum) has been planted as hedging in the Groudle area and at Tholt-y-will, *MD*. A specimen of Clementson's collected at Peel in 1939 is in hb BM.

P. padus L. Bird Cherry

N?H Upland thickets; lowland plantations. Very rare.

C — A solitary large tree above the east shore of Baldwin Reservoir, about half-way along, at c 600ft. Far from houses and perhaps bird-brought from the large native populations in the Lake District and Pennines rather than from one of the few (more recent?) planted local trees.

Wheldon (1909-10) listed this species in his flora of the Ballaugh Curraghs but not, suspiciously, the common ***P. cerasus.*** 'Bird Cherries' have been reported from there since but this name is often misapplied to all wild cherries indiscriminately. The true tree, however, has been planted in some of the old northern gardens and plantations. The one mentioned by Quayle (1973, 71), which was on the Claughbane estate, came into this category.

P. avium (L.) L. (Wild Cherry; Shillish) and ***P. cerasus*** L. (Sour Cherry) have both been widely planted but the latter is much the more plentiful, its habit of suckering freely doubtless causing it to be preferred for hedging — as along the field divisions in parts of the northern curraghs. ***P. laurocerasus*** L. (Cherry-laurel) has also been planted plentifully in one or two places.

Cotoneaster simonsii Bak. (Khasia Berry) is extensively planted at Arch-allagan as well as a frequent bird-sown escape. ***C. horizontalis*** Decne. (Wallspray) is well-naturalised in Billown and Ballahot quarries. ***C. microphyllus*** Wall. ex Lindl. (Rockspray) is abundantly naturalised on lead-mine 'deads' at the Eairy and occurs on waste ground and roadsides elsewhere.

Crataegus laevigata (Poir.) DC. (*C. oxyacanthoides* Thuill.) (Woodland Hawthorn) has been planted by the stream at Tholt-y-Will. Paton observed that Manx hawthorn hedges occasionally yield specimens with characters pointing towards this species and I have seen a bush near Ramsey that was clearly closer to it than the next. The stocks grown by nurserymen in England were evidently often partly, or even largely, of hybrid origin, the two species having crossed so freely in the wild already.

C. monogyna Jacq. Hawthorn; Drine (skeag = haw)

D Hedges, glens, pastures. Very common.

The Castle Rushen accounts show a consignment of trees bought in Dublin in 1696 for the garden of William, 9th Earl of Derby (Lord of Mann) included 12,000 examples of this. By the time of Townley (1791) hawthorn hedges were widespread, even general, at least in the more populous areas. Long before, however, the magico-religious beliefs associated with this tree caused it to be planted round walls and farmsteads. The frequency with which it features in Manx place-names bespeaks the usual special regard for oddly isolated thorns. Yet it is hard to believe it ever formed part of the primeval vegetation: in the natural climax woodland that survives on islets in the Connemara lakes it appears but a recent intruder and wherever elsewhere it has a native look it clings to calcareous habitats, ecologically well apart from the highly interfertile ***C. laevigata.*** Seemingly native populations in Peak District woods are formed of the ultra-dissected variety, var. ***laciniata*** Ledeb., which may represent the original, uncontaminated species. Nurserymen have inevitably distributed this variety too and Hobkirk (1866) noted that in Man, as elsewhere, it frequently grows intermixed with the 'type' in hedges. I have seen a bush of it in willow carr SW of Garey, Lezayre, but it is doubtless only adventive there.

Sorbus aucuparia L. Rowan; Cuirn

NH Glens, heaths, curraghs, hedges. Local. Calf (planted).

Credited with strong, always beneficent, powers in Manx folklore (a cross made of its twigs was hung over the door on May Eve), this was another tree once planted by homesteads. A preserve continues to be made from its berries.

S. intermedia (Ehrh.) Pers. (Cut-leaved Whitebeam) has been planted in many places. The mysterious '***S.? rotundifolia***' listed by Hiern (1897) was merely this, according to the specimens in hb RAMM, det. A. J. Wilmott. ***S. aria*** (L.) Crantz (Whitebeam) has been planted particularly extensively and increasingly occurs self-sown, notably on lead-mine 'deads'. A pronounced lime-lover, it is unlikely to be native.

Malus sylvestris Mill. Wild Crab

N?D Hedges in old lanes, usually singly. Very rare.

N — NE of Orrisdale, *D & G.* **C** — Narradale, *D & G.* **SE** — N of Mount Murray Inn. **S** — Near Great Meadow House*.

In Narradale this is the ultra-glabrous extreme accepted as native in Sessile Oakwood in the north and west of the British Isles. Other trees are probably relics of an early orchard stock later replaced by ***M.*** × ***domestica*** Borkh. (Apple; Gartag). Examples of the latter occur more widely, but again almost always singly.

Crassulaceae

Sedum rosea (L.) Scop. Rose-root

D Habitat(s) unknown. Apparently extinct.

Two early records — in McNab's unlocalised list of 1830-2 and by Forbes

(1848) 'near Peel' — have been taken to refer to a native, sea-cliff population, as on the Mull of Galloway and northwards. But Ralfe, in his diaries (though not in his record-book) noted it from the Lhoobs, near St. John's, where it must surely have been a relic of its one-time herbal use as a fragrance. That is 'near Peel' and could have been Forbes' locality too.

S. telephium L. subsp. ***telephium*** (Orpine) has been recorded on several occasions round old cottages, principally in the Dalby area. It is also an abundant escape E of Orrisdale. As "Midsummer Men" it was much used for divination; it was also valued medicinally and the leaves eaten as salad.

S. spurium Bieb. (Caucasian Stonecrop) is now a more frequent escape and naturalised on coast rocks at Scarlett.

S. anglicum Huds. White Stonecrop
N Rocks, dunes, hedgebanks, walls, dry grassland. Common, especially near the sea. Calf. Ascends to 1500ft on North Barrule, *LSG*.

S. acre L. Wall-pepper
NH Rocks, shingle, dunes, walls, roofs; also an escape. Local: mainly in the south (in plenty) and along the coast northwards from Kirk Michael. Calf.

S. album L. (White Stonecrop) is a not uncommon escape, especially round Peel. ***S. forsteranum*** Sm. (Rock Stonecrop) is naturalised in the St John's area and in Glen Mona. ***S. reflexum*** L. (Large Yellow Stonecrop), once grown as a spring salad, has been recorded from hedgebanks, walls and a roof in various parts of the north as well as at Bradda. ***Sempervivum tectorum*** L. (House Leek; Lus y Thie) still survives in at least six places. In Man it did not have its usual anti-fire reputation: planted round doors it averted the entrance of evil spirits (Gill, 1929). Quayle (1973, 69) also notes its use as a poultice for carbuncles and in the treatment of burns.

Umbilicus rupestris (Salisb.) Dandy Wall Pennywort; Woishleeyn
N Walls, rocks. Common. Calf.
A characteristic western species, often very luxuriant with us. It even grows up among the pebbles on beaches. It was used in Man, bruised with lard, for the treatment of erysipelas and sores on horses. '. . . In the highest esteem as a medicinal herb throughout the island', *P. Kermode MS.*

SAXIFRAGACEAE

Saxifraga* × *urbium D. A. Webb (London Pride) is abundantly naturalised in several glens and a frequent escape elsewhere. ***S. hirsuta*** L. (Kidney

Saxifrage) is naturalised on a grassy slope near Ballure Glen, well away from houses, *WHH*, and has escaped in at least three other places.

S. tridactylites L. Rue-leaved Saxifrage
N Dry-stone walls. Formerly rare, apparently now extinct.
Unlocalised records by Stowell (1860) and S. Kermode (1900) only. The latter's vague reference to it on 'walls' seems to imply that several localities were then still known to him. Extensive destruction of its habitat has made this a declining species in the British Isles generally.

S. granulata L. (Meadow Saxifrage) was listed by Forbes as an introduction and, in the cultivated double form, still persists plentifully in places. An 1893 find by Ralfe, on a grassy broogh at Gob ny Chassan, Patrick, is more likely to have been an escape than indigenous. Though accepted as native on the Co Dublin and Co Wicklow coasts, the species occurs solely as the double garden form on sea-cliffs in Kirkcudbrightshire.

S. aizoides L. Yellow Mountain Saxifrage
N Wet stony ground by base-rich mountain flushes. Very rare, perhaps extinct.
'Isle of Man', Aug 1830, *McNab* hb DBN — confirming the long-doubted record of his published by Watson (1832).

[***S. oppositifolia*** L. Purple Saxifrage
Cited in Black's Guide (1883, 104), patently as a slip for ***Chrysosplenium oppositifolium***. Unfortunately picked up by Gasking and long perpetuated.]

Tolmiea menziesii (Pursh) Torr. & Gray (Pick-a-back Plant) is naturalised by streams in Glen Auldyn, Glen Wyllin and Port Garwick, *MD*.

Chrysosplenium oppositifolium L. Opposite-leaved Golden Saxifrage
N Damp, shady places. Common. Calf.

PARNASSIACEAE

[***Parnassia palustris*** L. Grass of Parnassus
Listed by Gasking (1890), without details. Credibly reported from Blaber River, above Glen Helen, c 1957, *FC* per *LSG* but confirmation needed.]

HYDRANGEACEAE

Philadelphus coronarius L. (Mock Orange) is naturalised in several glens.

Escalloniaceae

Escallonia macrantha Hook. & Arn. escapes into glens and hedges.

Grossulariaceae

Ribes rubrum L. (Red Currant) and ***R. nigrum*** L. (Black Currant) are occasionally bird-sown from gardens but seldom look wild. ***R. sanguineum*** Pursh (Flowering Currant) is naturalised on Onchan Harbour cliffs.

R. uva-crispa L. (Gooseberry) is unusually widespread, nowadays mostly occurring singly; it was formerly planted for hedging and relics of this still survive in a few places. It has no claims to be considered indigenous in Man.

Droseraceae

Drosera rotundifolia L. Common Sundew; Lus ny Graih
N Bogs, especially in hilly areas. Locally frequent. Calf.
Stowell in the 1860s claimed it grew in 'boggy ground, everywhere' — which, if not a wild exaggeration, points to a great decrease since.

[***D. intermedia*** Hayne Long-leaved Sundew
Listed by Gasking (1890), without details. A likely species to occur.]

Lythraceae

Lythrum salicaria L. Purple Loosestrife; Lus Skeilley
N Swamps, ditches, riversides. Locally common in the curragh areas, scarce elsewhere. Calf.

L. portula (L.) D. A. Webb Water Purslane
N Margins of ponds and reservoirs. Frequent in the north, rare elsewhere. Calf.
This species exhibits a ratio cline in the length of the outer calyx teeth: in the west of the British Isles, as in Man, var ***longidentata*** (Gay) Vasc. predominates, gradually giving way eastwards to the short-toothed extreme, var. ***portula.*** The five Manx localities in which the latter has been noted have no seeming geographical or ecological distinctiveness and in two of them both extremes grow side by side accompanied by numerous intermediates.

Thymelaeaceae

Daphne laureola L. (Spurge-laurel), apparently grown as a herb as well as ornamentally, is widely naturalised, especially in the north. Solitary bird-sown bushes are usual, but on the steep bank of the Ballaglass stream near Rhenab it occurs in profusion.

Onagraceae

Epilobium hirsutum L. Great Willow-herb
NC Marshes (especially on cliffs), streams, ditches; increasingly on dry, bare waste ground. Local: like ***Myosotis scorpioides*** mainly in the far south, round Douglas and, more thinly, along the Peel-Ballaugh coast. Unrecorded by Forbes and perhaps spreading. With white flowers — Foxdale spoil-heaps, *MD*: garden, Onchan, *AMH*.

E. parviflorum Schreb. Hoary Willow-herb
N Marshes. Frequent.

E. montanum L. Broad-leaved Willow-herb
NC Shady places; roadsides, cultivated ground. Common.

E. roseum Schreb. Pale Willow-herb
C Stream-sides, gardens, damp, stony waste places. Local, but spreading.

C — Above Ballig Bridge, *LSG*: Ballamanaugh, Sulby. **W** — Glen Maye. **SW** — Railway track near Greeba. **SE** — Road to Clay Head (× ***montanum***?), hb BM: Calvary Glen and Museum grounds, Douglas. **S** — About Ballasalla, *BSBI*[1] hb K!: Atholl Park, Port Erin; W Colby; Silverburn near Great Meadow; Ochre Mill Dam, Silverdale; about Castletown.

First noticed in 1950, this has undoubtedly increased since. It is invading north-west England and very rare in Ireland, so despite three stream-side stations it seems probably a recent colonist.

E. ciliatum Raf. (*E. adenocaulon* Hausskn.) American Willow-herb
C Marshes, roadsides, gardens, tips. Local, but spreading fast.
This North American species has increased explosively over southern England since the early 1930s. First noticed in Man in 1958 (though not in Ireland till 1980) it has proved increasingly widespread, especially round Laxey. Most of its earlier occurrences have been in or by gardens, suggesting importations from England with soil. Hybrids with ***E. montanum*** appear not uncommon.

[***E. tetragonum*** L. subsp. ***tetragonum*** (*E. adnatum* Griseb.)
Square-stemmed Willow-herb
'With ***E. montanum*** by far the commonest species', *Paton.* Also listed by Gasking (1890) and Hiern (1896). This is a markedly southern species, virtually absent from Ireland, and the records doubtless all belong to the next.]

E. obscurum Schreb. Broad-fruited Willow-herb
NC Marshes, damp roadsides, walls. Common. Calf.
Hybrids with ***E. palustre*** and ***E. parviflorum*** have been determined by G. M. Ash.

E. palustre L. Marsh Willow-herb
N Bogs, less often in marshes. Frequent. Calf.
The only ***Epilobium*** of the moors. Surprisingly, on railway tracks near Peel and Ellanbane.

[***E. alsinifolium*** Vill. Chickweed Willow-herb
Head of Sulby Glen, *Stowell* (1860): Ballaugh Curraghs, *Bilton and Bostock* (1885), *Br. Ass.*[2] A plant of mountain rills, extremely rare in Ireland. Stowell's record is possible, but in each case dwarf plants of some other species were more probably mistaken for it.]

E. brunnescens (Cockayne) Raven & Engelhorn (*E. nerterioides* auct.)
New Zealand Willow-herb
H Bare stony ground in hilly districts. Local, but spreading fast.
First noticed in 1961 on the mountain roads near The Bungalow, *GSM*, and by the Round Table, *LSG*!, this began to spread aggressively around 1968. It has since been found profusely in Block Eary valley and the Dhoon Quarry and has spilled over from the Round Table into South Barrule quarries and Glen Rushen Plantation. A remote colony has also appeared in Kimmeragh gravel-pit, Bride. Imported into gardens as a 'filler' for crazy paving, its speedy colonisation of upland Britain since the 1940s is now predictably being repeated in Man.

E. angustifolium L. Rose-bay
N?C Open woodland, hedges, dry bare ground. Local, but spreading fast and in places abundant. Calf.
As elsewhere in the British Isles, this was scarce a century ago. Whether it was native in Man even at that period is uncertain. British botanists agree in according it this status only in upland birchwoods and on screes; and although recorded by Forbes from 'the mountain glens' and by Stowell from 'glens and streams' (and best known in Sulby Glen in later years), it was then already in hedges near Ramsey and by lime kilns at Port Cornaa, seemingly adventive. Its glen occurrences may thus have been merely secondary as well. Escapes from cottage gardens were con-

ceivably responsible for these in part; but if a specimen in hb Talbot from Maughold (c 1866) is representative, these were the always sterile var. ***brachycarpum*** Leight. and so unlikely to have run wild all that far.

Whatever the origin of these plants, the extensive deforestation of the 1914-18 war touched off an explosive spread in Great Britain, which eventually, in the 1940s, evidenced itself also in Man. Within the last twenty years the species has become common in the felled parts of the conifer plantations and by 1969 reached the Calf.

Oenothera erythrosepala Borbás (Evening Primrose) appears occasionally on waste ground and tips. ***Fuchsia magellanica*** Lam., much planted for hedging in Man, spreads vegetatively with ease and readily becomes naturalised.

Circaea lutetiana L. Common Enchanter's Nightshade
NC Glens; gardens. Local: mainly in the eastern glens.

Around Douglas this is common in artificial glens and shrubberies, its bristly fruits readily dispersed by dogs. ***Geum urbanum***, with similar fruits, characteristically accompanies it. Once in gardens it is hard to eliminate and easily travels accidentally in soil. In this way it has spread to parts of the Island (e.g. Newtown, Port Erin, Sulby) far outside it putatively native range. Its presence under a cattle grille half-way up Sulby Glen is, however, unexpected. The plant was used herbally in Man for kidney complaints.

C.* × *intermedia Ehrh. Upland Enchanter's Nightshade
C Bushy places. Very rare.

N — Port Cornaa, *WFS*! **E** — Crogga Glen, *BSBI*[2]*.

P. M. C. Kermode's notebook also includes an 1884 record of ***C. alpina*** in a river-bed at Ballure(?) which must surely have been this. A sterile hybrid between ***C. alpina*** L. and ***C. lutetiana***, it reproduces vegetatively with ease and can become a garden pest. The known stations are in areas where there has been extensive planting and no doubt it has come in with soil accidentally — as in Co Wicklow and Merioneth.

Haloragaceae

Myriophyllum verticillatum L. Whorled Water-milfoil
N Still lowland pools with base-rich water. Very rare, perhaps extinct.

N — Ballaugh Curraghs, *Wheldon* (confirmation desirable: the species is unknown in Scotland.) **S** — Formerly abundant in a flooded pit at Gansey*, since filled in.

M. spicatum L. Spiked Water-milfoil
N Still lowland pools. Rare. Calf.

N — [Near shore at Jurby, *S. Kermode*, YLM 4, 191. The next species, which he failed to record, occurs here.] Ballaugh Curraghs, Proc 1, 271, *Wheldon*!: Poyll-dhooie, Ramsey, 1943, *Paton** (now gone). **W** — Patrick Reservoir; Peel power station pool, *D & G*. **SW** — Glen Darragh, near Glen Vine, 1953: Calf Mill dam, *D & G, SCM*.

An aquarists' and water-garden favourite and possibly on the increase from this cause.

M. alterniflorum DC. Alternate Water-milfoil

N Still pools and ditches, less often in swift streams, especially in peaty water. Local.

Noted in 23 stations since 1949 as against a mere 4 previously; but because non-flowering aquatics were neglected in the past and many smaller pools left unsearched, it is unsafe to infer a spread from this. The amphi-Atlantic var. ***americanum*** Pugsl., with tiny leaves, takes the place of the type in several lakes in northern Ireland and is recorded for one in Dumfriesshire; it might therefore also occur in Man.

Gunnera tinctoria (Molina) Mirb. occurs spontaneously on a wet cliff at Onchan Harbour, beside a stream outside Ballamanaugh, Sulby, and at the back of Ramsey Mooragh. It is widely naturalised in Ireland.

Hippuridaceae

Hippuris vulgaris L. Marestail

N Pools, ditches. Very local: confined to the north (mainly the north-west) except for quarry pools at Billown.

Callitrichaceae

Callitriche stagnalis Scop. Water Starwort

N Shallow pools, ditches, marshes. Frequent. Calf.

In a rock-pool on Langness and a bog-pool above Dalby.

C. platycarpa Kütz.

N Still or flowing, often base-rich water in lowland areas. Rare or overlooked.

[**SE** — Ditch beside Pulrose power station, 'probably' fide J. P. Savidge.] **S** — Brook running into Fleshwick Bay, *JAR*, det. J. P. Savidge.

Long confused with ***C. stagnalis*** and accurately discriminated in Britain only recently. A record of '***C. verna*** var. ***platycarpa***' by Gasking (1890) is unacceptable in the absence of a specimen. '***C. verna***', a name often given to ***C. platycarpa*** in this country, appears in Hiern's 1897 list but his material in hb RAMM is indeterminable.

C. obtusangula Le Gall
N Ponds, ditches, brackish stream-mouths. Local.

Almost completely overlooked until 1951, this conspicuous species has since been noted in 16 stations, mainly in the north, round Douglas and along the south coast. It is particularly characteristic of, and in places abundant in, the watercourses draining the northern curraghs. This is the more noteworthy in view of its southerly range in Britain and absence from Scotland apart from the far south. Such plenty at a range limit is suggestive of a spread still in progress.

C. intermedia Hoffm.
N Cold, base-poor water in ditches, lakes and streams. Frequent.

C. brutia Petagna (*C. pedunculata* DC.)
N Shallow muddy pools, especially those drying up in summer. Very local.

N — Three pools E of Ballawhane, Andreas*. **W** — Ballacross dub, Peel. **S** — Near Fleshwick; below Cronk Moar, Rushen; by Glendown, Port Erin.

Although some authorities dismiss this as a habitat state of ***C. intermedia***, I follow Schotsman in regarding it as a good species. It has a distinct facies and ecology (typically associated with ***Montia fontana***, ***Lythrum portula*** and ***Veronica scutellata***), a different chromosome number and a markedly Atlanto-Mediterranean range. Easily overlooked, it may be much more widespread than these records suggest.

Loranthaceae

Viscum album L. Mistletoe
H On trees (usually apples). Rare.

N — Formerly at Ballachurry, Andreas, *JCC*. **C** — Claughbane, Ramsey, *P. M. C. Kermode*: Ivie Cottage, near Kirkmichael, *FC*. **SE** — Ballavale, Santon, *Talbot*: The Arragon, Santon, 1939-40, *BW & IDA*: formerly at Onchan, *BW*. **SW** — Crosby, *D & G*.

Cornaceae

Swida sericea (L.) Holub (Red-osier Dogwood) survives as a relic of one-time planting in a field hedge near Sandygate, well away from houses, *D & G*.

ARALIACEAE

Hedera hibernica (Kirchner) Bean — Atlantic Ivy; Hibbin
NH Shady places, cliff-faces, shingle. Common.

This recently separated species has twice the chromosomes of the usual British Ivy, ***H. helix*** L., and a strongly western distribution. All native-looking Ivy in Man is proving to belong here, as in Ireland, west Wales and south-west England. It is told by the scale-hairs appressed to the leaf surface, not standing out in all directions. 'Irish Ivy', its sub-arboreal clone (***H. hibernica*** hort.) with larger, waxy, softer, paler green, usually five-lobed leaves with deeply cordate bases, was introduced for cover late last century and has become very widely naturalised in Man (as in parts of Scotland, but not Ireland).

Two other species are well naturalised in Glen Maye: ***H. algeriensis*** Hibberd ('Canary Ivy' of horticulture), with large glossy leaves, and ***H. colchica*** (C. Koch) C. Koch, with very tough, leathery ones.

UMBELLERIFERAE

Hydrocotyle vulgaris L. — Marsh Pennywort; Ouw
N Bogs, swamps. Common. Calf.

Sanicula europaea L. — Wood Sanicle
N Shady glens. Local: mainly between Laxey and Ramsey.

Eryngium maritimum L. — Sea Holly; Hollin Traie
N Sandy shores. Local: mainly in the north.

Chaerophyllum temulentum L. — Rough Chervil
C Shady hedgerows on base-rich soil. Very local.

N — Sulby, *Paton*: Lezayre road, Ramsey; Orrisdale, *WHH*: Rhencullen, *D & G*. **C** — The Rhaa, Lonan, *LSG*. **S** — Near Great Meadow House, *LSG*.

Also an unlocalised specimen in hb Mrs Kermode (who collected mainly in Ballaugh). An unlocalised record by Forbes (in Watson 1873-4) can hardly be correct, as he did no fieldwork at the time of year it would have been out (Forbes 1837b); moreover, he failed to record the much commoner ***Torilis japonica***, which is repeatedly misreported as this (eg Chalmers-Hunt 1970, 24).

Anthriscus caucalis Bieb. — Bur Chervil
N Sandy banks, dunes. Local: confined to the north and Derbyhaven.

A. sylvestris (L.) Hoffm. — Cow Parsley
NC Wet shady places; hedges. Very local, but markedly increasing.

Unrecorded till 1889, this has an oddly scattered distribution and in several places (mainly in the centre and south-east) is clearly recently introduced — with grass seed or imported soil. At least one of these populations is the form prevailing in southern England, var. ***latisecta*** Druce. Most Manx plants, however, both native and introduced are the more glabrescent, boreal-montane var. ***angustisecta*** Druce with darker green, more rigid, more sharply-cut leaves. Large, convincingly native populations occur along Glen Auldyn, in Cooil Darry Glen (upper Glen Wyllin) and by the junction of the Glass and Baldwin streams. They apparently demand a relatively cold and wet climate combined with a not too acid soil — conditions in Man seldom found together.

Scandix pecten-veneris L. Shepherd's Needle

C Cornfields, gardens. Formerly occasional, now very rare.

N — Cottage garden, north Andreas, 1969, *MD*. **SW** — Dumped farm refuse, Cornelly mines, 1967, *LSG*. **S** — Around Castletown, *Holt*: Port St. Mary, *Ralfe*: near Colby station, *LSG*.

'A cornfield weed', *S. Kermode*. Unlocalised specimens in hbb Talbot, Mrs Kermode and Mrs Brearey.

Myrrhis odorata (L.) Scop. (Sweet Cicely; Myrrh), once a herb of peculiar importance in Man, occurs today in or by almost every farmyard. It was used for sweetening sour fruit and its seeds did duty for caraway. But it was also a plant of especial power, very unlucky to uproot. It supposedly flowered at midnight on Old Christmas Eve (January 4) and the custom still survives of going out to witness this.

Torilis japonica (Houtt.) DC. Hedge Parsley

C Roadsides. Locally common, especially in the north, and apparently still spreading.

T. nodosa (L.) Gaertn. Knotted Bur Parsley

N Dry sunny banks, especially by the sea. Local: mainly S, W and N coasts. A southerly species, barely penetrating into Scotland.

Coriandrum sativum L. (Coriander) occurred as a casual on Ramsey tip, 1967*.

Smyrnium olusatrum L. Alexanders; Lus yn Ollee

D Roadsides, waste ground, mostly near the sea and seldom above 600ft. Common along the south and west coasts round to Bride, scarce elsewhere.

The predecessor of celery, once widely grown as a vegetable and salad. It was also valued for toothache as well as chopped up and fed to cattle with sore mouths — whence the Manx name: 'cattle herb'. In recent years its habit of dying off in midsummer has been found unsightly, giving rise to intensive spraying.

Conium maculatum L. Hemlock; Aghaue
NC Beaches; hedgebanks, waste ground, on light soil, mainly near the sea. Local: largely in the north and (especially) round Castletown.
Appears native on stony and sandy beaches just above the drift-line (cf ***Sonchus asper***), as at Poyllvaaish and the Point of Ayre. Absent from the inland waterside habitats it favours in England.

Bupleurum intermedium Poir. (Narrow-leaved Thorow-wax), a bird-seed casual, began appearing in 1965 and has turned up in many parts of the Island since, usually in gardens.

Apium graveolens L. (Wild Celery) was recorded by the Kermodes on waste ground in and near Castletown c 1883-1900 — presumably the var. ***dulce*** (Mill.) DC., escaped from gardens. A notable absentee from the native flora.

A. nodiflorum (L.) Lag. Fool's Watercress
N Ditches, marshes, pools (sometimes brackish), sea-cliff trickles. Frequent in the lowlands, but mainly coastal away from the north and all but absent between Douglas and Ramsey. Calf.

A. inundatum (L.) Reichb. f. Marshwort
N Shallow pools in neutral to strongly acid water. Frequent in the north, very rare elsewhere. Calf.
Until 1950 there were only two records for this, both by Paton, who knew it in Lough Gat-y-Whing by 1919. It has since proved to occur in most pools and dubs on the northern plain, often in profusion. Ballacross dub, near Peel, floristically an outlier of the north, also harbours it and, more surprisingly, it occurs in the mill pool and at Caigher Point on the Calf as well. Although aquatic plants were much neglected by earlier workers, a similar recent rush of records in Galloway suggests that a genuine increase has taken place. The distribution of the species in the British Isles shows little obvious pattern apart from a strong coastal trend towards the north. There is thus no apparent climatic reason for such a spread, which may accordingly be no more than the initial, explosive radiation so characteristic of newly-introduced aquatics.

Petroselinum crispum (Mill.) Nyman (Parsley; Parsal) has long been established, in its old non-crisped form, on a few sandy hedgebanks in the north. There are also two records from near Castletown, one of them the crisped form as a recent escape.

[***P. segetum*** (L.) Koch Corn Parsley
'Hedges', *S. Kermode* (1900). It is evident from a statement in YLM 3, 287 that Kermode mistook this as the scientific name of the preceding species.]

Cicuta virosa L. Cowbane
N Peaty pools, in reedswamp. Very rare, perhaps extinct.

N — (Jurby?) Curraghs, *Garner* (1867). Also recorded from an unspecified locality by Keegan (1888).

Though Garner's record (believed to date from 1854) has long been doubted, I now think this over-hasty. He had, after all, considerable experience and is likely to have been familiar with this species in his home area. Moreover, he listed on the same day its characteristic associate, ***Ranunculus lingua*** — and the peaty pools SW of Ballamoar where this still occurs are certainly suitable. The plant, which is sometimes half-floating, has a reputation for being scarce and elusive.

Ammi majus L. occurred in 1980 in a garden on Minorca Hill, Laxey, apparently as a bird-seed derivative, *MD**.

Carum verticillatum (L.) Koch Whorled Caraway
N Damp acid grassland. Locally abundant but markedly disjunct: mainly concentrated in the northern curraghs and along the south flank of the hills from Ballakilpheric to Ballamodha, with connecting populations at Ballavarane, Groudle and below the Glen Mona Hotel; also an outlier in the Great Meadow, Castletown.

Characteristic of a late stage in the vegetational succession following the drying up of lakes — a rather narrow ecological preference which seemingly accounts for its sharply localised occurrence. The pattern in Ireland is strikingly similar.

C. carvi L. (Caraway) was reported to Forbes (1837b), presumably as a stray from cultivation. It is said to have been grown in Man formerly for flavouring cheese.

Conopodium majus (Gouan) Loret Pignut; Curlan
N Fields, shady places. Common — but unrecorded from the Calf.

Pimpinella saxifraga L. Burnet Saxifrage
N or C Dry roadsides. Very local: now only in the northernmost tip.

N — Abundant round Kirk Bride, *Backwell's*, *Paton**!: by Phurt, Cranstal, *D & G*. **W** — Near Peel Road Station, *Clementson* (since gone).

The Bride population is genetically heterogenous, much of it coming under f. ***dissecta*** (Retz.) Neum.

Aegopodium podagraria L. (Ground Elder; Lus yn Aspick) is frequent in hedgebanks near houses and in gardens, including on the Calf. Formerly much prized as a cure for various disorders, especially gout, and now an ineradicable weed. Surprisingly, unrecorded by Forbes and Stowell.

[***Sium latifolium*** L. Great Water Parsnip
Listed by Wattam (1901), without details. Undoubtedly an error.]

[***Berula erecta*** (Huds.) Coville Lesser Water Parsnip
Sulby Glen, *S. Kermode* (1900). A likely species to occur but an unlikely locality. Kermode was prone to error and perhaps mistook for it luxuriant ***Apium nodiflorum***.]

Crithmum maritimum L. Rock Samphire; Lus ny Greg
N Sea cliffs, shingle or (rarely) dunes. Locally abundant, mainly in the southern half. Calf.

Once extensively gathered — and exported — for use as a sauce with meats: see Allen & Garrad (1980) for a detailed history.

Oenanthe fistulosa L. Tubular Water Dropwort
N Marshes. Very rare, perhaps extinct.

N — Curragh Beg, Bride, *P. M. C. Kermode*, YLM (1890), 183. **SE** — 'The Lake', by Douglas Nunnery, 1878, *Holt**.

[***O. pimpinelloides*** L. was invariably recorded in error for the next by pre-1860 authors.]

O. lachenalii C. C. Gmel. Parsley Water Dropwort
N Brackish rock-pools, wet saline turf. Rare.

C — Port Cornaa. **W** — Creglea, Dalby, *MD*! **SE** — Between Banks Howe and Clay Head, *Stowell*. **S** — 'Castletown etc.', *Backwell's*: Scarlett, *Davies*, *Forbes* etc!: St. Michael's I., *BSBI*[1]! and gully opposite: near ruined farmhouse, W Langness.

The Scarlett plant, often only 2 cm, is the var. ***minima*** Camus & Rouy. Though also known in Anglesey, Wexford and Cork, this may be a mere environmental state.

O. crocata L. Hemlock Water Dropwort; Aghaue
N Streams, ditches, marshes. Common. Calf.

Aethusa cynapium L. Fool's Parsley
C Gardens, waste ground, railway tracks. Local: confined to the lighter soils of the north, far south and Peel area.

Unrecorded last century and only twice up to 1930, this has noticeably increased in recent years.

Foeniculum vulgare Mill. (Fennel; Lus y Vooyn, Pinkeyl) has been naturalised since early last century on sandy hedgebanks in the north. There have also been two occurrences on the south coast.

[***Ligusticum scoticum*** L. Lovage
Listed as a component of cliff-top vegetation in the Port Erin area by Russell (1967). The recorder now believes the winter state of ***Smyrnium*** was taken for it.]

Angelica sylvestris L. Wild Angelica
N Streams, ditches, swamps. Common — but unrecorded from the Calf.

Peucedanum ostruthium (L.) Koch Masterwort
D Damp grassy places. A rare relic of old herbal use.
N — Keilthusthag lane, Andreas, *P. M. C. Kermode*: Sulby Curraghs, 1924; near Cronk-bouyr, Ballacregga, Bride, 1929, *Paton**: Close y Kee, St. Jude's, *JCC*: Lambhill, Bride; dub by Smeale chapel, *MD*.

Anethum graveolens L. (Dill) occurred in a garden in Castletown in 1973, *LSG*, det. D. McClintock, probably as a bird-seed derivative.

Heracleum sphondylium L. Hogweed; Farrain
N Grassy places, glens, roadsides, banks. Very common. Calf.

H. mantegazzianum Somm. & Levier (Giant Hogweed) is a rapidly increasing escape of moist, shady places and waste ground, first noted outside gardens as recently as 1957. It has already colonised the banks of the middle stretch of the Sulby R. and appeared on both the Killane and Lhen trenches.

Daucus carota L. subsp. ***carota*** Wild Carrot; Carradje marrey
N Dry ground, mainly near the sea. Common — but unrecorded from the Calf.

As remarked by Forbes (1849), cliff-top populations of this species in Man often exhibit some of the characters of the western race, subsp. ***gummifer*** Hook. f. (*D. maritimus* Lam., non With.), notably in having the flowering umbels more or less globular and, at least in some cases, the achene prickles ascending. Similar populations recur to the north, in Wigtownshire and Islay. It is uncertain whether they merit inclusion within this taxon and more intensive work on them is needed.

EUPHORBIACEAE

Mercurialis perennis L. Dog's Mercury
D Old gardens. Very rare.
N — Ballakillingan, Lezayre, three large patches, 1975, *D & G*.

The total absence of this species from the native flora bewilders visitors accustomed to its abundance in England; but in Ireland too it is very rare, confined to the old planted demesnes except for one passably indigenous colony on the limestone of the Burren.

M. annua L. Annual Mercury

C Gardens, waste ground. Rare.

N — Ballaugh, 1955, *WHH*. [**W** — Rumoured to have occurred at Peel, *Paton*, Proc 4, 126.] **SE** — Circular Road, Douglas, 1979, *LSG*. **S** — Port Erin, 1945 onwards, *JRB*: Castletown, 1957.

Beginning to occur as an accidental import from southern England but (unlike in Ireland) showing little tendency yet to spread.

Euphorbia lathyrus L. (Caper Spurge), listed by Gasking (1890), still lingers on as a herbal relic in and near gardens and on tips.

E. helioscopia L. Sun Spurge; Lus y Bwoid Mooar

C Cultivated fields, waste ground. Common.

E. peplus L. Petty Spurge; Lus ny Fahnaghyn

C Gardens, waste ground, preferring less acid soils than the last. Common.

E. exigua L. Dwarf Spurge

C Cultivated ground, railway tracks. Rare.

N — Mooragh Park, Ramsey, 1965, *MB*: Ramsey tip, *D & G*. **C** — Christ's Church parsonage, Maughold, *Stowell*. **SE** — Near Tromode, *Ralfe*: Castleward, 1902, *Hardaker*. **S** — Near Kirk Malew, *Stowell*: near Reash, Malew, *Ralfe*: Malew road N of Castletown, *LSG*: Billown quarries, *D & G*.

Also unlocalised records by Forbes, S. Kermode and Wattam (1901). In 1960 this was found to occur in four places on the railway between Port Soderick and Port Erin and, abundantly, W of St. John's. It had probably been there some years. Spraying and destruction of the lines have doubtless now eliminated it.

E. portlandica L. Portland Spurge

N Stony and sandy ground by the sea. Rare and disjunct: dunes of north and Marine Drive cliffs.

N — The Lhen, *F. Craine**, *MBB*: Ayres N of Rue Point, *BSBI*[1]! **SE** — Marine Drive, Wallberry, *Forbes*, *Cowin*!: Douglas Head, *Backwell's*: The Whing, between Little Ness and Keristal, *Ralfe*.

Also unlocalised records by Jowett, Webb, Talbot and Murray. Apparently a recent arrival in the north, unrecorded there till 1939.

E. paralias L. Sea Spurge

N Fore-dunes, a stony drift-line. Very local.

N — At intervals along the Ayres, 'very rare' according to Forbes (1837b) but now fairly frequent. **C** — The Dhyrnane, Port Mooar, one plant, 1975.

E. cyparissias L. (Cypress Spurge) has escaped near West Craig, Andreas, *MD*.

POLYGANACEAE

Polygonum aviculare L. Knotgrass; Finigagh, Glioonagh Veg

N?C Beaches; cultivated and waste ground. Frequent. Calf.

P. arenastrum Bor. (*P. aequale* Lindm.) Knotgrass

NC Muddy pool margins, bare ground, trampled grassland. Locally abundant.

As a native characteristic of a community including ***Potentilla anserina***, ***Rumex crispus*** and ***Lythrum portula*** — as at West Nappin dub, Jurby.

P. oxyspermum C. A. Meyer & Bunge ex Ledeb. subsp. ***raii*** (Bab.) Webb & Chater Slender Sea Knotgrass

N Drift-line of sandy shores. Local.

N — Common in the north-west, as at Ballaugh, *Forbes*: near Blue Point, *Wheldon*: Rue Point, *MBB**: NNW of Ballaghennie, *MD*: Ramsey foreshore. **S** — Derbyhaven, *Forbes*.

Also an unlocalised specimen in hb Holt.

[***P. maritimum*** L. Sea Knotgrass

Listed by Wattam (1901), without details. Doubtless an error for the preceding.]

P. bistorta L. Bistort; Glioonagh ghuiy

D Roadsides, damp fields. Rare.

N — Ballaugh Curraghs, *Wheldon*. **SE** — Port Grenaugh, *J. Kewley*, Proc 1, 26: Saddle Road, Kirk Braddan!; Pulrose, *Cowin*. **S** — Ballaclague, Kirk Arbory, *Teare*: S of Ballakilpheric.

Formerly grown herbally, the boiled leaves and shoots substituting for cabbage.

P. amphibium L. Amphibious Bistort

N Ponds, ditches, dry banks. Common in the north, local elsewhere, absent from much of the centre and east.

P. persicaria L. Redleg
NC Water margins, river shingle; cultivated and waste ground. Common. Calf.

P. lapathifolium L. (incl. ***P. nodosum*** Pers.) Pale Persicaria
NC Marshes, water margins, shingle. Cultivated and waste ground. Frequent. Calf.
Prefers a richer, more acid soil than the last, in wet habitats typically accompanying ***P. hydropiper.*** Unlike ***P. persicaria*** it seems to have formed an important Bronze and Iron Age food, suggesting that it may once have been much the commoner.

P. hydropiper L. Water-pepper; Glioonagh Cheh
N Mildly acid damp mud. Local: mainly in the north, central valley and far south-west, in abundance where conditions permit.

P. convolvulus L. Black Bindweed; Glioonagh Ghoo
C Cultivated and waste ground. Frequent. Calf.

P. cuspidatum Sieb. & Zucc. (Japanese Knotweed) is now a common and widely naturalised escape, especially on river and beach shingle.

P. polystachyum Wall. ex Meisn. is naturalised by the Silverburn just N of Rushen Abbey, *D & G*. ***P. campanulatum*** Hook f. (Himalayan Knotweed) is spreading along the Narradale stream by Sulby Claddagh, *D & G*!, and has also appeared in Greeba Curraghs, *MD*. The Manx climate clearly suits these Asian species.

Fagopyrum esculentum Moench (Buckwheat) occurred as a bird-seed casual in a garden N of Ramsey in 1967, *MD**.

Rumex acetosella L. Sheep's Sorrel
N Dry barish ground, acid grassland. Common. Calf.

R. tenuifolius (Wallr.) Löve Slender Sheep's Sorrel
N Acid sandy heathland. Very local.

> **N** — Between Ballaugh and Orrisdale, abundant,* conf. J. E. Lousley. Mitchell (1958) has also found this in a Late-Glacial deposit near Ballaugh.

A 'Continental' species with a strongly eastern range in Britain and in Ireland, though widespread in the Late-Glacial deposits, so far known only from Wexford.

R. acetosa L. Common Sorrel; Shughlaig
N Damp grassy places, marshes, bogs, swamps. Common.
Ascends to 900 ft on North Barrule, growing among sphagnum, *Paton**.

[***R. hydrolapathum*** Huds. Great Water Dock
Listed by Gasking (1890), without details. Reputedly once planted as an ornamental.]

R. alpinus L. (Monk's Rhubarb) was planted on a Port Soderick farm early this century for the use of its leaves to wrap up butter, *T. Ruddy* per *A. A. Dallman*, NW Nat (1935) 143. Not reported since.

R. crispus L. var. ***crispus*** Curled Dock; Cabbag (all docks)
NC Muddy pond- and lake-margins, stream shingle; cultivated and waste ground. Common. Calf.

var. ***littoreus*** Hardy (all three perianth tubercles equal)
N Shingle, sea-cliffs, dunes. Common.

R. crispus × ***obtusifolius*** (***R.*** × ***acutus*** L.) is probably frequent, usually being found wherever the parents occur together, but so far definitely noted only near Loughdoo, Jurby, det. J. E. Lousley.

R. obtusifolius L. subsp. ***obtusifolius*** Broad Dock
N?C Lake-shores; waste ground, field-margins. Common. Calf.

R. sanguineus L. var. ***viridis*** Sibth. Wood Dock
N Shady places, marshes, pond-margins. Frequent.

R. conglomeratus Murr. Clustered Dock
N Marshes, stream-sides. Locally frequent.

R. maritimus L. Golden Dock
N Mineral-rich ponds and ditches within two miles of the sea. Rare and very local.

N — Jurby and Bride (parishes), *Backwell's*: Ballakinnag dub, Andreas; dub SSW of Jurby church; dub NE of Braust, Andreas: E end of Lough Cranstal drain, *D & G*. Fluctuates greatly in quantity; especially profuse in 1951 and 1975.

Not in Scotland and exceedingly rare in Ireland, this is here virtually at its British Isles northern limit.

Urticaceae

Parietaria judaica L. (*P. diffusa* Mert. & Koch) Pellitory of the Wall
ND Maritime rocks; walls. Very local.

SE — River walls between Douglas Harbour and Nunnery, *Paton*! **S** — Strandhall to Poyllvaaish, abundant, *Holt*, *Keegan* etc. hb K!: Ballabeg,

S. Kermode, *Paton* etc: The Howe, *Ralfe*: near Port St. Mary; by entrance to Ballakeigan.

This looks native along the E side of Bay ny Carrickey, just as it does on rocks elsewhere along the north coast of the Irish Sea and at least as far north as Gigha. The populations on walls in this neighbourhood have clearly spread to these from the rocks; but other wall colonies, while doubtless ultimately of the same origin, are probably relics of herbal use of the plant as a diuretic.

Soleirolia soleirolii (Req.) Dandy (Mind your own business), a common greenhouse carpeter, has begun to escape in various places, including on the cliffs below Gibbdale Bay on the Calf.

Urtica urens L. Small Nettle; Undaagagh Rangagh
C Cultivated ground (mainly gardens). Common in the drier areas, largely absent from the moist east and centre. Calf.

U. dioica L. Stinging Nettle; Undaagagh, Onn
N Grassy and shady places, fens, beaches. Very common. Calf.

Cannabiaceae

Humulus lupulus L. Hop; Lus-y-gharghid, Lus Lhionney
N?D Fen thickets; hedges, cliffs. Occasional.

Normally an obvious relic of one-time cultivation, but in the Ballaugh Curraghs widespread and in places looking very wild. S. A. P. Kermode, first to report it here, in 1896, was sufficiently impressed to refrain from his usual dismissiveness, describing it as 'apparently naturalised'. The species is a characteristic constituent of alder-willow carr in England and has been claimed as native on a moss in Wigtownshire; it also occurs in post-glacial peats on the coast of South Lancashire. But against this must be set R. Lloyd Praeger's verdict that it is nowhere indigenous in Ireland.

Cannabis sativa L. (Hemp; Kennip), a bird-seed casual, has been recorded several times since 1957.

Ulmaceae

Ulmus glabra Huds. Wych Elm; Lhiouan
H Glens, hedges. Common.

Although the Manx trees mainly have the narrower leaves of the northern extreme, subsp. ***montana*** (Lindq.) Tutin, probably they are wholly descended from planted stocks. The species prefers base-rich soils, which are virtually absent from Man; and although its pollen shows up strongly in Boreal and Atlantic levels in peat near the Point of Ayre (Phillips 1967), the evidence suggests it became much reduced later, after 3000 BC, all over the Irish Sea region, apparently through its popularity as forage for cattle. In an island desperately short of timber it seems unlikely that so sought-after a tree would have been spared.

Many of the similar-looking Elms to be found in plantations and glens are segregants of the cross between this species and the very variable ***U. minor*** Mill. Three random gatherings by the BSBI party in 1950 were determined as this by R. Melville. ***U. procera*** Salisb. (Common Elm) has also been planted quite widely, mainly by houses. ***U. minor***, a complex mass of local clones, is represented by trees formerly separated as '***U. carpinifolia*** G. Suckow' at St. Mark's (hb K, det. R. Melville) and Rockmount, German*; and by others doubtfully referred to the Jersey Elm ('***U. sarniensis*** Loud.') — which is especially favoured as a windbreak in maritime climates — at Andreas, Peel, St. Mark's and elsewhere. These ***U. minor*** forms require fuller study in Man.

Moraceae

Ficus carica L. (Fig; Billey Figgagh) is naturalised on a wall in Ramsey and on the bridge and beach at Old Laxey. It also occurs on tips.

Myricaceae

Myrica gale L. Bog Myrtle; Roddagagh

N Curraghs. Very local: confined to the north-west (in places abundant) and the central valley from Union Mills to Peel Road Station. Also twice recorded from the Silverburn head-waters near St. Mark's.

Formerly used in Man for a yellow dye, as a substitute for hops, for tanning and as an insecticide.

Betulaceae

Betula pendula Roth Silver Birch; Beith Argid, Billey Veih

NH Dry heaths; plantations. Rare and very local.

N — Thinly scattered over Sulby Curraghs; field by Ramsey tip, one tree; Rhendhoo curragh, Jurby: boggy hollow by The Berrag, *D & G.*
C — Two old trees in wood on steep bank of Laxey stream opposite Minorca, with abundant holly.

Clearly introduced on Sky Hill and E of Union Mills Station.

B. pubescens Ehrh. subsp. ***odorata*** (Bechst.) E. F. Warb. Downy Birch

N Heathy scrub, glens, especially in the hills. Occasional.

N — Many in relic(?) oak-birchwood alongside railway N of Sky Hill; field by Ramsey tip. **C** — Upper Blaber R., *JR*: Old Laxey, one small tree; heath N of Kirk Lonan, one tree; N tip of Baldwin Reservoir. **W** — Upper Glen Wyllin*. **SW** — Quayle's Orchard, Grenaby; top of Barnell Glen, Patrick.

Till 1955 its mainly hairless leaves led this to be passed over as ***B. pendula***. In all the above localities it looks passably indigenous, the last fragments of what must once have been an extensive fringe of birchwood, principally along the upper limit of the oakwoods. On geographical grounds this northern and upland race, so abundant in the Highlands, is just what one would expect the aboriginal Manx trees predominantly to have been. Those in the Sky Hill and Glen Wyllin localities, moreover, have an appearance of great age, being notably tall and laden with 'witch's brooms'.

Sometimes accompanying these trees but considerably more numerous and widespread in the lowlands (especially in the northern and central curraghs) and in some cases clearly planted are examples with pubescent twigs, more or less viscid buds and leaves subdeltoid with the teeth pointing upwards, i.e. intermediate between subsp. ***odorata*** and ***B. pendula***. These one would automatically assume to be hybrids were it not for the fact that experimental work shows that the two species are highly intersterile and that most intermediates have the chromosome number of ***B. pendula.*** Either some odd breeding mechanism is at work, therefore, or the variation range of ***B. pendula*** is much wider than generally supposed.

Much more obviously introduced, and plentiful (often with pines) in several glens, are hairy-leaved trees intermediate between ***B. pendula*** and ***B. pubescens*** subsp. ***pubescens.*** This is the 'Silver Birch' also normally sold and planted in Ireland. A sterile hybrid is easier to believe in the case of stocks in use commercially, but even these sometimes seem self-sown. The presence of several small trees in a very wild-looking garey in Santon (317745) also calls such an assumption in question. These at least seem more likely to be relics of a one-time native population of subsp. ***pubescens*** in the south of the Island — or else segregates of a distinctive, hairy-leaved population of ***B. pendula***. The presence of 'pure' subsp. ***pubescens*** anywhere in Man has yet to be confirmed, however.

Alnus glutinosa (L.) Gaertn. — Alder; Farney

NH Glens, curraghs. Common.

Paton (in litt. to A. J. Wilmott, 1939) thought this very likely not native at all in view of how extensively it is known to have been planted. Certainly, the populations along the Neb have leaves suspiciously large for so northerly and westerly an area in the light of the geographical gradient in this character that is known to occur across the British Isles. Even so the species looks indigenous enough in some of the curraghs.

A. incana (L.) Moench (Grey Alder) has been planted along the N side of the Eairy Dam and beside the railway E of Crosby Station.

Corylaceae

Carpinus betulus L. (Hornbeam) has been planted on one or two of the older estates and is naturalised in Colby Glen, Glen Helen and Tholt-y-Will Plantation, *D & G.*

Corylus avellana L. Hazel; Couyll
NH glens, hedges. Local: mainly along the north-east edge of the hills.
'Hazel nuts are found in the bogs', observed Feltham (1798, 219); 'this is singular, as very few traces of the hazel are now to be found growing in the island'. At least one recent worker has also described this tree as rare. Yet though scarce (and doubtless planted) in many glens, it is still abundant in Glen Coul ('glen of the hazels') off Glen Auldyn and in Glen Mona. Hazelwoods on steep slopes, as in lower Glen Maye and Cass-ny-Hawin gorge, seem unquestionably indigenous. The more accessible native woods even so may once have been cropped, for Townley (1791, 195) records that vast quantities of hazel sticks were used for spitting herrings when the catch was landed.

Fagaceae

Fagus sylvatica L. (Beech; Faih) thrives well in the Manx climate but appears never to have been native. Rev. James Wilks (in Nichols 1822, 687) implies that it was being planted by as early as 1700, while the isolated plantation at Montpelier in Druidale, at 750ft, now notably rich in fungi, is mentioned in documents by 1768 (Garrad 1972b, 153). Today the tree is widespread and sometimes self-sown.

Castanea sativa Mill. (Sweet Chestnut; Castan Spaainagh) has also been widely planted but only sets viable seed in exceptional years. The trees in Glen Maye are mentioned by Woods (1811, 149) and no doubt this is the 'chestnut' implied by Wilks to have been growing by 1700 at Lewaigue.

Quercus cerris L. (Turkey Oak) has been planted in a few places.

Q. petraea (Matt.) Liebl × ***robur*** L. Oak; Darrag
NH Steep slopes, mainly by the sea; glens, hedges, plantations. Common, but rare and very local as a native.
Archaeological evidence suggests there were still sizeable oakwoods in the first centuries AD and perhaps into the Viking period, and on ecological grounds one would expect these to have been at least mainly of the

Durmast or Sessile Oak, ***Q. petraea***. The seemingly relic oak scrub on the side of the Santon gorge, however, has a mean petiole length intermediate between this and ***Q. robur*** (Garrad 1972a). Biometric analysis by Dr Garrad of other native-looking populations — notably in Glen Maye and straggling down the east coast cliffs at intervals from Clay Head to Traie ny Halsall (see map in Garrad 1972b, 149) — has yielded the same result. In Scotland, too, pure ***Q. petraea*** apparently no longer exists — and there is next to no 'good' ***Q. robur*** either. This is attributed to the long tradition there of planting ***Q. robur*** to maintain the stocking of the indigenous ***Q. petraea*** coppice woods, with mass crossing between two such freely interfertile species as a result; but it is hard to believe this explanation holds for Man in view of the earliness of its deforesting. The few oakwood relics that survive are also too inaccessible to have lent themselves to management. It must therefore be inferred that even the indigenous populations in Man had undergone some crossing. The few ***Q. robur***-like trees that occur today, however, all look patently planted. They, too, invariably seem in some degree intermediate.

Salicaceae

Populus alba L. (White Poplar) is sparingly planted and barely naturalised. ***P. canescens*** (Ait.) Sm. (Grey Poplar; Pobbyl), also sparingly planted, by contrast looks impressively wild in the Ballaugh Curraghs near Ballavolley and was recorded by Paton from Sulby Curraghs too. Though probably native in similar habitats in England, it is too far north, however, for this to be likely here. Paton believed he had evidence that it was present in Man before the period of reafforestation, but this was based on a misunderstanding of Bishop Hildesley's remark that 'abeles' were already around at the time he began planting. In fact the Castle Rushen accounts mention 'abeles' being imported well before, in 1696 — and these may have been ***P. alba*** in any case. ***P. nigra*** L. subsp. ***nigra*** (Black Poplar) has been planted in a glen N of Cronk-y-Voddy, Michael, its var. ***plantierensis*** (Simon-Louis) C. K. Schneid. in a glen above Fleshwick, and subsp. ***betulifolia*** (Pursh) W. Wettst. by Andreas Parish Hall. ***P. × canadensis*** Moench var. ***serotina*** (Hartig) Rehd. (Black Italian Poplar) is represented by solitary trees in several places. ***P. gileadensis*** Rouleau (Balsam Poplar) grows in two places near Ballakeigan, Castletown, and is also being used on the edge of Forestry Board plantations.

P. tremula L. Aspen; Chengey ny Mraane, Cron Craaee

NH Curraghs, stream-sides, glens, hedges. Occasional.

Often planted but clearly native in wet habitats in the north and elsewhere.

Salix L. (†det. R. D. Meikle)

S. pentandra L. Bay Willow; Shellagh Voainee

NH Curragh thickets, stream-sides. Rare.

N — Curraghs W of Sandygate, *Garner*, *BSBI*[1]: ditch N of Close Taggart; Ballaugh Curraghs by Ballavolley: Sulby Curraghs NW of Close an Allan, *LSG*. **C** — Sulby Glen, *Forbes*. **W** — S of Ballacraine, St. John's, *BSBI*[1] hb K!: Congary curragh, *WFS*, *MD*! and Neb bank nearby: garey SW of Cronk-y-Voddy, *D & G*.

'Wet places' *Stowell*. Planted in a garden on Sulby Claddagh! and, in quantity, on the E side of Lough Cranstal, *D & G*.

S. alba L. (White Willow) has a wild look along the rivers in the central valley and reappears by one or two pools in the south. Some have thought it native in similar country in England and central Ireland, but so accessible a tree seems unlikely to have survived in an island so bereft of timber. There is no record of it before 1896 and elsewhere in Man it always appears planted. ***S. fragilis*** L. (Crack Willow) is represented only by forms of horticultural origin: the Bedford Willow, var. ***russelliana*** (Sm.) Koch, is frequent by rivers, streams and ponds and occurs even in curraghs †; the White Welsh Willow or Varnished Willow, var. ***decipiens*** (Hoffm.) Koch, grows in the Congary curragh near Peel † and in three places in the north; and the Basford Willow, var. ***basfordiana*** (Scaling ex Salter) Bean, has been planted at Rhendhoo farm, Jurby, from withies wrapped round a consignment of apple-trees, *MD*!†. The reddish twigs and ultra-long catkins of the last have made it a prized ornamental in many parts of England. [***S. triandra*** L. (Almond Willow) is cited for vice-county 71 in Druce (1932) apparently through a clerical error. Druce is not known to have visited Man.]

S. purpurea L. Purple Willow

N?H Curraghs, bushy places. Very local.

Conceivably native in alder carr (once a lake margin) in the Congary curragh, near Peel, where some of the trees look old — though forms of the planted ***S. fragilis*** accompany it. It reappears further east in the central valley, from Crosby Station to Glen Vine and again N of Kirk Braddan, along the railway and the edge of the curraghs, apparently as an escape. It is grown in some quantity in the Forestry Board's nursery at St. John's, whence doubtless came a recent planting by the stream in lower Glen Wyllin. The Manx record in Druce (1932) is presumably derived from Hiern's list (1897), in which it is bracketed as merely cultivated — but Hiern's specimen in hb RAMM is not this species.

S. daphnoides Vill. (Violet Willow) has been planted by a stream near Four Roads, Rushen*; by a ditch near Ballakeigan, Castletown; and by a pond at Ballaclucas, Andreas.

S. viminalis L. Osier; Shellagh Ushtey

D Beside water, roadsides, quarries. Local: absent from most of the east and the Peel area, but frequent round St. John's and Port Erin. This oddly patchy distribution betrays its former cultivation (the twigs are used for lobster pots). It is doubtfully a native of the British Isles.

S. caprea L. subsp. ***caprea*** Pussy Willow

N or H Sea-cliffs, roadsides, sand-pits. Rare and very scattered, usually singly.

N — The Dollagh, Ballaugh, *WHH*: N of Ellanbane, *MBB*: dub by The Lhaggagh, *MD*: railway N of Sky Hill, in two places; Leodest, Andreas. **C** — Riverside, Old Laxey. **W** — Ballakinnag, Michael; sand-pit, St. John's. **SE** — Near Oakhill, *Talbot**: Onchan Harbour: Spring Valley, *LSG*. **SW** — S of Crosby; N of Ballanank, Malew. **S** — Ballasalla, *Wheldon*: cliff, Port Erin. Also unlocalised records by Gasking and Hiern.

The rarity of this common Britannic species is doubtless due to its preference for the margins of oakwoods on dryish, base-rich soils. The small cluster of finds at the east end of the northern curraghs is possibly the remnant of a native population, but generally in Man it has the appearance of a wind-borne adventive. The four or five trees at Spring Valley seem to have been planted ornamentally, so cultivation may be the primary (or even only) source.

S. cinerea L. subsp. ***cinerea*** Grey Sallow

N Very wet fens. Very rare or overlooked.

N — Curraghs S of Ballamoar, Jurby, *BSBI*[1]†.

A 'Continental' race mainly confined to the east in England. In Ireland so far known only from one base-rich lakelet in Co Down.

subsp. ***oleifolia*** Macreight (subsp. *atrocinerea* (Brot.) Silva & Sobrinho) Common Sallow; Shellagh

N Curraghs, glens, water-sides, on drier and more acid ground. Common. Calf.

S. aurita L. Eared Sallow

N Wet, acid ground. Frequent. Calf.

S. repens L. Creeping Willow; Tuig-y-Yeeigey

N Bogs, wet roadsides, ditch-banks at low elevations. Local: widespread in the north and the central valley, thinly scattered down the moist east side (with a concentration in Malew and Santon), reappearing on the Mull Peninsula and in plenty on the Calf.

The dune-slack form, var. ***nitida*** (Sér.) Wender (subsp. *argentea* (Sm.) G. & A. Camus), is locally abundant on the Ayres, especially between Ballaghennie and Ballakinnag, but absent from the other dune areas.

S. herbacea L. Least Willow

N Bare ground on mountains. Very rare.

C — Snaefell, *A. Templeman* hb OXF, BEC (1924) 596. Refound in 1962, on NW side of summit 30 yd W of radar station, *JEL*; in 1971 on S side between the cairn and the hotel, *LSG, MD & GLQ*. The latter population consists of some ten distinct patches sheltering against small rocks at just over 2000 ft.

The only true arctic-alpine flowering plant in Man, sought in vain on several of the other summits.

Several of the above species are highly interfertile and, being mainly insect-pollinated, very prone to cross. ***S. aurita*** × ***cinerea*** is the commonest occurring spontaneously in Man, followed by ***S. cinerea*** × ***viminalis***. There are three records of ***S. aurita*** × ***repens*** and a bush of putative ***S. aurita*** × ***viminalis*** grows by the railway W of Glen Vine. ***S. caprea*** × ***cinerea*** probably also occurs but needs re-study: broad-leaved ***S. cinerea*** may have been largely mistaken for it. The numerous records of ***S. aurita*** × ***caprea*** are likewise suspect, for these two scarcely overlap in their flowering periods. ***S. caprea*** × ***viminalis***, however, certainly occurs: Glen Grenaugh*†; Spaldrick Bay cliffs, Port Erin†; Dalby Glen; Congary curragh, near Peel; near Ballakilpheric Mill; N of Ballachrink, East Baldwin. Some of these localities are well outside the known range of ***S. caprea*** and presumably originated from plantings — for certain crosses were formerly favoured by growers for particular specialised uses. Thus ***S.*** × ***smithiana*** Willd. (***S. cinerea*** × ***viminalis***), known commercially as the Silky-leaved Osier, has clearly been widely planted on its own account in Man, especially in the north. Forby's Osier, ***S.*** × ***forbyana*** Sm. (***S. purpurea*** × ***viminalis*** × ***? cinerea***), several clumps of which grow by the Dhoo midway between Union Mills and Braddan bridge*†, was preferred for coarse basket-making and continues in use commercially as a shelter-belt. The large clump of willows by the Calf Mill dam — the most substantial vegetation on the islet — is also this hybrid*†. Another old commercial favourite, ***S.*** × ***mollissima*** Ehrh. (***S. triandra*** × ***viminalis***), prized for its vigour and known for preferring rich soil, constitutes the equally conspicuous clump at Derbyhaven, hb K†.

ERICACEAE

Rhododendron ponticum L. is well naturalised in some glens and in Oakhill railway cutting but on the whole is surprisingly non-invasive.

Pernettya mucronata (L.f.) Gaudich. ex Spreng. is naturalised above Onchan Harbour and on the railway at Union Mills.

Calluna vulgaris (L.) Hull Ling; Freoagh Mooar

N Heathy ground, moors. Locally abundant. Calf.

White flowers are not uncommon and especially plentiful on the Calf. The glaucous and hairy var. ***pubescens*** Hull, the predominant form in many maritime areas elsewhere, has not been reported in Man.

Erica tetralix L. Cross-leaved Heath; Freoagh Frangagh
N Bogs, wet heaths and moors. Locally common, especially in the southern hills — but missing from the Calf.

White-flowered in several places, especially on and near South Barrule.

E. cinerea L. Bell Heather; Freoagh Tessen
N Dry heaths and moors. Locally abundant. Calf.

'The only species found for miles together in the greywacke of the Isle of Man', *W. Thomson*, Mag Nat Hist (1830) 417. Very variable in flower and foliage colour. White flowers are frequent.

Vaccinium vitis-idaea L. Cowberry
N High moorland, usually around summits. Rare.

C — Hill NE of Snaefell, *Davies*: Beinn-y-Phott, *Backwell's*, *JS*, *MC & RM*: Snaefell, *Conolly*: Slieau Freoghane, *LSG*. **SW** — South Barrule, *Paton**!: The Carnanes, *Conolly* (since gone through burning).

V. myrtillus L. Bilberry; Freoghane Ghorrym
N Moors, glens, open heathy ground. Locally common.

Unusually, in a dry sandy field near the sea at Ballaugh, *WHH*.

V. oxycoccus L. Cranberry
N Upland valley bogs. Very rare.

C — Near top of the Cluggid stream below Slieau Managh at c 900ft, *GEQ*, *NK* per *LSG*. Mr Quayle showed me a freshly-gathered specimen in 1960 shortly after his discovery.

A rare plant in Ireland too, but there characteristic of raised bogs in the lowlands.

Pyrolaceae

[***Pyrola minor*** L. Common Wintergreen
Spanish Head, *M. Everton*, WF Mag (1931) 7.

Though seemingly a species that is unmistakable, others in Miss Everton's MS list (per Marjorie Cross, of Millom) are highly unlikely. On reflection, despite the suitability of the locality, this record would have been better withheld from the *Atlas* and treated as doubtful.]

Empetraceae

Empetrum nigrum L. Crowberry
N Heathery moorland mostly over 1000ft. Locally abundant but absent from large areas.

Plumbaginaceae

Limonium vulgare Mill. Common Sea Lavender
N Saltmarshes, crevices of rocks washed by the tide. Very rare.

N — Ballaugh shore, *Hoyle* (now gone). **C** — Port Mooar, a solitary patch of about 20 plants, discovered in 1972, per *D & G*!*, det. L. A. Boorman. **S** — Gully opposite St. Michael's Island, one plant, 1971 only, *MD*.* Also listed by Gasking, without details.

L. binervosum (G.E.Sm.) C. E. Salmon Rock Sea Lavender
N Sea-cliffs. Very rare.

SW — High perpendicular cliffs between The Chasms and Port St. Mary, 1881, *Holt**, JB (1896) 448. Presumably the Sea Lavender reported 'on cliffs' in Black's Guide (1883). Resighted there by AH in 1966 and FBG in 1971.

This species is apomictic (like the Brambles) and so consists of numerous true-breeding local populations. The Irish Sea ones fall into three groups: 'var. ***intermedium*** Syme' of most of Wales and NW England, 'var. ***procerum*** (Rouy) C. E. Salmon' of NW Wales and E Ireland, and an unnamed one peculiar to the Mull of Galloway. Miss C. W. Muirhead finds Holt's specimens differ from the latter as well as from the plant on St. Bees Head, Cumberland; but whether this means they belong under 'var. ***procerum***' remains unsettled.

Armeria maritima (Mill.) Willd. subsp. ***maritima*** Thrift; Kione Jiarg
N Coast rocks, shingle, saltmarshes. Common. Calf.

White-flowered specimens have been recorded in the south, including on the Calf.

Primulaceae

[***Primula farinosa*** L. Birdseye Primrose
Listed by Gasking, doubtless on the strength of Miss Dodd's assertion in YLM 1, 98 that 'the bird's eye primrose is to be found near Ramsey' — which was evidently a misnomer for the reddish variety of the Common Primrose recorded thence by Stowell.]

P. veris L. Cowslip
CD Grassy places. Rare and usually impermanent.

Repeatedly recorded since c 1826, sometimes singly, sometimes abundantly in one particular field, but typically disappearing after two or three years — though a colony at Kirk Michael has now persisted half a century at least. Just the same pattern is reported in NE Ireland. Past sowings (for Cowslip wine was esteemed for insomnia) or imports with grass seed are presumably responsible, for the species becomes too markedly a lime-lover on the margin of its range for Man to have it as a native.

P. veris* × *vulgaris occurred at Mount Murray following the sowing there of ***P. veris*** last century, *Holt**.

P. vulgaris Huds. Primrose; Sumark
N Banks, pastures, shady places, wet sea-cliffs, bogs. Very common. Calf.

With reddish or purplish flowers at: **N** — Plantation on Lough Mollagh road near Ramsey, *Stowell*: Ohio, Andreas, *P. M. C. Kermode*: old plantation S of Ballamoar, Jurby, *D & G*. **C** — Glen Joughlin, Rhenab, *P. M. C. Kermode*: Carmodil Glen, Ballaugh; behind Ravensdale, *D & G*. Doubtless introduced originally in all cases. Also several with green flowers in a native population on Shellag Point, *AP*.

Lysimachia nemorum L. Yellow Pimpernel
N Glens, stream banks. Frequent, but absent from large areas.

L. nummularia L. (Creeping Jenny), a not infrequent escape, is well naturalised in ditches and on shady hedgebanks in at least three places. Its total sterility makes it unlikely to be native.

L. vulgaris L. Yellow Loosestrife
NH Fen-swamps. Very rare as a native.

N — Garey along the Sulby Drain SW of The Dhoor, several scattered patches, *D & G**. Discovered only in 1976, this seems a relic of an old lake-margin (cf ***Crepis paludosa***). **C** — Greeba Curraghs near Northop Farm, forming a brilliant sheet for at least half a mile. The discoverers, Cowin & Karran (1945), assumed this population was native; but it proves to be the cultivar 'Grandiflora', with showier, wholly terminal flowers suffused with red at their base. It is partly on disturbed ground and spreading aggressively. This form is widely grown in Man and occurs elsewhere as an obvious escape.

L. punctata L. (Dotted Loosestrife) is naturalised in a ditch in the same part of the Greeba Curraghs, by the Silverburn, in Ramsey 'hairpin' quarry and at Cornelly mines, *MD*; in the bog above Onchan Harbour, *RWD*; and transiently elsewhere.

Anagallis tenella (L.)L. Bog Pimpernel
N Bogs. Common. Calf.

A. arvensis L. Scarlet Pimpernel; Sooill y Laa
NC Bare stony places by the sea; cultivated and waste ground. Common. Calf.

Rather frequent in open maritime habitats as the ordinary sprawling form with scarlet flowers. On dunes in the west of the British Isles stricter, suberect populations occur which are often wholly the pale pink recessive, var. ***carnea*** (Schrank) Boenn.; but in Man plants combining these characters have been noted only on the Point of Ayre, *WFS*! Var. ***purpurascens*** Thurston & Vigurs, an extremely rare variant with dark purple flowers, occurred at Orrisdale Head in 1972, *MD*. The blue-flowered, mainly Mediterranean var. ***azurea*** Wilmott, another recessive, also turns up rarely and very locally:—

N — Ballacrebbin, Andreas, sporadically, *MBB*: roadside N of Ellanbane, several plants 1958-60, *GEQ*!: garden, W Ramsey, *MD*. **S** — Near Castletown, *S. Kermode*: Scarlett, *Paton**.

The two last were erroneously published as ***A. foemina*** Mill.

A. minima (L.) E. H. L. Krause — Chaffweed

N Bare ground where water has stood in winter. Very local. Calf.

N — Andreas! and Bride! (parishes), *Backwell's*: 'Curraghs' (S of Ballamoar?), *Garner*: Ballakinnag dub, Smeale; Ballasalla dub, Jurby; wet hollows on the Ayres at Sartfield, near Knock-e-Dooney, and W of Ballaghennie. **SE** — Douglas Head, abundant in damp rock fissures; above Onchan Harbour; green lane near Newtown 314744, very abundant. **SW** — Calf, in several places.

'Wet places on gravel, rarely', *Stowell*. 'Isle of Man', 1827, *Jowett* hb K.

Glaux maritima L. — Sea Milkwort

N Salt-marshes, rock-pools, spray-drenched turf. Local. Calf.

Samolus valerandi L. — Brookweed

N Sea-cliff trickles, marshes and pools by the sea. Local: mainly south and south-west coasts. Calf.

Buddlejaceae

Buddleja davidii Franch. is widely naturalised, especially on quarry rubble.

Oleaceae

Fraxinus excelsior L. — Ash; Unjin

NH Hedges, glens, curraghs. Common. Calf.

Though such an important component today of the glens, this has undoubtedly been much planted. Its timber was greatly valued; and pollen analysis shows that in Ireland it was very rare before 2500 BC, implying that it owes its prevalence largely to human intervention.

Syringa vulgaris L. (Lilac) is occasionally naturalised, often the only sign of former habitation. ***Ligustrum vulgare*** L. (Privet) and ***L. ovalifolium*** Hassk. (Japanese Privet) have been planted here and there as hedging.

Apocynaceae

Vinca minor L. (Lesser Periwinkle) is naturalised in several places, mainly in the north. ***V. major*** L. subsp. ***major*** (Greater Periwinkle) also runs wild.

Gentianaceae

[***Centaurium pulchellum*** (SW.) Druce Slender Centaury
Listed by Gasking, without details. Doubtless derived from the claim in Black's Guide (1883) that it 'flourishes in several spots near Ramsey' — which surely must be an error for a form of the next.]

C. erythraea Rafn Common Centaury; Keim-Chreest
N Maritime turf, dry and damp pastures inland; bare waste ground. Locally common. Calf.
White-flowered plants have been noted on the Calf and at Cranstal. The dwarf, cushion-like var. ***subcapitatum*** (Corb.) Ubsdell is frequent on cliffs; it was misreported as ***C. latifolium*** (Sm.) Druce by early workers and as ***C. capitatum*** (Willd.) Borbás by Wheldon, Proc LBS (1920) 16 (later corrected in his herbarium).

C. littorale (D. Turner) Gilmour Seaside Centaury
N Damp saline turf. Very rare, perhaps extinct as a pure species.

W — Creglea, Dalby, a solitary specimen, 1972 hb BM. Dr R. A. E. Ubsdell pronounced this extremely puzzling: on the whole intermediate between this species and the last but tending towards the former, yet unlike any hybrids seen elsewhere and quite devoid of the dense scabridity characteristic of ***C. littorale*** up the west coast of Britain. In this latter respect its affinity is North European. A chromosome count alone could have clinched the matter, but the material was insufficient.

In 1950 on the BSBI Field Meeting I collected from an unremembered spot (I believe Port Cornaa) another specimen which J. S. L. Gilmour accepted as 'almost certainly' this hybrid. There is no apparent sign of hybridity, however, in the ***C. erythraea*** populations on Ramsey Mooragh and the Ayres.

Arthur Bennett, JB (1896) 448, claimed to have received a Manx specimen of ***C. littorale*** from H. Platts of Clydebank; but this is not in Bennett's herbarium and his checking is known to have been inadequate. Holt's repeat of this record in Proc led him to be miscredited with finding this species by Paton (1933). Stowell's '***C. littorale***', which he found far more common than his '***C. latifolium***', can only have been one of the forms of ***C. erythraea***.

Gentianella campestris (L.) Börner Field Gentian

N Damp grassy, usually base-rich ground near the sea; lead-mine 'deads' inland. Very local.

N — Sartfield, Jurby, *Dickson, MBB* etc: inner Ayres W of Ballaghennie, *MBB, D & G*: widespread (and spreading) on Ballakinnag — Ballaghennie outer Ayres, *D & G*. **W** — Brows near White Strand, *Young* hb BM. **SW** — Common on old mine waste, Foxdale and Eairy, *RH*! hb CGE. **SE** — Mount Murray, *Holt*. **S** — Castletown golf links, *Hannay, Dickson*: near Langness lighthouse, *CB, D & G*.

'Scarce', on the clay-slate, *Forbes*. A white-flowered plant at Foxdale, 1969, *MD*.

Menyanthaceae

Menyanthes trifoliata L. Bogbean; Lubberlub, Lus-ny-tree-Ghuillag
N Pools, swamps, hill flushes. Local: mainly in the north and central valley.

Polemoniaceae

Polemonium caeruleum L. (Jacob's Ladder) was listed by McNab (Watson 1832). A garden favourite, it not uncommonly escapes.

Boraginaceae

[***Cynoglossum officinale*** L. Houndstongue
A photograph of this species by H. M. Rogers labelled 'a first time for us' is in the Manx Museum. It is believed to have been taken on the Ayres around 1930, but this is not certain.]

Symphytum officinale L. (Common Comfrey; Cumfurt) is occasional on waste ground, usually singly and usually with cream flowers. Its roots and stems were formerly in herbal use for curing coughs (Quayle 1973, 69). Stowell (1860) recorded it on 'stream sides, Ballaglas Glen, etc' and it has also been noted by the Glass at Tromode in recent years, but though accepted as native in this habitat in England, its status here is at best doubtful. ***S.* × *uplandicum*** Nyman (Russian Comfrey), introduced for fodder late last century, has become established in many places thanks to its deep roots. At Glen Wyllin and near Ellerslie it is grown in gardens, perhaps for the benefit of bees. ***S. tuberosum*** L. (Tuberous Comfrey) is established in hedges by Great Meadow House*, by Knocksharry Farm, above Waterfall Halt, Foxdale and also at The Crogga. ***Borago officinalis*** L. (Borage) occurs occasionally, usually fleetingly, near gardens and on tips. A beekeepers' favourite, it has also been prized herbally.

An infusion of the flowers was used to ease lung infections (Quayle 1973, 69) — presumably in lieu of ***Pulmonaria*** — while its cucumber flavour made it a popular seasoning in salads and drinks. ***Trachystemon orientalis*** (L.) G. Don f. (Abraham, Isaac and Jacob) is naturalised along the Crogga stream and at Mount Murray, *LSG**. ***Pentaglottis sempervirens*** (L.) Tausch ex L. H. Bailey (Green Alkanet), originally grown for the red dye from its roots which was used in Man for rouge, is now popular in gardens for its early blue flowers and frequently escapes.

Anchusa arvensis (L.) Bieb. Small Bugloss; Lus Chengey Dow
N?C Dry heathy ground (rare); cultivated fields on light soils. Common in the north, local elsewhere. Calf.
On the Welsh coast accepted as native on sandy and pebbly beaches. At Glen Wyllin mouth, on sandy ground regularly associated with ***Fumaria muralis*** subsp. ***boraei***, it possibly also has this status.

Pulmonaria officinalis L. (Common Lungwort) is an uncommon escape.

Myosotis scorpioides L. Water Forget-me-not
N Beside running or (rarely) still water. Local: mainly in the far south and inland from Douglas.
Preliminary sampling suggests that the Manx populations of this species may be separable into two distinct groups. On the central south coast the corolla limb averages 8-9·5 mm and the stem hairs are partly appressed, partly spreading or bent. Further east, on the Silverburn, and on the Glass at Douglas specimens have the smaller (7-9 mm) corolla limb and mostly appressed stem hairs reportedly characteristic of northern and upland Britain. Wrongly referred to the Continental ***M. strigulosa*** Reichb. in the past, these latter plants may well constitute a separate subspecies. But wider study is needed to test the consistency of the variation, which may prove merely clinal.

M. secunda A. Murr. Creeping Water Forget-me-not
N Bogs, especially in upland areas. Frequent. Calf.

M. laxa Lehm. subsp. ***caespitosa*** (K. F. Schultz) Hyland. ex Nordh. Tufted Forget-me-not
N Lowland marshes. Common. Calf.

M. sylvatica Hoffm. (Wood Forget-me-not) has twice been noted on roadsides in the north as an escape.

M. arvensis (L.) Hill Common Forget-me-not
C Dry places, including cornfields. Locally frequent. Calf.

M. discolor Pers. Changing Forget-me-not

NC Wet fields, marshes; bare dry ground, maritime turf, cornfields. Locally frequent; mainly in the north. Calf.

The Britannic range of this species is oddly bicentric: Scottish and south English, with a zone in between in which it scarcely occurs at all. This suggests two separate races, the northern of which may prove to correspond with subsp. ***dubia*** (Arrondeau) Blaise, with flowers creamy-white (instead of orange-yellow) before turning blue and a preference — at least in Norfolk — for damper habitats. There is one record for this (Dog Mills, *BSBI*[1] hb K, det. A. E. Wade) but Manx material has not otherwise been critically examined. The species is mainly on disturbed ground in Man and thus likely to be an incomer from the south; but on Cally beach, Port Cornaa, it looks native in dry close turf, while a wet ground form is widespread round Peel, especially in rushy places, and occurs in at least one slack on the Ayres.

M. ramosissima Rochel — Early Forget-me-not

N Bare ground near the sea. Very local: north-west and north coasts and near Derbyhaven and Poyllvaaish in the south-east.

With white flowers at Glen Mooar, Michael, *MBB* hb BM and near Poyllvaaish, *LSG*.

Buglossoides arvense (L.) I. M. Johnston — Common Gromwell

C Cultivated ground on light soils. Very rare.

S — Garden, Castletown, c 1906, *Hannay*: cornfield between Colby station and Kentraugh, 1965, *LSG*.

Mertensia maritima (L.) Gray — Oyster Plant

N Shingle beaches. Very rare.

N — The Lhen, one plant since 1977, *G & G*, *D & G*. Many seedlings produced annually. **S** — Poyllvaaish Bay, one plant c 1866, later crushed by a passing cart, *Talbot**, *Murray*, JB (1897) 147.

This species is withdrawing northwards and Man is now on the very edge of its British Isles range.

Echium vulgare L. — Viper's Bugloss

N or C Grassy fields on light dry soils. Very rare.

N — Fields at Ballaugh, *S. Kermode*: fields near Ballacregga, Bride, *Paton**. **S** — Ballaclague, Kirk Arbory, *Teare*, *Ralfe*.

'Cold clay', *Holt* (1874). Last recorded in 1928.

Convolvulaceae

Convolvulus arvensis L. — Field Bindweed; Lus y Lheaney

NC Eroding sea-cliffs; roadsides, footpaths, dry waste ground.

Frequent in the north and far south, scarce or absent elsewhere. Like ***Linaria vulgaris*** unknown to Forbes and probably mainly a recent invader. But along the base of the brooghs S of the Killane mouth it forms a constituent of a landslip community (including ***Equisetum arvense*** and ***Tussilago farfara***) in which it is believed native in Merioneth. It is also considered 'certainly native near the sea' in Kerry.

Calystegia sepium (L.) R.Br. subsp. ***sepium***
Great Bindweed; Lillee Hallooin
NC Stream-banks, tall marshes; beaches, hedges, roadsides. Local: mainly in the south and centre, rarer in the north. Calf.
Especially plentiful along the west half of the south coast. Forbes called it 'very rare' and Stowell believed it absent, but it is only so in the areas each knew best. Yet it must surely have increased, as it now also occurs as an apparent adventive in and around Douglas, Castletown and Ramsey. These urban populations may consist in part of the fertile hybrid with ***C. silvatica*** and need closer study. The mainly coastal and western pink-flowered race, subsp. ***roseata*** Brummitt, ought to occur in Man and should also be looked for.

C. pulchra Brummit & Heywood (*C. dahurica* auct.) (Pink Bindweed) has escaped here and there, especially in the south-west corner.

C. silvatica (Kit.) Griseb. (American Bellbind) is increasingly frequent on roadsides and waste ground. A garden specimen in hb Mrs Brearey dated 1866 shows that its history in Man as an ornamental is a lengthy one. The earliest record as an escape is 1930.

C. soldanella (L.) R.Br. Sea Bindweed
N Maritime sands. Local; north coasts, E of Castletown and near Dalby.
Paton noted an unusually large-flowered form near the Dog Mills up to c 1936.

Cuscuta epithymum (L.) L. Common Dodder
N Near the sea on heather, thyme and ***Leguminosae***. Rare.

W — on ***Calluna***, bottom of Glen Maye, *BSBI*[1]! **SW** — on ***Calluna***, Cregneish: on ***Calluna***, Easy Cushlin, *JBD*. **S** — Port Erin, *Holt*: on ***Ulex gallii*** (mostly), ***Erica tetralix***, ***Thymus***, near Langness lighthouse, *S. Kermode*, *Ralfe* etc: on ***Anthyllis***, between Scarlett and Balladoole, *VSS* hb K: on ***Calluna***, near Langness tower, *D & G*, and near the hotel.

A great rarity in Ireland and seemingly extinct in Scotland.

Solanaceae

Nicandra physalodes (L.) Gaertn. (Shoo-fly Plant) occurred as a casual on a tip near Crosby, 1964, *CB* and in a Ballaugh garden, 1975, per *LSG*. ***Lycium barbarum*** L. (*L. halimifolium* Mill.) (Duke of Argyll's Tea Tree) has escaped in a few places, mainly in the far south. ***Atropa belladonna*** L. (Deadly Nightshade) grew in a hedge near Ballanank, Malew, till destroyed by building c 1972, *HSP*. The record by Howarth in Allen (1954) I now believe to have been an error.

Hyoscyamus niger L. Henbane; Connagh ny Giark
ND Drift-line of shores. Occasional and sporadic: south-east, south-west and far north coasts. Also a rare casual in gardens and farmyards as a relic of herbal use as a narcotic.

Solanum dulcamara L. Bittersweet; Croanreisht
ND Pond and stream sides, swamps, hedges, sea-cliffs, shingle; waste ground, gardens. Local: mainly in the north, the central valley and the far south, largely avoiding the uplands. Calf.

To Stowell this seemed 'very rare', to Paton 'common'. In fact it is widely but very thinly scattered except along the lower reaches of the Colby (plentiful for 1½ miles) and Dhoo/Glass streams and in one or two scarcely acid curraghs in the north. After these its most favoured natural habitat is well-silted, mineral-rich ponds — extending to a brackish marsh at NW Langness. In sharp contrast, it also occurs widely on stony storm-beaches, in a subprostrate form also known on the coasts of Wales and Kerry. This is less extreme than the South England ecotype var. ***marinum*** Bab. and may be a mere state of the type, plants indistinguishable from which occur here and there in dry cliff and cliff-foot vegetation. Like the plants that turn up (more frequently) in artificial habitats, these may be bird-brought from wet ground; alternatively, they may have come from gardens — for the number of occurrences round ruined cottages strongly points to one-time cultivation. It was certainly to be seen last century in gardens in Donegal and that this was for herbal use, as a narcotic, is suggested by its Irish folk-name. Cregeen's dictionary records that the Manx held it in repute for healing internal bruises.

S. nigrum L. Black Nightshade
NC Sandy ground near the sea, gulleries; gardens, waste ground around houses, tips. Very local. Calf.

In plenty on the Calf (Caigher Point and along the east coast), especially among the gulleries — just as on Skokholm, off Pembrokeshire. Gulls may also be responsible for its several records on the Ayres and the adjoining sandy arable, just as they must surely have been for old Wigtownshire occurrences in profusion where seaweed had been drying. Like those other two bird-dependent nitrophiles, ***Vicia lutea*** and ***Chenopodium rubrum***, it seems an incontestable, if transient, native.

Solanum nitidibaccatum Bitter (*S. sarrachoides* auct.) occurred in a market garden, Ballavolley, Ballaugh, 1979, *JS*, det. E. J. Clement. ***Datura stramonium*** L. (Thorn-apple), an accidental import, turns up in newly-disturbed or newly-laid soil, especially in gardens: Ballacain, Ballaugh, 1895-6, *Keig*: Bradda East, 1949 onwards, *JRB*: Lambhill, Bride, 1957, *PRF-R*: Ramsey Mooragh and Wildlife Park, 1966, *NHAS*: Mull Hill, 1966, 1966, *AB*: Andreas, 1977; potato-field, Gretch Veg, Laxey, 1977, *MD*. Perhaps increasing.

SCROPHULARIACEAE

Verbascum thapsus L. Common Mullein; Cainle Voirrey
CD? Sandy maritime turf, quarries, tips, hedges, wall-tops. Occasional and usually singly.

Absent from the gravelly banks and high beach-ridges elsewhere believed to be its native habitat, in Man appearing no less of an adventive on the coast than inland. The very few records last century and Ralfe's (1892) description of it as 'seemingly recent' suggest it has increased considerably. Possibly escapes from herbal use have been supplemented by later incomers.

V. phlomoides L. (Orange Mullein) and ***V. virgatum*** Stokes (Large-flowered Mullein) have lately been recorded on waste ground near gardens.

Antirrhinum majus L. (Snapdragon; Blaa Laanee) has been naturalised on Rushen Abbey ruins for at least a century and occasionally appears elsewhere on walls and tips.

Misopates orontium (L.) Raf. Lesser Snapdragon
C Cultivated and waste ground. Rare and very local.

N — Unlocalised, *Garner* (1878): near railway at Lezayre, *Paton*: field by Ramsey Grammar School, *MQ*: railway N of Milntown, abundant, 1962*; Ramsey tip, 1967. **SE** — Gardens, Upper Douglas, *LSG*. **S** — Garden, Castletown, 1966; Derbyhaven tip, 1968, *LSG*.

Linaria purpurea (L.) Mill. (Purple Toadflax) is occasional on tips and walls. ***L. repens*** (L.) Mill. (Pale Toadflax), naturalised in several places in the south and round Douglas, has become an ineradicable weed in gardens in Port Erin; it has also crossed with the next (***L.*** × ***sepium*** Allman) in Billown quarries, *MD*.

L. vulgaris Mill. Common Toadflax
C Roadsides, hedge-tops, waste ground. Occasional, slowly spreading.

Pronounced absent by Forbes and unrecorded till 1874, this is especially fond of the railway and tramway tracks, to the laying of which it may have owed its orginal introduction. It occurs up to 650ft on Dalby Mt.

Chaenorhinum minus (L.) Lange (Small Toadflax) occurred on the track at Peel Road station, 1945-6, *Wagstaffe**, no doubt introduced from England with railway ballast. In this habitat in Man it is replaced by the close-related ***Kickxia elatine*** (L.) Dumort. (Sharp-leaved Fluellen). Previously known only as a weed in the 1860s in Stowell's parsonage garden in Maughold*, this was found in 1960 to be widespread, even abundant, on various stretches of the railway in the north and centre of the island, *BSBI*[2]! The subsequent abandonment of these sections has doubtless led to its extinction. ***Cymbalaria muralis*** Gaertn., Mey & Scherb. (Ivy-leaved Toadflax), collected by Talbot c 1866 and 'frequent' according to Ralfe (1892), continues to be a widespread escape on walls, including on the Calf. It also occurs in plenty on shingle at Scarlett, competing with natural vegetation.

Scrophularia nodosa L. Common Figwort; Arym
N C or D Watersides, shady scrub; roadsides, bare waste ground. Frequent.
Like ***Lapsana communis*** this appears mainly adventive. It was formerly a favourite folk medicine, in Ireland the Queen (or King) of Herbs, the swellings on its roots prompting its use for piles and skin lesions; and plants in artificial habitats may have come largely from this source.

S. auriculata L. (*S. aquatica* auct.) (Water Figwort) was found growing in patches on a damp roadside round Upper Ballaclucas, Braddan, 1962, *WFS*!*. A herbal relic or an accidental import in soil, it had gone by 1969. Holt claimed this species was frequent by rivers and streams, but his specimen is merely a form of ***S. nodosa*** — as was that recorded in Proc BSBI (1956) 144 and doubtless that in Proc (1897) 196 too. The descriptions of it in the standard books have long been misleading.

Mimulus guttatus DC. × ***luteus*** L. (Monkey Flower), first recorded as an escape in 1916, on the Silverburn, is now established on numerous other streams in the eastern half of the Island, though usually very locally. It formerly also occurred in Glen Maye. Its sterility no doubt accounts for its still fairly limited distribution. ***M. moschatus*** Dougl. ex Lindl. (Musk) is well naturalised in boggy ground between Cregneish and Port Erin. It also haunts an old garden in Sulby*, in which it was doubtless once grown for its now lost scent. ***Erinus alpinus*** L. (Fairy Foxglove) grows in great profusion along an old farm wall at Ballamona Hospital, Braddan, wholly white-flowered, *MD*.

Digitalis purpurea L. Foxglove; Sleggan-Sleeu
N Hedges, glens. Common. Calf.

White-flowered plants are not uncommon. After Tower Hill Wood, near Ramsey, was cut down in the First World War Foxgloves appeared of an extraordinary robustness, 5ft or more high, and in such profusion that the whole hillside was crimson, *Wheldon* (in litt. to H. J. Riddelsdell, Oct. 1919, in hb BM). The leaves of this species were used in Man for treating scab in sheep (Quayle 1973, 93), also as a poultice for boils etc (Moore 1898).

Veronica beccabunga L. Brooklime; Burleek
N Marshes, ponds, streamsides. Frequent, especially in the north.
With pink flowers near Arragon Veg, Santon.

V. anagallis-aquatica L. Water Speedwell
N Streams, ditches, ponds, wells. Rare and very local.

N — Old well, Ramsey, *P. M. C. Kermode*, *Paton** (since demolished): Ballaugh Curraghs, *Wheldon*: pond by Ballavarkish, Bride, 1965, *MD*: Killane trench, in two places; Lhen trench, near Kiondroghad, *LSG*. **W** — Congary curragh, Peel, *Clementson*, *Cowin*!: Peel golf links, 1956, *LVC*: Union Mills curragh, *LSG*. **S** — Poyllvaaish, *WFS*!: rivulet beside Silverburn weir N of Castletown; Strandhall; near Ballakeigan.

V.* × *lackschewitzii Keller (***V. anagallis-aquatica* × *catenata***). Abundant along the Dumb River drainage ditch and its feeders from Great Meadow to Poyllvaaish, *Ralfe* hb BM!*, det. J. H. Burnett. Ralfe's specimen dates from 1897 and was the basis for the new county record claimed for ***V. anagallis-aquatica*** by Arthur Bennett in JB (1898) 441. However, this was doubtless what P. M. C. Kermode recorded here under that same name in 1883 and very possibly also the ***V. anagallis-aquatica*** noted for 'Castletown' in Backwell's Guide c 1856. This sterile F_1 hybrid has great vegetative vigour, enabling it to withstand the periodic cleaning-out of the ditch far better than its parents, which today cling on only at the two far ends.

V. catenata Pennell Pink Water Speedwell
N Ponds, ditches. Very rare.

N — Dub, Rhencullen, *D & G*. **S** — Ditch off the Dumb River near Ballakeigan, in tiny quantity*.

V. scutellata L. Marsh Speedwell
N Bogs, acid pools. Local: frequent in the north, reappearing very thinly in the east central area and again on the Mull peninsula and the Calf.
The flowers vary from blue through to white (pink has also been reported), but no one colour form predominates more than very locally and there is no detectable overall pattern in their occurrence.

V. officinalis L. Heath Speedwell
N Dry acid grassland. Locally common. Calf.

Variable in flower colour: from very pale to very deep purple in adjacent patches near Laxey Head. With very small and narrow leaves (var. ***integra*** (Druce) Druce) and pink flowers on Cashtal Lajer earthwork, Ballaugh, *Paton*. On shingle at Port Cornaa.

V. montana L. Wood Speedwell

N Shady stream-banks. Very rare.

C — Bottom of Narradale by N end of Sulby Claddagh and at rear of Ballameanagh garden, *D & G*! Discovered in 1973. Convincingly native, in the second locality growing in semi-natural woodland with ***Moehringia*** and ***Carex sylvatica.***

V. chamaedrys L. Birdseye Speedwell; Foillyean

N Grassy places. Common. Calf.

V. serpyllifolia L. subsp. ***serpyllifolia*** Thyme Speedwell

NC Thinly grassy places, leys. Common. Calf.

On shingle at Port Garwick and Point of Ayre. In a marsh behind Ballagawne, Rushen.

V. arvensis L. Wall Speedwell

NC Dunes; walls, dry banks. Frequent. Calf.

Seemingly native on the Ayres in association with ***Aphanes microcarpa***, ***Geranium molle*** and ***Trifolium ornithopodioides***. Also on Castletown links.

V. sublobata M. Fischer Ivy-leaved Speedwell

N Shady places on rich humus. Locally abundant.

All material of the aggregate ***V. hederifolia*** so far examined has proved to be this recently separated tetraploid species. It also seems to be the common one in Wales, where the hexaploid ***V. hederifolia*** L. sens. strict. is local and almost exclusively a weed in gardens. ***V. sublobata***, however, also occurs in Welsh gardens, so this habitat in Man (in which it can be prolific) may not necessarily yield both. The hexaploid is best told by its blue (not pale purple) corolla, rather fleshy leaves and a style twice as long at 0·8 mm. Most surprisingly, not even the aggregate was known to Forbes (1837b): either it has spread greatly or his field coverage was grossly insufficient. Its absence from the Calf is hardly significant in this connection, for suitable habitats there are largely lacking (though at Port Mooar it grows on shingle).

V. persica Poir. Common Field Speedwell

C Cultivated and waste ground, roadsides. Very common. Calf.

An invader from Asia first recorded in England in 1825, in Ireland c 1845 and in Man c 1866 (hb Talbot). It was abundant in the Island by 1892, if not earlier.

V. polita Fr. Grey Field Speedwell

C Cultivated ground, field banks. Rare.

N — Andreas; near Regaby gate, *Paton**: field S of Point of Ayre, *D & G*. **SE** — Groudle, *MD*. **SW** — The Howe, near Cregneish, one plant, 1952.

More southerly than the previous species and the next and much confused with both. Paton called it 'common', but his specimens, like Hiern's, are largely misnamed. As a result there is no reliable record earlier than 1929, though it must surely have occurred before.

V. agrestis L. Green Field Speedwell

C Gardens, less often in cultivated fields. Local: mainly in the north and far south.

V. filiformis Sm. (Slender Speedwell) is a rapidly increasing escape, especially in parks and cemeteries and on road verges, first reported in 1946. ***Hebe × franciscana*** (Eastwood) Souster (*H. lewisii* auct.) is the Hedge Veronica extensively planted as a windbreak which often occurs self-sown. ***Hebe salicifolia*** (Forst. f.) Pennell is also naturalised round Laxey and elsewhere.

Pedicularis palustris L. Red Rattle; Lus y Vill

N Bogs, swamps. Local: widespread in the north, reappearing on cliffs N of Peel, in the Greeba Curraghs, at Ballavarane, Groudle, and in the region of the upper Santon Burn.

P. sylvatica L. subsp. ***sylvatica*** Lousewort; Lus y Chellan Veg

N Damp heathy ground, bogs. Common. Calf.

A semi-albino form is not uncommon. The West Irish and Hebridean race, subsp. ***hibernica*** D. A. Webb, with long white curled hairs above, has been sought in vain.

Rhinanthus minor L. Yellow Rattle

N Bogs, marshes, wet fields, mine rubble, damp roadsides, dry grassland. Locally abundant.

The prevailing form, as in Scotland, is var. ***stenophyllus*** Schur, formerly distinguished as a separate northern race but now considered a mere autumnal ecotype. Certainly in Man var. ***minor*** occurs in much the same areas and habitats, differing only in monopolising dry roadsides in the Bride hills.

Melampyrum pratense L. subsp. ***pratense*** Common Cow-wheat

N Wet acid woodland and heath below 600ft, bilberry moor above 1250ft. Rare.

C — The Dhoon, *Backwell's*: North Barrule, *Paton*, *FR*: Narradale, locally abundant at 500ft, *D & G**; Beinn y Phott, *JS*, *MC & RM*. **SE** — S of Ballavarane, Groudle, *JTW**. **SW** — South Barrule summit, *S. Kermode*, *Ralfe* etc!*

Unexpectedly scarce and remarkably disjunct. The moorland plants are dwarfer and probably ecotypically distinct. The North Barrule and Narradale colonies are wholly golden-flowered (var. ***hians*** Druce, the form of the older rocks of the North and West), but on South Barrule the pale yellow type prevails.

Euphrasia L. (†det. P. F. Yeo) Eyebright; Lus y Tooill

Great variability, extensive crossing and a shortage of reliable characters make much of this genus extremely difficult. Random gatherings of just a specimen or two tend to be unsafe for the specialist to pronounce upon: at least a dozen from any one place should be submitted. The account below is probably broadly accurate but more detailed study of populations in the field is needed.

E. micrantha Reichb.

N Among ***Calluna*** on lowland heaths and moors. Occasional. Calf.

E. tetraquetra (Bréb.) Arrond. (*E. occidentalis* Wettst.)

N Short turf by and near the sea, slate rubble on the coast and (rarely) inland. Occasional, in places abundant. Calf.

A lilac-flowered form at Port Cornaa, *MD*†. Along the sandy north-west coast, at intervals for 9 miles, a densely hairy form replaces the type. First collected and remarked upon by Forbes† (1837d), this has hitherto been assigned to the ambiguous '***E. curta***' but Dr Yeo now considers it best placed here. It appears to be a local race peculiar to the Manx, Lancashire and north Wales coasts.

E. nemorosa (Pers.) Wallr. (incl. ***E. curta*** (Fr.) Wettst.)

N Damp pastures, grassy roadsides, slate rubble, sandy maritime turf. Locally abundant, especially in the foothills, with a concentration in the south central area.

The only species found plentifully in secondary habitats (particularly quarries) and almost wholly inland. A large-flowered variant characteristic of upland districts, formerly distinguished as var. ***collina*** Pugsl., occurs very locally at 600-800ft along the southern flanks of South Barrule.

E. confusa Pugsl.

N Dry heathy pastures (to 1000ft), bare stony ground, maritime turf. Local. Calf.

A particularly variable species, withstanding intense grazing. Hybrid swarms with ***E. tetraquetra*** occur on the coast and crosses with ***E. arctica*** and ***E. nemorosa*** also appear not uncommon.

E. arctica Lange ex Rostrup subsp. ***borealis*** (Towns.) Yeo (*E. brevipila* auct.)
N Damp fields and roadsides, typically in longish grass. Common in the northern and central curraghs, very local elsewhere. Calf.

The cross with ***E. nemorosa*** is the most plentiful Eyebright in the north as well as common in Billown quarries. A hybrid swarm with ***E. tetraquetra*** (an unusual cross) occurs on Castletown golf links.

E. anglica Pugsl.
N Damp heathy grazings, especially at 350-750ft, often with gorse. Locally abundant on the flanks of the northern hills and of South Barrule, reappearing on The Mount (by The Braaid) and on Cronk ny Arrey (by Cregneish); also in isolated lowland colonies in and by curraghs near Ballacain, E of Ballamona and SW of Union Mills.

With its dense long glands this is the one unmistakable Manx species, doubtfully ever crossing. Endemic to the British Isles, it has a southerly range and is surprisingly widespread in Man in view of its near-absence from Scotland.

Odontites verna (Bellardi) Dumort. Red Bartsia
NC Wet fields. Marshes, muddy pool-margins, roadsides. Locally abundant in the north, frequent elsewhere. Calf.

In wet saline turf by Creglea, Dalby, but (unlike West Scottish plants in this habitat) not differing morphologically. In common with authors of other recent local Floras I do not find the supposed differences between subsp. ***verna*** and subsp. ***serotina*** (Dumort.) Corb. sustainable.

Parentucellia viscosa (L.) Caruel Yellow Bartsia
C Damp grassland. Very local, but spreading.

N — E edge of Ballaugh Curraghs, in three places, *GEQ*, *WFS* etc!: leys N of Kella, Sulby. **C** — Roadside, Sulby Glen, 1974, *MD*.

First noticed near The Rule c 1958, this must have come in with grass seed. A native of south-west Britain, it has turned up widely elsewhere by this means in recent years.

OROBANCHACEAE

[***Lathraea squamaria*** L. Toothwort
Listed by Gasking, presumably on the strength of Garner's remark in Trans. NHAS (1879-84) 89: 'Mr Harrison mentioned a plant found which it struck me might be the Tooth-wort'. Though frequent in north-east Ireland, this is mainly a lime-lover and so rather improbably Manx.]

Orobanche rapum-genistae Thuill. Great Broomrape
N On the roots of gorse and broom. Rare and very local.

N/C — Lezayre, *Forbes*: Ballaugh, *Brearey**, *Holt**. **C** — On gorse, top of Bellvue Hill, Ramsey, one plant only, c 1925, *Quayle*: on broom, Cronkshamerk, Sulby, 1950, *RH*. **SE** — On gorse, bank of Santon Burn by Arragon Mooar, *BW*.

The concentration of records along the north edge of the hills is noteworthy. A southerly species, this only just penetrates Scotland and is not north of Dublin in Ireland.

O. minor Sm. Common Broomrape

NC On the roots of ***Leguminosae***, ivy, etc. Rare and sporadic.

N — Near "Ohio" cottage, Andreas, *Paton** (from 1916), *MBB* etc: ***Olearia*** hedge by Ramsey Mooragh, *Paton*, *Cowin* etc: Ramsey foreshore, on ***Eryngium***, up to 400 spikes, *ADW*, *GEQ* etc! **W** — Near Glen Maye mouth, on ivy, *LVC* (from 1944), *MD*, conf. D. J. Hambler. **S** — Near Red Gap farm, Castletown, 1906, *Moore-Lane*.

A southern species, widely introduced northwards with clover crops. It appears native at Glen Maye, but may be adventive elsewhere.

Lentibulariaceae

Pinguicula lusitanica L. Pale Butterwort

N Boggy seepages. Rare (formerly locally common).

Forbes knew this abundantly in damp ravines along the coast N of Douglas, but from here like other Atlantic species it has long since inexplicably vanished. Paton, who termed it 'common', was used to it in roadside ditches in the north; but otherwise its records are all from the central hills and the moist east lowlands with outliers in the Mull Peninsula.

P. vulgaris L. Common Butterwort; Lus-y-Steep

N Bogs, wet rocks, wet roadsides. Local: especially mid west coast and base-rich curraghs in Jurby (in at least one in abundance).

On dry slate rubble at Cornelly mines. As in Scandinavia, formerly used as a substitute for rennet to curdle milk.

Utricularia vulgaris L. agg. Greater Bladderwort

N Peaty ditches. Very rare.

N — Ballaugh Curraghs, *Wheldon*, *Ralfe* etc!* hb NMW.

This is more likely to be ***U. australis*** R. Br. (*U. neglecta* Lehm.) than ***U. vulgaris*** sens. strict., which prefers base-rich water; but the two are distinguishable only by their flowers, which at this latitude never appear.

U. minor L. Lesser Bladderwort

N Peaty ditches. Very rare.

N — Ballaugh Curraghs, 1909, *Wheldon* hb NMW, det. P. M. Hall, BEC (1938) 104 (where the sheet is erroneously attributed to hb Leeds University). A single specimen unwittingly collected by Wheldon along with ***U. vulgaris*** agg.

Verbenaceae

Verbena officinalis L. (Vervain) is a rather rare weed in gardens and waste places, presumably mainly or wholly as a relic of herbal use. To the Manx, however, 'Vervine' or 'Yn Lhus' ('The Herb') is normally the plant known to the English as Motherwort, ***Leonurus cardiaca.*** Valued as a febrifuge and emetic, this rated supreme in warding off ills, to the extent that mothers sewed it into their babies' clothes and fishermen tied a sprig of it to their nets to bring them luck (Moore 1898). Reflecting this, ***Leonurus*** is much the more often met with today as an escape. Perhaps therefore the English Vervain is a mere late introduction.

Labiatae

Mentha L. (†det. R. M. Hartley ‡det. R. A. Graham)

M. pulegium L. Pennyroyal; Lurgadish

N Mineral-rich ponds, especially where geese are kept. Rare and very local.

N — In many places where there are marl-pits, in Ballaugh, Jurby and Andreas, *Forbes*, *Stowell*: common in wet clay, Curraghs, *Garner*: Ballaugh, *Holt*: Gat-y-Whing, *Paton**: Ballakinnag dub, Smeale; Ballasalla, Jurby: N of Orrisdale House, *MD*: Rhencullen, *D & G*.

A western species, only in Scotland as a rare introduction. Mixed with barley meal it was valued in Man for burns.

M. arvensis L. Corn Mint

NC Lake and river shingle; cultivated ground. Rare.

N — Sulby, *Paton**: E of the Cronk. **C** — Baldwin Reservoir, frequent along both shores, *MBB*! **SE** — Douglas, 1929-32, *Cowin*: shingle bank upstream of Tromode Dam, one plant, 1971, *MD*. **SW** — Ballakilpheric.

Also unlocalised records by Talbot*, Teare and S. Kermode.

M. × gentilis L. (***M. arvensis × spicata***) Bushy Mint

D Beside streams and ponds. Rare.

N—Ballakinnag dub, Smeale, *D & G*. **C**—Sulby Milldam†. **SE**— Stream near The Arragon. **SW** — Ballakilpheric, *FHT*‡. **S** — Mouth of R Colby‡.

Though well naturalised (as elsewhere in the British Isles) this very variable hybrid betrays its herbal origins by its anomalous distribution.

M. aquatica L. Water Mint; Mynthey Yiarg
N Marshes, bogs, watersides, dune slacks. Common. Calf.

M.* × *verticillata L. (***M. aquatica*** × ***arvensis***) Whorled Mint
C Arable land. Very rare.

SW — Ley by Awin ny Reash SSW of Ballamodha, 1960, *BSBI*[2]!†

'Marsh Whorled Mint', possibly intended for this, was listed by Wattam (1899) without details.

M.* × *piperita L. (***M. aquatica* × *spicata***) Peppermint; Mynthey-garg
D Wet roadsides, lake shores, hedgebanks. Very local.

N — St. Jude's, *Paton**: Sulby, *WHH*: Ramsey Mooragh, *WFS*: Ballachurry, Andreas, *MD*. **C** — NE shore of Baldwin Reservoir, a small patch. **SW** — Roadside fork S of Ballamodha.

Also unlocalised records by Talbot* and Murray.

M. spicata L. (Spear Mint) is an occasional escape on waste ground, also naturalised beside at least two ponds in the north. ***M.* × *villosa*** Huds. (***M. spicata*** × ***suaveolens***; *M. niliaca* auct.) (Large Apple Mint) is established in a lane at Ballafesson, Port Erin†. ***M. longifolia* × *suaveolens*** (*M. longifolia* var. *horridula* auct.) is established above Glen Mona† and has also occurred in Ramsey‡. ***M. suaveolens*** Ehrh. (*M. rotundifolia* auct.) (Apple Mint) also not uncommonly escapes.

Lycopus europaeus L. Gypsywort; Nep Curree
N Ditches, ponds, swamps, dune slacks. Very local: widespread in the north, elsewhere only at Tromode Dam.

Thymus praecox Opiz subsp. ***britannicus*** (Ronn.) Holub (*T. drucei* Ronn.)
Wild Thyme; Lus ny Vrat
N Maritime turf, dry hedgebanks, hillsides. Common, especially on the coast. Calf.

A pink-flowered and very hairy form predominates round Peel and reappears near Dalby and on Bradda Head. Many such local races are known in this species but are too numerous to be worth naming.

Origanum vulgare L. (Marjoram; Lus Villish) occurred as an escape near Onchan in 1931, *Paton**. ***Calamintha sylvatica*** Bromf. subsp. ***ascendens*** (Jord.) P. W. Ball (Common Calamint) has been known since Forbes's day on dry banks and roadsides in various places in Ballaugh, Andreas and Bride parishes; it also occurs in the south near Colby Bridge Hotel. A pronounced lime-lover as a native in Ireland, it is presumably only a herbal relic in Man (French peasants used it as an indigestion cure). ***Melissa officinalis*** L. (Balm; Millish), a herbal alternative to Borage, is naturalised outside Ramsey and near Ballaugh.

[***Acinos arvensis*** (Lam.) Dandy Basil Thyme
Listed by Gasking, without details. A possible Manx species on geographical grounds, but its preference for lime makes its presence unlikely.]

[***Clinopodium vulgare*** L. Wild Basil
'Cultivated ground', *S. Kermode*. Apparently a name confusion: this is not a habitat of this species. It is also a lime-lover and absent from Ireland except as a rare alien.]

Prunella vulgaris L. Self-heal; Dooan y Chione Cast
NC Grassland, bogs, base-rich flushes, dune slacks. Very common. Calf.
White flowers are not uncommon. A pink-flowered form is also quite widespread and seems characteristic of leys, in some of those by the Silverburn N of Castletown occurring almost to the exclusion of the type. A pale blue form is persistent in lawns in Union Mills, spilling over into nearby pastures; it is also on record from Cornaa. Both may have been sown.

[***Betonica officinalis*** L. Betony
'Cultivated ground', *S. Kermode*. Again, quite the wrong habitat — unless this occurred as a herbal relic. It has been noted recently in a garden at the Eairy Dam.]

Stachys arvensis (L.) L. Field Woundwort
C Cultivated ground. Common. Calf (1943 only).
A southerly species with a western trend, in Scotland and all but south-east Ireland rare and markedly coastal.

S. palustris L. Marsh Woundwort
NCD Watersides, marshes, upper beaches; cultivated and waste ground. Locally frequent.
On beaches at Port Cornaa and The Dhoon (as in Arran). Rarely, in or by gardens and farmyards, suggesting it sometimes substituted herbally for either of the next. Var. ***segetum*** (Hagen) Mutel (var. *canescens* Lange), a probably genetic variant combining strong hairiness with a much shorter spike, has been noted in eight localities, mainly among corn and on wall-tops and more especially in the far south.

S. × ***ambigua*** Sm. (***S. palustris*** × ***sylvatica***)
ND Ponds, marshes; waysides, waste places. Frequent in the far south, especially round Ballasalla, rare and scattered elsewhere.

As in some other areas in west and north Britain this sterile hybrid appears to occur largely independently of its parents, noticeably more often than either hanging round houses and farmyards. It must have been the preferred 'All-heal' of folk medicine, the roots of which were boiled and eaten as a purgative and the leaves and spike-tips powdered into a snuff (Quayle 1973, 69). Forbes described it as 'frequent in the damper parts of the northern sandy districts', but its conspicuous absence there today suggests he mistook as this a form of ***S. palustris***. Both vary a lot, even to the extent — in a Billown Mooar population, unique in the British Isles, studied biometrically by C. C. Wilcock, Watsonia (1972) 62 — of overlapping in their characters.

S. sylvatica L. Hedge Woundwort; Lus y Lhott
ND Glens; waysides, waste places, gardens. Locally frequent but seldom in quantity and absent from large areas.

Ballota nigra L. subsp. ***foetida*** Hayek Black Horehound; Nep
D Roadsides, waste ground. Rare, but increasing.
N — Ballacorey, Andreas, 1932, *Paton** hb BM: near Curragh Beg, *JEL*: Rhencullen, outside a garden. **W** — Peel, 1939-45, *Clementson*, *Cowin*: St. John's, *BSBI*[2]!: SW of Ballacross, Peel.

[***Lamiastrum galeobdolon*** (L.) Ehrend. & Polatsch Yellow Archangel
A single plant at Ballaterson, Maughold, 1917, *Miss Graham* per *Ralfe*. This 'yellow dead-nettle' was doubtless ***Galeopsis speciosa***, already on record in that area.]

Lamium amplexicaule L. Henbit
C Cultivated ground. Local: mainly north and south-east.
In Ireland and Scotland largely confined to the coast.

L. molucellifolium Fr. Intermediate Dead-nettle; Ard Firryn Jiarg
C Cultivated ground. Frequent. Calf.
Forbes implied that this northern species was the prevailing one in his day; if so, it has seemingly decreased — as it has in Ireland too.

L. hybridum Vill. Cut-leaved Dead-nettle
C Cultivated and waste ground. Local, but increasing: mainly in the north and far south.
First recorded by Gasking (1890) and all but overlooked till 1938, this appears to have been expanding in the west of the British Isles during the past century at the expense of the previous species.

L. purpureum L. Red Dead-nettle
C Cultivated and waste ground. Frequent, especially in the south-east.

Unrecorded till 1896 and probably much increased. Several white-flowered at Ballahick, Ballasalla.

L. album L. White Dead-nettle

C Roadsides, gardens, nurseries. Rare.

N — Ditch NW of Lough Cranstal, *Moore*: Closelake, St. Jude's, *MBB*: Glentramman farm, *GEQ*: S of Ballachurry, *JCC*. **C** — Glen Auldyn, *P. M. C. Kermode*, *MQ*. **W** — St. John's, *Cowin*, *MD*! **SE** — Onchan, c 1855, *Murray*, JB (1897) 146; Bibaloe farm, *RH*: Falls nursery, Braddan, *BW*. **S** — Colby, 1874, *Brearey**. Also an unlocalised record by Forbes (1848).

Though in herbal use elsewhere, in Man this seems exclusively an accidental import with soil.

L. maculatum L. (Spotted Dead-nettle) is a garden favourite often running wild.

Leonurus cardiaca L. (Motherwort; Vervine, Yn Lus), once the herb of herbs to the Manx — see under ***Verbena officinalis*** — recurs in and near old cottages and farmyards, mainly in the north. Intriguingly, it is relatively much more plentiful than in either Ireland or Scotland.

[***Galeopsis segetum*** Neck. Downy Hemp-nettle

Cited for Man by Clapham, Tutin & Warburg (1962) consequent upon Paton's admission of this species to his 1933 list on the strength of records by both Gasking and Stowell. But Gasking's listing of it — as always, without supporting details — was almost certainly a mere uncritical repeat of Stowell. And Stowell's records clearly relate to ***G. speciosa***.]

G. tetrahit L. Common Hemp-nettle

C Cultivated and waste ground. Common. Calf.

Except by the Dhoo near Union Mills (a stray?) absent from the damp, shady natural habitats in which it frequently occurs in Britain. Most plants appear referable to the controversial '***G. bifida*** Boenn.', reportedly intersterile with ***G. tetrahit*** but distinguished by only trivial characters.

G. speciosa Mill. Large Hemp-nettle

C Arable fields on rich, often peaty soil. Rare.

N — The Craig, Andreas, *Paton**. **C** — Booilyvelt, Maughold, *Stowell*: (Ballaterson, Maughold, *Graham* as ***Lamiastrum galeobdolon***, doubtless this): N of St. Luke's, Baldwin, *MD*: Grawe, Laxey, *IMK*. **W** — Lhergydhoo, near Peel, *Stowell*. **S** — Between Colby and Gansey, *JTW*, *LSG*.

Glechoma hederacea L. Ground Ivy; Ard Losserey

N Glens, hedges, under bracken. Locally abundant, especially along the west and north coasts, ascending to 1000ft. Calf.

Marrubium vulgare L. (White Horehound; Nep Vane), once in herbal use for coughs, has been recorded three times on the north-west coast.

Scutellaria galericulata L. (Common Skullcap) has been a plentiful weed in a garden in Onchan since before 1943, *Mrs Hardy**, *WSC*; clearly imported with soil — perhaps from Scotland, where it frequently grows in cultivated land. Forbes marked this species as 'rare' in his original list of c 1832, but in the absence of any further mentions of it by him this must be presumed a slip.

S. minor Huds. Lesser Skullcap

N Bogs. Rare: mainly central valley curraghs and central east coast.

N — Andreas, *Backwell's*: Close William, Sulby, *D & G*. **C** — Glen Auldyn bank, *Spanton*: Glen Roy, *S. Kermode*, *Ralfe*: Port Cornaa, *ADW*! **SE** — Frequent in damp ravines, opening to the sea and abundant in those between Douglas Crescent and Banks' Howe, *Forbes*: Banks' Howe; Groudle, *Holt*: Drury's bog, Braddan; Castleward, *Ralfe*: Union Mills curragh, *BSBI*[2]: Clay Head. **SW** — Greeba Curragh, *Ralfe*! (SW of Greeba).

Also unlocalised records by Garner (1878) — Glen Dhoo? — and Jowett, 1827 hb K.

Teucrium scorodonia L. Wood Sage; Lys y Toar Vrein, Creaghlagh

N Hedgebanks, glens, heaths. Common. Calf.

Ajuga reptans L. Bugle; Lus y Chayrn

N Marshes, wet fields, glens, roadsides. Common. Calf.

With white flowers in Glion Mooar, Eary Cushlin, *LSG & GLQ*.

Plantaginaceae

Plantago major L. subsp. ***major***

Ratstail Plantain; Duillag-Pherick, Cabbag-Pherick

C Waysides, lawns, cultivated and waste ground. Common. Calf.

subsp. ***intermedia*** (Godr.) Lange

N Marshes and pond-margins near the sea. Very local.

N — West Nappin dub, Jurby. **S** — N of Strandhall; behind Ballagawne; W Langness; Cass-ny-Hawin.

Characteristically associated with ***Potentilla anserina***, ***Cerastium glomeratum*** and ***Gnaphalium uliginosum***.

P. media L. (Hoary Plantain) occurred at Douglas, c 1866, accidentally introduced with grass seed, *Talbot**.

P. lanceolata L. Ribwort Plantain; Slane Lus
NC Maritime turf; dry fields, waste ground. Very common. Calf.

P. maritima L. Sea Plantain
N Maritime rocks and turf, bare ground inland, hill-tops. Locally common. Calf.

The relatively high oceanity and its liking for slaty rubble have enabled this species to spread along the railway tracks in German, Patrick and Santon and thereby establish itself unusually far inland on lead-mine 'deads' and roadside banks. It flourishes 3½ miles from the sea in Foxdale and South Barrule quarries. A population on the summit of North Barrule, at 1800ft, may be a distinct arctic-alpine ecotype.

P. coronopus L. Buckshorn Plantain; Bossan Vreeshey
N Rocks and bare ground mostly by the sea. Locally common. Calf.

A notably robust form apparently corresponding with var. ***maritima*** Gren. & Godr. (var. *ceratophyllon* Rapin?) occurs along the south and west coasts and is particularly plentiful round Peel. It seems more spray-tolerant than the type and tends to avoid the close sward. Similar plants are known elsewhere on the southern Atlantic coasts of the British Isles. They retain their distinctiveness from seed and appear to constitute a separate geographical race, probably meriting subspecific rank.

P. arenaria Waldst. & Kit. (*P. indica* L.) occurred abundantly in a market garden by Ballacross, Andreas, for several years during the 1950s, *MBB**. It was probably introduced with wallflowers.

Littorella uniflora (L.) Aschers. Shore-weed
N Beds and margins of reservoirs and peaty pools. Very local. Calf, *JS*.

N — Curragh-y-Cowle, Andreas, *Paton*!: Ballasalla dub, Jurby: rear of Ballakinnag Ayres, *G & G*, *D & G*: old gravel-pits W of Point of Ayre, *D & G*. **C** — Mountain near the Dhoon, *Backwell's*: Baldwin Reservoir, very abundant. **SW** — Near Calf Sound, *Billups*: Eairy Dam, *BSBI*[1]: Cringle Reservoir; Barnell Reservoir.

Campanulaceae

Wahlenbergia hederacea (L.) Reichb. Ivy-leaved Bellflower
N Damp peaty turf. Very rare and very local: flanks of hills from sea level up to 800ft.

N — Near St. Jude's, *S. Kermode*: Curraghs near The Rule, *Cowin*, *MBB*.

C — Glen Auldyn, *Stowell*; near Milntown, *Backwell's*: Sulby Glen, *Backwell's, Holt* (plentiful by the roadside, 1915): Maughold (parish), *Talbot*: above Glen Dhoo (?), *Garner*: Port Cornaa, *P. M. C. Kermode, Ralfe*: Tholt-y-Will; Laxey Glen, *S. Kermode*: Sulby Claddagh, *Mrs Hoyle*: near Close-ny-Mona, Narradale, *NHAS:* head of Glen Dhoo, *D & G*. **W** — Glen Mooar, *P. M. C. Kermode, Holt**.

An unlocalised specimen collected by Jowett in 1827 is in hb Watson at Kew. Of all the Atlantic species this appears to require the heaviest precipitation, which thereby largely restricts it to the more benign areas of the main upland mass. Unlike some others in this group it seems to have been rare all along, never even heard of by Forbes. Nevertheless it conforms to pattern in having died out in several of its former stations, for reasons that must surely be climatic.

Campanula latifolia L. (Giant Bellflower) is widely grown in gardens and not uncommonly escapes. Though found on stream banks in two or three places, it does not have the indigenous look it has in Galloway (where it is comparatively common) and is doubtless only naturalised, as in Ireland.

C. trachelium L. (Nettle-leaved Bellflower) is naturalised in a hedge near Sandygate, *MD*.

C. giesekiana Vest (*C. rotundifolia* auct.)
Northern Harebell; Mairane Ferrish

N Dry pastures, railway banks, bare slaty ground. Locally common. Calf.

Visitors from England — for example, Hemsley (1887) — have long remarked on the distinctive appearance of Manx Harebells. It has now been discovered by Dr H. A. McAllister (1973 etc) that some at least of this is taxonomically well-founded. Chromosome counts on material from The Cronk and Cornelly mines show that some, if not all Manx plants differ from those in most of Great Britain in being hexaploid, not tetraploid. The same is true of Cornwall, Ireland, the inner and outer Hebrides (except Arran) and the adjacent mainland districts, several Scottish mountain summits (two of them in Galloway), Teesdale, Snowdon and the Little Orme — a peripheral distribution suggestive of a once-prevailing entity largely displaced by a later invader. The hexaploids tend to have fewer (often solitary), larger flowers, hemispherical ovaries and shorter rhizomes; they are also weaker competitively. They tally morphologically (though not cytologically) with this Greenland species. White-flowered specimens are not uncommon along the sandy north coast.

Jasione montana L. Sheepsbit; Bossan Gorrym

N Heaths, rough pastures, hedgebanks. Common. Calf.

White flowers are not uncommon. The diffuse maritime form with tiny heads, var. ***litoralis*** Fr., recently found to differ cytologically as well, occurs on the Ayres, *Wheldon* hb NMW, *Paton*! Var. ***latifolia*** Pugsl., a very robust plant with heads at least twice the normal size, probably a distinct Atlantic race, occurs at Onchan Head and Creglea, Dalby, *MD*.

RUBIACEAE

Sherardia arvensis L. Field Madder; Maddyr y Vagheragh
N?C Calcareous turf (rare); walls, dry banks, railway banks, cornfields. Common.

[***Cruciata laevipes*** Opiz (*C. chersonensis* (Willd.) Ehrend.) Crosswort
Oakhill, *Talbot*. Also listed by McNab, without details. These two beginners made several obvious errors and name confusion with ***Galium verum*** seems likely. The species is a lime-lover, very rare and not native in Ireland.]

Galium odoratum (L.) Scop. (Woodruff), long established in old gardens, is occasionally naturalised far from habitation — for example, in Silverdale, Groudle and Dhoon Glens. Being a lime-lover, it seems unlikely to be native — and this is borne out by the absence of last-century records.

G. verum L. Lady's Bedstraw; Lus y Volley
N Maritime turf, dry grassy places. Common. Calf.
var. ***maritimum*** DC. occurs on the dunes, and in saline turf at Scarlett.

G. saxatile L. Heath Bedstraw; Follan Fing
N Dry heathy ground. Locally abundant. Calf.

G. palustre L. Marsh Bedstraw
N Marshes, bogs, watersides. Common. Calf.

G. elongatum C. Presl
N Swamps. Frequent.

[***G. uliginosum*** L. Fen Bedstraw
Listed by Gasking, without details. A likely species to occur in the northern curraghs, but so far sought in vain.]

G. aparine L. Goosegrass; Lus y Chollane
NC Shingle beaches, hedges; cultivated and waste ground. Common. Calf.
Rather widespread on shingle but in a form doubtfully extreme enough to be equatable with the boreal ecotype var. ***marinum*** Fr.

Caprifoliaceae

[***Sambucus ebulus*** L. Dwarf Elder
Listed by Gasking, doubtless on the strength of the '***S. edulis***' said by Black's Guide (1883, 104) to grow in 'the damp dark hollows'. The next species was obviously intended.]

S. nigra L. Elder; Tramman
D Hedges, sea-cliffs, fixed dunes. Frequent. Calf.

Like the Hawthorn, this has been so extensively planted, and is so readily bird-sown, that it seems a very doubtful native at best. In Ireland, too, it is seldom seen in uncultivated districts. It was believed that the souls of ancestors resided in its hollow stems, with the result that 'even at the present time', wrote Train in 1845 (2, 170), 'an elder tree may be observed growing by almost every cottage in the Island'. As with most plants of potency its esteem extended into medicine, leading it to be used for bites and other ills (Moore 1898).

Viburnum opulus L. (Guelder Rose) was formerly naturalised in lower Glen Tramman, Lezayre, *GEQ* (the 'Water Elder' of Quayle 1973, 71). It was also listed by Gasking. ***Symphoricarpos rivularis*** Suksd. (Snowberry) has been extensively planted for hedging and in glens. ***Leycesteria formosa*** Wall. (Himalayan Honeysuckle) is well naturalised in various places, including on the sea-cliffs and in quarries.

Lonicera periclymenum L. Honeysuckle; Ullaagagh
N Hedges, thickets, cliffs. Common. Calf.

Valerianaceae

Valerianella locusta (L.) Betcke Cornsalad; Burley Frangagh
NC Sandy coastal turf; walls, dry banks. Frequent.

The native coastal form is the dwarf, cushion-like var. ***dunensis*** D. E. Allen. This is common along the north coast (the type locality is the Ballaghennie Ayres) and was also recorded by Wheldon (1918) on Ramsey Mooragh. The large-fruited form once cultivated for salads, var. ***oleracea*** (Schlecht.) Breistr., was noticed in Peel in 1942 by Paton*.

V. dentata (L.) Poll. Smooth-fruited Cornsalad
C Cornfields. Very rare, perhaps extinct.

SE — Santon, *Backwell's*. Also an unlocalised specimen in hb Mrs Kermode*, c 1880, probably from round Ballaugh or Castletown.

Much decreased in both Scotland and Ireland as a result of cleaner seed.

Valeriana officinalis L. Common Valerian; Kere Hallooin
N Marshes, streamsides, bogs, wet roadsides. Locally frequent.

V. dioica L. Marsh Valerian
N Fens. Very rare.

N — Ballaugh Curraghs, *S. Kermode* (1900), *Wheldon* (1909).
Of particular interest in being unknown in Ireland.

V. pyrenaica L. (Giant Valerian) is plentifully naturalised on streamsides in upper Glen Roy and Glen Helen (and on the Neb S of there) and on the roadside between Ballasalla and Silverdale. It has also been recorded from Ballaugh and Laxey. ***Centranthus ruber*** (L.) DC. (Spur Valerian) is extensively naturalised on cliffs and walls, in quarries, etc.

Dipsacaceae

Dipsacus fullonum L. (Wild Teasel; Leaddan) occurs sporadically and usually singly, mostly in or near old gardens or on tips. It never looks indigenous and is either a relic of cultivation or, in some cases, a recent bird-seed derivative.

Knautia arvensis (L.) Coult.
Field Scabious; Lus ny Crammanym Gorrym
C Railway banks, hedge-tops, waste ground. Locally common in the south-east, elsewhere sparse and often singly.
Several white-flowered in Scarlett quarry and one in a quarry by Balladoole.

[***Scabiosa columbaria*** L. Small Scabious
Listed by Gasking, on unknown evidence. Records by S. Kermode ('hedges') and Hoyle ('common') more clearly relate to the preceding. A pronounced lime-lover and absent from Ireland, so most unlikely to be Manx.]

Succisa pratensis Moench Devilsbit Scabious; Lus y Chengey Veg
N Damp acid grassland, marshes, sea-cliffs. Locally common.
Abundant on grassy, sheltered cliffs behind Douglas Head lighthouse. White-flowered near Foxdale and at The Dhoon; pink-flowered on Jurby brooghs and at St. John's.

Compositae

Helianthus annuus L. (Common Sunflower) occurs on tips as a bird-seed derivative.

Bidens cernua L. Nodding Bur-marigold
N Margins of eutrophic pools near the sea. Very rare.

N — West Nappin dub, Jurby; Ballavair dub, Bride.
Listed by S. Kermode (1901) for 'wet places'; but as he calls just this species 'Bur-marigold' and cites no records of his own under the next, it can safely be assumed that he found only the latter.

B. tripartita L. Trifid Bur-marigold
NC Ponds, ditches, marshes, cornfields, railway tracks. Frequent and locally abundant in the north, reappearing near Peel (Ballacross dub and by Ballacosnahan).

Galinsoga ciliata (Raf.) Blake (Shaggy Soldier) appeared in 1971-2 in a greenhouse at Glen Vine, introduced with soil, *MD**. This species is colonising south Lancashire and may well recur.

Senecio jacobaea L. Common Ragwort; Cushag
NC Pastures, roadsides, waste ground. Common. Calf.
The prevailing form in Man, as elsewhere in the North and West, is var. ***stenoglossus*** Brenan & Simpson, which combines narrow ray-florets with more dissected leaves; it may represent the original native plant and its ecology merits study. Where this species occurs in natural habitats in Ireland, however, it appears a marked lime-lover, and it is noteworthy that the rayless form frequent on Irish dunes is absent from those in Man. The variety of Manx superstitions clinging to the 'Cushag' even so suggests this plant has long been a plentiful inhabitant.

S. aquaticus Hill Marsh Ragwort
N Marshes, bogs, watersides, wet meadows, fens. Locally common. Calf.
Especially plentiful along the Santon Burn. Hybridises freely with ***S. jacobaea*** and clearly introgressive plants are not uncommon. Hybrid swarms occur particularly in the far south.

[***S. erucifolius*** L. Hoary Ragwort
Listed by Gasking without details. A rather unlikely Manx plant in view of its near-absence from Ireland and Scotland. Probably a form of ***S. aquaticus*** × ***jacobaea*** was mistaken for it.]

S. squalidus L. (Oxford Ragwort) arrived from Britain in 1980, as a solitary plant off Strand Street, Douglas, *LSG**.

S. sylvaticus L. Heath Groundsel
N Hedgebanks, dry sandy ground. Locally common, but rare in the south. Calf.

S. vulgaris L. Groundsel; Grunluss
NC Dunes; cultivated and waste ground. Very common. Calf.

The adventive rayed form, var. ***hibernicus*** Syme (var. *radiatus* auct.), which has spread widely in Britain in recent years, has become established on waste ground in Douglas since 1967, *LSG*. A rayed form reported on Ramsey Mooragh dunes by Wheldon (1918), however, was probably the native subsp. ***denticulatus*** (O. F. Muell.) Sell; unfortunately he took no specimen and it now appears extinct. This boreal-atlantic race is not yet on record for Ireland.

S. doria L. (Saracen's Woundwort; Bossan Mollagh Mooar, Cuishag Vollagh), an old cottage-garden herb long known as an escape in the north and round Port Erin, is well naturalised at Hillberry, Fistard and near Fleshwick. ***Doronicum pardalianches*** L. (Leopardsbane) is naturalised in Crogga Glen, *LSG**, and in a lane near Sulby Claddagh, *D & G*.

Tussilago farfara L. Coltsfoot; Cabbag ny Hawin, Duillag Soor
NC Eroding cliffs and stream-banks; roadsides, waste ground. Locally abundant. Calf.

Petasites hybridus (L.) Gaertn., Mey. & Scherb. Butterbur
N?D River-banks; old gardens, farmyards. Very local.

S — Abundant along the Silverburn from Castletown to Ballasalla, *Backwell's*, *Talbot** etc! with an outlying patch on the Ballamodha 'straight' as it crosses the stream.

Of doubtful status, as only the 'male' plant occurs (as in most of the British Isles away from the Pennines) and the species would readily spread vegetatively if once introduced. It is known to have been prized medicinally and the leaves used to wrap up butter or serve as fire-lighters — the North Country name 'eldin' being from an Old Norse word for fuel. No Manx name or uses appear to have been recorded, but it occurs today in farmyards round Dalby and in old gardens in Lower Ballanorris, Arbory and near Sulby Bridge, betraying a one-time herbal value.

P. japonicus (Sieb & Zucc.) Maxim. (Creamy Butterbur) is naturalised in a glen behind the Slieau Lewaigue inn, Maughold, *D & G*. ***P. fragrans*** (Vill.) C. Presl (Winter Heliotrope), introduced as a winter food-plant for bees, has become ineradicable in gardens and thrusts out of them in many places. ***Inula helenium*** L. (Elecampane; Lus y Rollage) is wide-spread in the far south-west corner, including on the Calf, as a relic of herbal use. It has also been recorded at Ballaugh.

Pulicaria dysenterica (L.) Bernh. Common Fleabane; Lus y Taghys
N Cliff trickles, ditches, mainly by the sea. Very local: central west coast, brooghs N from Ramsey, Port Mooar area, and three scattered stations inland along the Silverburn drainage.

Filago vulgaris Lam. (*F. germanica* L., non Huds.)
Common Cudweed; Lus ny Croshey
NC Dry, bare ground. Locally common in the north, scarce and largely casual elsewhere.

F. minima (Sm.) Pers. Small Cudweed
N Bare, sandy and gravelly ground. Very local: common near Orrisdale and the Point of Ayre and sporadically elsewhere in the north; formerly also at Peel (1918) and along stretches of the central valley railway track.

Gnaphalium sylvaticum L. Heath Cudweed
N Dry heathy ground, at sea-level and in the hills. Very rare.

N — Point of Ayre, a large patch, *D & G**. **C** — Near Tholt-y-Will, *Br Ass*[1] hb RAMM.

Also unlocalised records by Forbes ('rare') and by Backwell's ('mountains'). But S. A. P. Kermode's 'pastures etc' is too suspiciously sweeping to be trustworthy.

G. uliginosum L. Wayside Cudweed
NC Marshes, damp bare ground, cornfields. Common. Calf.

Anaphalis margaritacea (L.) Benth. (Pearl Everlasting), once popular for graveyards, was naturalised last century on hedgebanks in Andreas and beside the Ballaglass stream, but has not been recorded since the 1860s.

Antennaria dioica (L.) Gaertn. Mountain Everlasting
N Dry heathy and rocky ground, especially at highish altitudes. Very rare.

C — 'Occurs with ***Viola lutea*** as a mountain plant', *Forbes* (1848): bank, Glen Auldyn, 1880, *Spanton*. Also an unlocalised record by McNab, c 1830.

A. A. Slack believes he saw this by a cliff-path near Spanish Head c 1937. He was familiar with the species in Scotland and the area is a likely one.

Solidago virgaurea L. Golden-rod
N Dry banks, cliffs, shady places. Locally frequent.

Oddly, the Golden-rod Pug moth, ***Eupithecia virgaureata*** Doubl., which feeds exclusively on this species, is seemingly rare in Man.

S. canadensis L. (Canadian Golden-rod) is an increasing garden escape.

Aster tripolium L. Sea Aster
N Salt marshes. Very local: Castletown area and Ramsey.

A. puniceus L. (Michaelmas Daisy) is naturalised by the Neb at Ballig and in the Greeba Curraghs near Northop farm, det. T. G. Tutin. Other Michaelmas Daisies frequently occur as escapes but have yet to be critically studied; they probably include ***A. novi-belgii*** L. ***Conyza canadensis*** (L.) Cronq. (Canadian Fleabane) has begun to arrive as a casual from England and is liable to spread rapidly: roadside S of Grenaby, for some years only, *VLW*: Glen Vine nurseries, 1968; Christian St., Douglas and gardens in Union Mills and Andreas, 1976, *D & G*. ***Olearia macrodonta*** Bak. (New Zealand Holly) has been extensively planted for hedging and, very rarely, occurs self-sown.

[***Erigeron acer*** L. Blue Fleabane
Some records entered under this species in P. M. C. Kermode's notebook were published as such in his brother's 1900 list. Paton repeated them in all innocence. But the localities are known ones for Common Fleabane, ***Pulicaria dysenterica***, and undoubtedly a mismatch of the English and scientific names occurred.]

Bellis perennis L. Daisy; Eaynin
NC Short grassland, dunes. Very common. Calf.

Eupatorium cannabinum L. Hemp Agrimony; Jeshal
N Sea-cliff trickles, stream-banks. Local: W coast up to Peel and E coast up to Ramsey. Calf.

Anthemis cotula L. Stinking Chamomile
C Waste ground. Rare and probably only casual.

N — Waste heaps, Ramsey Mooragh, 1918, *Wheldon*: Lhen; Jurby, *Paton**. **SW** — Ballakilpheric, *FHT*.

Also listed by Gasking, Wattam (1899) and S. A. P. Kermode, by the last two probably erroneously.

A. arvensis L. Corn Chamomile
C Cultivated ground on light soils. Rare.

N — NE of Ballaghaie, Jurby, *MD*. **W** — Near Peel Road station, 1936, Paton*. **SE** — Near Kirk Onchan, 1912, *Holt*.

[***Chamaemelum nobile*** (L.) All. Common Chamomile
Listed by Stowell (1856), without details; but not repeated in his more substantial accounts, so presumably withdrawn as an error. The record attributed to Holt by Paton is merely a reference to this mention by Stowell. Nevertheless this western species could well occur.]

Achillea millefolium L. Yarrow; Airh Halllooin
N Short grassland, including maritime turf. Common. Calf.

A. ptarmica L. Sneezewort; Lus y Chreoid
N Wet places in general. Locally frequent. Calf.

Common in slacks on the Ballaghennie Ayres. More unexpectedly, on the dry railway track through Greeba Curraghs, in two areas.

Matricaria maritima L. Sea Scentless Mayweed
N Sandy and stony places by the sea. Common. Calf.

M. perforata Mérat (*M. inodora* L.) Scentless Mayweed
C Cultivated and waste ground. Common.
Hybrids with the above are doubtless frequent, as the two are fully interfertile; however, this can be established only by chromosome counts.

Chamomilla recutita (L.) Rauschert Scented Mayweed
C Waste ground round farms, hen-runs. Occasional.
N — Garey farmyard, plentiful, *MD*: near Ellanbane; Close Taggart. **SE** — Tromode. **SW** — N of Grenaby.
Undetected till 1958 and probably overlooked. Apparently introduced with poultry food.

C. suaveolens (Pursh) Rydb. (*Matricaria matricarioides* (Less.) Porter) Pineapple Weed
C Waysides, cornfields, waste ground. Common — but not yet on the Calf.
This North American invader was first noticed in England in 1871 and in Ireland in 1894. The first Manx record was at Castletown in 1924.

Chrysanthemum segetum L. Corn Marigold; Bastag Wuigh
C Cultivated fields, especially on drained curragh land. Locally abundant. Calf.

Leucanthemum vulgare Lam. Ox-eye Daisy; Bastag Vane
C Permanent long grass, quarries. Locally common in the north and south-east, local elsewhere. Calf.
There is no sign of the native-looking, probably diploid populations that occur on mountain rock-ledges in Wales. It nowhere looks indigenous in Man.

L. maximum (Ramond) DC. (Shasta Daisy) is a frequent throw-out, readily becoming naturalised. ***Tanacetum parthenium*** (L.) Schultz Bip. (Feverfew; Lus y Chiassaghey), once a popular herb, is also an occasional escape. Garner found it called 'Camphor Plant' in Man. ***T. vulgare*** L. (Tansy) is frequent on dry hedgebanks and wall-tops, especially in the north, apparently always near houses. It seems absent from the drift-line habitats in which it is elsewhere accepted as a native. ***Balsamita major*** Desf. (Costmary) was once used extensively in Man in brewing. 'It grows about old cottage enclosures, and the Manx call it Sweet-leaf' (Garner 1878); but unrecorded since.

Artemisia vulgaris L. Mugwort; Bollan Bane, Bollan Feaill' Eoin
C or D Roadsides, waste ground. Locally common, scarce in the east and uplands.

For some obscure reason this unprepossessing plant had a great reputation, in Man and elsewhere, as a protector from evil influences, rivalling ***Hypericum pulchrum*** in its St. John's Eve potency (whence one Manx name and whence the custom, revived c 1924, of wearing it on Tynwald Day). Elsewhere herbalists recommended it for nervousness, its leaves were often smoked like tobacco and it was held in especial esteem for women's complaints. These uses taken together seem to point to an ancient narcotic bound up somehow with the old mother goddess religion. Intriguingly, in the Irish deposits the pollen of this species suddenly much increases after 500 AD. Its native habitat, at least in Scandinavia, appears to be drift-lines.

A. absinthium L. (Wormwood; Ullymar), a former general-purpose herb, is still occasional on roadsides and waste ground, especially round old cottages, mainly in the north-west and far south.

A. maritima L. Sea Wormwood
N Rocks by the sea. Very rare, perhaps extinct (last record 1902).

W — Dalby, *Wesley Sci Soc.* **SE** — Near Seafield, Santon, abundant, *Forbes* (1848), *Stowell*: Traie ny Gill, by Port Grenaugh, *Ralfe* (same locality?). **SW** — The Chasms, *Garner.* **S** — Port Erin, *Hardaker.* Also an unlocalised gathering, 1832, *McNab* hb DBN.

A mainly eastern species in Britain which has vanished from most of its other former stations in the North and West, presumably for a climatic reason.

Carlina vulgaris L. Carline Thistle
N Sandy and rocky ground by the sea. Rare and very local.

N — N Ramsey brooghs, *S. Kermode*: Dog Mills; Ayres E of Rue Point, *BSBI*[1]! **C** — Port Cornaa, *S. Kermode*: Dhoon beach, *S. Kermode*, *Ralfe*! **S** — Langness, *S. Kermode*, YLM (1916) 79.

Also unlocalised records by Gasking, Wattam (1901) and Holt (JB (1905) suppl 52). The rocky habitats this favours in Maughold have counterparts in Galloway and Arran.

[***Arctium lappa*** L. Great Burdock
Most earlier workers listed ***A. minus*** subsp. ***pubens*** as this, in an aggregate sense. A recent record in Proc BSBI (1954) 173 was a misdetermination. This southern species is unlikely to be Manx.]

A. minus Bernh. subsp. ***pubens*** (Bab.) J. Arenes Burdock; Bollan-dhoa
D Waysides, farmyards, waste ground. Locally frequent, mainly near the south and west coasts. Calf.

Often singly and round habitations, betraying its former herbal popularity — for purifying the blood, skin diseases and nervousness (Moore 1898), for eating as a stand-in for asparagus, and for making into a beer.

subsp. ***nemorosum*** (Lej.) Syme
N Woodland on minimally acid soil. Very rare.

W — S margin of putatively relic oak-hazel wood halfway down Glen Maye, with ***Bromus ramosus***.

[subsp. ***minus***
Ballasalla, *Wheldon*, Proc (1910) 213. Probably just an unusually small-headed subsp. ***pubens***. I have seen no sign of true ***minus*** in Man, which lies outside its known Britannic range.]

Carduus tenuiflorus Curt. Seaside Thistle
N Dry waste ground near the sea. Locally frequent.
Occasionally white-flowered.

C. nutans L. Musk Thistle
C Sandy cultivated and waste ground. Rare, impermanent and very local.

N — Ballure; Ballaugh Curraghs, *P. M. C. Kermode*: fields at Ballaugh, *S. Kermode*: Ballacain, Ballaugh, *Ralfe*: about Jurby airfield; all over a field at Squeen, Ballaugh, 1973, *JH*: Lhen sandpit, 1973; Kirk Michael; abundant in field N of Ballagarrett, Bride, *D & G*.

[***C. acanthoides*** L. Welted Thistle
'Fields and waste ground, but not common', *Stowell*. As no one else has recorded this, Stowell must be presumed to have understood by the name some other species.]

Cirsium vulgare (Savi) Ten. Spear Thistle
N?C Drift-line of beaches; pastures, waste ground. Common. Calf.
In exposed maritime turf at Peel Castle and elsewhere, singly, on beaches. It is accepted as native on rocky shores in Scilly and I have seen it in closed turf on the coast of Brittany.

C. palustre (L.) Scop. Marsh Thistle
N Damp pastures, marshes, bog. Frequent. Calf.
Not uncommon with white flowers. On the Calf and the adjacent Mull Peninsula a form with pinkish-purple flowers occurs, intermixed with the type. A wholly white-flowered population in marshes at Orrisdale Head differs also from typical specimens nearby in having more congested inflorescences, simple stems and more deeply-cut leaves. Similar plants

but with rather numerous yellowish spines as well (and normally purple flowers) have been noted on a dry hillside in Glen Auldyn, on the brooghs at Peel and Knockaloe, at Ballameanagh, Sulby and in Druidale. A specimen with copious yellow spines is in hb Paton from Sulby and there is another, unlocalised, in hb Talbot. These last certainly, the others possibly also, are var. ***armeniacum*** (Ten.) Grande (var. *spinosissimum* Willk., var. *ferox* Druce), which has a wide Atlanto-Mediterranean distribution and appears to be a separate race, meriting subspecific rank. It favours drier ground, tolerating even limestone pavement. Great variability in the expression of the characters, however, renders its delimitation elusive.

C. arvense (L.) Scop. Creeping Thistle
NC Drift-line of shores; artificial grassland. Common. Calf.

Often white-flowered. Looking native (as in Scandinavia) on shingle at Port Soderick and Port Cornaa, on embryonic dunes near The Cronk and in slacks on the Ayres. Subsp. ***incanum*** (Georgi) J. Arènes (var. *vestitum* Wimm. & Grab.), an adventive form from South Europe, was noted near St. German's by Hartley & Wheldon (1914b).

Silybum marianum (L.) Gaertn. Milk Thistle
D Sandy fields, farmyards, usually near the sea. Very rare, perhaps extinct.

N — Sandy fields, Ballaugh, *Forbes* (1845): Lhen, 1919, *Ralfe*. **C** — Maughold parsonage garden, *Stowell*. **S** — Scarlett, *Ralfe*: Poyllvaaish, *Hardaker*: Balladoole hill, *Hannay*.

Formerly eaten as a salad and a vegetable, nowadays a hen-food casual.

Onopordon acanthium L. (Scotch Thistle), recorded near Ramsey by Forbes, resurfaced on newly-disturbed ground in an Orrisdale garden in 1974, *MD*. S. A. P. Kermode had it in his 1900 list ('hedges and waste places . . . fairly common now') in error for, probably, ***C. vulgare.***

[***Centaurea scabiosa*** L. Greater Knapweed
Listed by McNab. A strong lime-lover, unlikely to occur. Doubtless a 'radiate' ***C. nigra***.]

C. cyanus L. Cornflower; Sumark gorrym
CH A not uncommon cornfield weed up to 1900, extinguished by c 1925 through a more vigorous cleaning of seed. A temporary reappearance at Ballaterson, Maughold, in 1966, *GEQ*, resulted from a use of Continental seed. Other recent records are likely to have been escapes from gardens.

C. nigra L. Hardhead; Lus ny Gramman
NC Fens, marshes, stream-banks, cliffs; artificial grassland. Common. Calf.

Once with white flowers: Port Mooar, *P. M. C. Kermode*. 'Radiate' specimens occur here and there in the north, probably representing an adventive strain. The plants in the low-rainfall areas as a whole tend to differ from the rest morphologically and are likely to be a later immigrant wave, but the former recognition of two subspecies is not now considered sustainable. Marsden-Jones & Turrill (1954) thought the species native on sea-cliffs unreached by forest in north and west Britain. Dry, grassy ones at the Niarbyl certainly harbour it, but it looks more convincingly aboriginal in cliff marshes N of Peel — and even more so inland in fens (as in Norfolk), forming a frequent constituent of that at Rhendhoo, for example. Its presence on the drift-line at Port Soldrick is similarly suggestive.

C. diluta Ait. (Lesser Star Thistle), an increasing bird-seed derivative, occurred on Ramsey tip in 1969*. ***Cichorium intybus*** L. (Chicory; Lus y Shugr) has been much sown in leys and is often to be found lingering on.

Lapsana communis L. Nipplewort; Duillag Vreeshey
N?CD? Shady places, roadsides, gardens, open waste ground. Common. Calf.

Too successful a colonist of shrubberies and plantations to be more than doubtfully native on glen margins. A weed since the Neolithic, its seeds have been found in two prehistoric corpses, one a twelfth-century Dublin woman. In parts of England it was rated the sovereign remedy for piles.

Hypochoeris radicata L. Common Catsear; Cleaysh Chiyt
NC Dry pastures, heaths; cultivated fields, roadsides. Very common — but scarce on the Calf.

H. glabra L. Smooth Catsear
N Sandy ground near the sea. Very local: Orrisdale to Point of Ayre, at rare intervals.

A mainly eastern species in Britain, in Ireland only in Derry.

Leontodon autumnalis L. Autumn Hawkbit; Croag Phartan
NC Marshes (salt and fresh), sea-cliffs, lake-shores, dunes; pastures. Common. Calf (1931).

[***L. hispidus*** L. Greater Hawkbit
Listed by Gasking without details. A lime-lover, not very likely to occur. Robust plants of the next are sometimes reported as this in error — as in Proc BSBI (1956) 143.]

L. taraxacoides (Vill.) Mérat Lesser Hawkbit
N Dry pastures, maritime turf. Locally common. Calf (abundant).

Picris echioides L. (Bristly Ox-tongue) is a recently-arrived (bird-seed?) casual: Union Mills, 1975; Ballaglass, 1976; Andreas, 1977, *D & G*.

[***P. hieracioides*** L. Hawkweed Ox-tongue
Near Port Soderick, *Talbot* in Kermode (1900). A lime-lover unlikely to occur as a native, but a potential introduction with grass seed (as in Ireland and Norway). No Talbot record, however, can be accepted unsubstantiated.]

Tragopogon minor Mill. (Goatsbeard) has recurred for many years on waste ground in and around Ramsey*. A solitary plant was also noted by Paton in Andreas c 1937. ***T. porrifolius*** L. (Salsify) has been noted in several places since the War, mainly in the north, presumably after being grown as a crop. ***Lactuca tatarica*** (L.) C. A. Mey. was a recent weed in a Port Erin garden, per *LSG*, det. E. J. Clement.

Mycelis muralis (L.) Dumort. Wall Lettuce
D Walls, farmyards. Very rare and local.

N — Ballakillingan, Lezayre, *GEQ**, *JCo*: near Glentramman, Lezayre, *GEQ, D & G*. **C** — Ballure hill, *Stowell*.

An unlocalised record by Wattam (1899) was perhaps an error for ***Lapsana***.

A native of wooded, typically rocky places on rich humus; in Man (as in most of Ireland) apparently merely a relic of kitchen-garden use.

Sonchus arvensis L. Corn Sow-thistle
NC Shingle-beaches; cornfields, farmyards, roadsides. Common. Calf.

S. oleraceus L. Smooth Sow-thistle; Bee Muck
NC Drift-line of shores, ledges of sea-cliffs; cultivated and waste ground. Common. Calf.

A regular member of the strand association in parts of the south (including a form with very narrow, subentire leaves from Perwick to Port St. Mary), reappearing at Port Mooar and on the sands of the north. Along the rocky east and south-west coasts it is equally frequent in damp places on cliffs, as in south-west England and Brittany. These maritime plants are markedly glaucous.

S. asper (L.) Hill Prickly Sow-thistle
NC Drift-line of shores, ledges of sea-cliffs; cultivated and waste ground. Frequent. Calf.

Almost as widespread as the last in maritime habitats but more exclusively a strand plant. On the brooghs near Orrisdale it even grows in close turf.

Cicerbita macrophylla (Willd.) Wallr. subsp. ***uralensis*** (Rouy) Sell (Blue Sow-thistle), an aggressive garden spreader, has escaped in at least three places.

Hieracium murorum L. agg. Hawkweeds

NC Woods, rocks; walls, roadsides, artificial grassland. Very local. The remarkable scarcity of this group in Man, elsewhere as productive as the Brambles of microspecies of particular value to the geographer, is extremely disappointing. A mere six out of well over two hundred occur as evident natives (though the odd one more may yet be detected on the precipitous Dhoon cliffs). The unexciting geology and the paucity of exposed rock can never have supported many, but even these few have been all but extinguished by the intense grazing of sheep. The populations of most of them are now so tiny that they should not be collected further. All except the recent ***H. umbellatum*** finds have been determined by P. D. Sell and/or Dr C. West.

H. argenteum Fr. **C** — By cliff-path in cove just N of Dhoon beach*.

H. subrude (Arv.-Touv.) Arv.-Touv. **C** — Abundant on rocks, stony rubble and cliff turf above the beach at The Dhoon, *Paton*! hb BM, CGE: abundant on rocks, tramway and roadside above Bulgham Bay; Dhoon quarry. Also on wall of Avondale House, York Road, Upper Douglas, *MD*! hb CGE, presumably introduced with soil; a similar-looking plant, perhaps this species, formerly grew not far away on Governor's Bridge, Onchan, *Cowin*.

H. caledonicum F. J. Hanb. **C** — Rocks above Dhoon beach, *JEL* hb CGE!*

The above three are all northern species.

H. exotericum Jord. ex Bor. agg. **C** — Lonan churchyard, presumably introduced with grass seed*. Almost certainly ***H. grandidens*** Dahlst., but less advanced material has yet to be collected. Another alien, ***H. scotostictum*** Hyland., was found in 1978 outside Corvalley, near The Braaid, perhaps introduced with shrubs, *MD**.

H. cravoniense (F. J. Hanb.) Roffey **C** — Rocks in Sulby R by fall below Tholt-y-Will, hb CGE. Unknown in Ireland.

H. vulgatum Fr. **W/C** — Neb bridge, Ballig, *Cowin*!*: below Rhenass falls, Glen Helen, *MBB* hb CGE: below Tholt-y-Will, with ***H. cravoniense***, *MBB*! hb CGE. The conspicuous Ballig colony was discovered only in 1937; as it seems to be spreading, it may be of recent origin from fruits borne down from Glen Helen. Elsewhere in the north of the British Isles this is abundant and an aggressive colonist of walls; its extreme localisation in Man, despite suitable conditions, is the mark of a depauperated native relic. '***H. sylvaticum***' agg., recorded by Ralfe from the Santon Burn mouth in 1898 may also have been this.

H. umbellatum L. subsp. ***umbellatum*** **N** — Roadsides at Jurby East chapel (spreading into adjoining fields), NE of Loughan (since gone) and by Dollagh Mooar, Ballaugh (one plant), all discovered 1963, hb BM. **SW** — Cregneish, 1897, *Roeder**. Also listed by Gasking, without details. Apparently adventive.

H. perpropinquum (Zahn) Druce **C** — Spooyt Vane, *Garner*! hb CGE. The plants resemble the British, not the Irish form.

H. vagum Jord. **C** — Abundant round Laxey, recurring S to Baldrine, on railway banks and adjacent roadsides and cliffs, *Whellan*, BEC (1946-7) 300! hb CGE. Presumably introduced: unknown in Ireland and as a native normally in woods. Hardaker assured me he knew this at Laxey (as '***H. boreale***' agg.) shortly after the Manx Electric Railway opened in 1899; but if it was also the '***H. boreale***' listed by Gasking (1888-9), it must antedate the railway's construction.

Pilosella officinarum C. H. & F. W. Schultz Mouse-ear Hawkweed
N Dry short turf, shingle beaches, wall-tops. Common.

P. aurantiaca (L.) C. H. & F. W. Schultz subsp. ***aurantiaca*** is invading mown grass in Ballure park, *MD*, and subsp. ***brunneocrocea*** (Pugsl.) Sell & West (Fox and Cubs) has also escaped in many places.

Crepis capillaris (L.) Wallr. Smooth Hawksbeard
C Wall-tops, roadsides, dry pastures. Frequent, especially in the north. A taller and more robust form with heads up to twice as large, var. ***glandulosa*** Druce (*C. druceana* J. Murr) is common in the south-east and round Peel, chiefly along main roads. This appears to be a recent adventive, perhaps of Continental origin. In Cornwall an association of it with root crops has been noted.

C. paludosa (L.) Moench Marsh Hawksbeard
N Shady, swampy ground. Very rare.

SW — Greeba Curraghs SW of Greeba Bridge, on margin of one-time lakelet, *WFS*!*

Taraxacum Weber Dandelion; Lun y Minnag
Like the Brambles and Hawkweeds, an assemblage of numerous microspecies — but unlike them, mostly adventive and so of limited value for tracing geographical affinities. Because they must be collected before June, earlier than most of my visits, and because there was no British specialist till c 1965, this is the one major group still much underworked in Man. The few gatherings made down to 1962 were deposited in hb BM for naming by the leading European specialist, Prof J. L. van Soest. Dr A. J. Richards has since re-examined these and named more recent

collections by E. F. & B. D. Greenwood and H. McAllister. The former are in hb LIV. As collecting to date has mainly been at random, detailing of localities is pointless in most cases and merely their number is given instead.

Section ***Erythrosperma*** (H. Lindb. f.) Dahlst. ('***T. laevigatum*** (Willd.) DC.' agg.)
NC Dunes; dry bare ground, roadsides. Local:—
T. brachyglossum (Dahlst.) Dahlst. (4, including Ayres), ***T. lacistophyllum*** (Dahlst.) Raunk. (1), ***T. rubicundum*** (Dahlst.) Dahlst. (Ayres), ?***T. laetum*** (Dahlst.) Dahlst. (Ayres, common), ***T. oxoniense*** Dahlst. (dunes near Lhen).

Section ***Obliqua*** Dahlst. ('***T. obliquum*** (Fr.) Dahlst.' agg.)
N Open sandy turf by the sea. Very local:—
T. platyglossum Raunk. (Castletown golf links, abundant). A northern species, unrecorded for Ireland.

Section ***Spectabilia*** Dahlst. ('***T. spectabile*** Dahlst.' agg.)
NC Bogs, wet grassland, dune slacks, roadsides. Common:—
T. unguilobum Dahlst. (9; probably general), ***T. landmarkii*** Dahlst. (1), ***T. faeroense*** (Dahlst.) Dahlst. (common), ***T. praestans*** H. Lindb. f. (1), ***T. laetifrons*** Dahlst. (2), ***T. nordstedtii*** Dahlst. (4), ***T. adamii*** Claire (11; probably general), ***T. maculosum*** A. J. Richards (3).

Section ***Taraxacum*** ('***T. officinale*** Weber' agg.)
NC Marshes; roadsides, cultivated and waste ground. Very common. Calf:—
T. subcyanolepis M. P. Chr. (Scarlett and Derbyhaven; a lime-lover), ***T. ancistrolobum*** Dahlst. (marsh at Scarlett; not Irish or Scottish), ***T. pannucium*** Dahlst. (1), ***T. alatum*** H. Lindb. f. (1), ***T. croceiflorum*** Dahlst. (2), ***T. expallidiforme*** Dahlst. (1), ***T. longisquameum*** H. Lindb. f. (1), ***T. haematicum*** Hagl. (1), ***T. bracteatum*** Dahlst. (2), ***T. christiansenii*** Hagl. (1), ***T. hamatum*** Raunk. (2), ***T. hamatiforme*** Dahlst. (2), ***T. marklundii*** Palmgr. (2), ***T. subhamatum*** M. P. Chr. (1), ***T. maculatum*** Jord. (1), ***T. fasciatum*** Dahlst. (1), ***T. raunkiaerii*** Wiinst. (3), ***T. polydon*** Dahlst. (1), ***T. privum*** Dahlst. (1).

Monocotyledones

Alismataceae

Baldellia ranunculoides (L.) Parl. Lesser Water Plantain
N Peaty ditches and pools. Very local: widespread in the north, recently found at Baldwin Reservoir and rediscovered on the Mull Hill.

Alisma plantago-aquatica L. Common Water Plantain
NH Ditches, ponds. Rare.

N — Mouth of Killane trench. **S** — Castletown Mill dam, *Ralfe* (now gone): Dumb River, *Paton**!

Also planted ornamentally — including in at least one Ballasalla mill dam, from which these South occurrences may have derived.

A.* × *rhicnocarpum Schotsman Hybrid Water Plantain
N Ditches. Very local: north only.

What appears to be this sterile hybrid between ***A. lanceolatum*** With. and ***A. plantago-aquatica*** is much the most plentiful Water Plantain in Man (though confined to the north). Evidently more tolerant than its parents of the repeated cleaning of the Curraghs drainage-ditches, its abundance along the Killane trench and the presence of ***A. plantago-aquatica*** only at the mouth of this neatly parallels the situation in the Water Speedwells on the Dumb River near Castletown. A disturbed habitat has also been noted in Sweden as a precondition of its occurrence. Previously passed over as ***A. lanceolatum***, its intermediate character was first noticed in 1963. At that time this hybrid was unrecorded for the British Isles, but putative examples have since been reported from Ireland and the Fens. How far the southerly ***A. lanceolatum*** occurs in Man is still uncertain; records of it from various ponds in the north are likely to be correct in part but await critical re-examination.

HYDROCHARITACEAE

[***Hydrocharis morsus-ranae*** L. Frogbit
The record in Garrad (1972, 139) was a slip for ***Baldellia***.]

Elodea canadensis Michx. Canadian Waterweed
C Well-silted lakes and rivers. Local.

N — Along Lhen trench (in flower, 1970, *MD*). **C** — Baldwin Reservoir, *RH*. ***SE*** — Mount Murray lake, *Paton*!: Tromode Dam, *MD*: Union Mills, *LSG*: Glass at Pulrose; pool in Nunnery grounds. **S** — Along the Silverburn, *Hunter*, *Ralfe* etc!* (up to Atholl Bridge).

A North American invader first noticed in the British Isles c 1836 but in Man not till 1915.

JUNCAGINACEAE

Triglochin palustris L. Marsh Arrow-grass
N Marshes, swamps, bogs. Local: mainly in the north-west corner and the southern two-thirds, with a coastal tendency and largely avoiding high-rainfall districts. Calf.

In saline marshes with the next at Scarlett and Creglea, Dalby.

T. maritima L. Sea Arrow-grass
N Salt marshes, rock-pools. Local.

Zosteraceae

Zostera marina L. Common Eel-grass
N On sand below low-water mark. Rare?

N — The Carrick, Ramsey Bay, *Savage*, *Spanton* etc: Ballaugh shore, thrown up by storms, *Hoyle*. **SE** — Douglas, *Talbot*. **W** — Peel, *Clementson*. **S** — Derbyhaven, *Ralfe*, *LSG*: Port St. Mary, *Knight & Parke* (1931, 69, 102): Port Erin, *JRB*, *LSG & DJS* etc*. 'Sea shores', *Backwell's*.

I have seen material only from Port Erin: ***Z. angustifolia*** (Hornem.) Reichb. may well also occur.

Potamogetonaceae

Potamogeton natans L. Broad-leaved Pondweed; Lus ny Lhingey
NH Pools, ditches, slowish streams. Local: common in the north, reappearing thinly along the central valley and round the head waters of the Santon Burn. Elsewhere (including two pools on the Calf) apparently introduced.

P. polygonifolius Pourr. Bog Pondweed
N Peaty ditches and ponds, bog-pools. Locally common. Calf.

P. alpinus Balb. Reddish Pondweed
N Peaty pools. Very rare.

N — Dub below Jurby church, in plenty,* hb BM.

P. perfoliatus L. Perfoliate Pondweed
N Well-silted still water. Apparently extinct.

N — Lhen Mooar, 1881, *Murray* hb BM: Lhen trench, *Paton**.

P. berchtoldii Fieb. Slender Pondweed
N Ponds, ditches. Very local: frequent in the north, reappearing in Eairy Dam and quarry pools near Ballasalla.

P. crispus L. Curly Pondweed
N Ditches, ponds. Rare and very scattered.

N — Pond N of Jurby (Lhen Mooar?), *Wheldon*: Lhen trench, *Paton**!: old gravel-pits W of Point of Ayre; pond by Ballacottier, Lezayre, *D &*

G. **W** — Peel power station quarry, abundant, *D & G*. **S** — Dumb River, by main road, *BSBI*[2]!

P. pectinatus L. Fennel Pondweed
N Brackish pools. Rare and very local.

N — Old gravel pits W of Point of Ayre, *D & G*. **S** — Abundant in pool by shore at Castletown (Scarlett?), *Holt**, *Wood* etc hb BM, RAMM: ponds, Derbyhaven, *S. Kermode* (now gone): freshwater pool and quarry, Scarlett, *Paton**, *BSBI*[1]!: formerly abundant in pit at Gansey, since filled in.

ZANNICHELLIACEAE

Zannichellia palustris L. Horned Pondweed
N Ditches and pools near the sea. Very rare.

N — Dub below Jurby church; Glascoe dub, Bride. **S** — Balladoole, *Paton**. 'Ditches etc', *S. Kermode*. Also listed by McNab.

LILIACEAE

Narthecium ossifragum (L.) Huds. Bog Asphodel; Lus y Niew
N Boggy heaths, moors, wet rocks. Locally common, mainly in the hills. Calf.

Phormium tenax J. R. & G. Forst. (New Zealand Flax) is self-sown here and there and survives spectacularly in the Ballaugh and Greeba Curraghs from abortive attempts (in 1932 and the First World War respectively) to establish an industry based on its fibre. It has also been tried as a crop in Wigtownshire, Connemara and Scilly. ***Polygonatum* × *hybridum*** Brügger (Garden Solomon's Seal) is naturalised at the bottom of Glen Tramman, Lezayre, *D & G*. The '***P. multiflorum***' listed by Gasking was doubtless this. ***Asparagus officinalis*** L. subsp. ***officinalis*** (Asparagus; Croau-muc-feie) occurs casually on tips. ***Ruscus aculeatus*** L. (Butcher's Broom) is naturalised in old plantations and one or two hedgebanks. ***Lilium martagon*** L. (Turkscap Lily) is naturalised in plantations at Ballakillingan, Lezayre, and (white-flowered) Lambhill, Bride, *VR*. ***L. croceum*** Chaix (Cottager's Orange Lily) is also at Lambhill, *MD*. ***L. pyrenaicum*** Gouan (Pyrenean Lily) is well-established by Tosaby curragh, near St. Mark's, *D & G*; and naturalised in several other places. ***Fritillaria meleagris*** L. (Fritillary) has occurred as a stray in a meadow near Sulby, *AQR*. ***Ornithogalum umbellatum*** L. (Common Star-of-Bethlehem) is also naturalised in many places, including maritime turf.

Scilla verna Huds. Spring Squill; Unnish Varrey
N Maritime turf. Common round most of the coast. Calf.

A freak autumn flower of this was doubtless responsible for McNab's record in Watson (1832) of ***S. autumnalis*** L. White and pink flowers are not uncommon.

Endymion non-scriptus (L.) Garcke Bluebell; Gleih-vuc
N Glens, cliffs, hillsides, hedgebanks, often in full sun. Common. Calf. Up to 1100ft between Keppel Gate and Windy Corner. On the treeless Calf under bracken, among heather on a hill-top, even in a swamp. Occasionally white-flowered.

E. hispanicus (Mill.) Chouard (Garden Bluebell) commonly escapes and has been extensively sown in glens. It readily crosses with the native species.

Colchicum autumnale L. (Meadow Saffron) has escaped on to roadsides at Smeale corner, Andreas, *MD*. A solitary plant also occurred in a Sulby Curraghs field off Ellanbane road c 1944, *GEQ*.

JUNCACEAE

Juncus squarrosus L. Heath Rush
N Heaths and moors. Locally abundant.

J. tenuis Willd. Slender Rush
C Waysides. Rare, but slowly spreading.

C — Dhoon Glen entrance, 1951; Grawe Farm lane, Lonan, abundant, 1958; E of Clypse Reservoir, 1958. **SE** — NE of Groudle Glen, 1957. **SW** — By Archallagan Plantation E of Eairy Dam, 1962: railway by Marown church, 1971, *D & G*.

An American invader gradually colonising the British Isles. Dates denote year of first noticing: it may have been present well before in each instance.

[***J. compressus*** Jacq. Round-fruited Rush
Records by Talbot and Murray (who worked closely together) were accepted by Paton; but the specimen in hb Talbot is ***J. acutiflorus***. The name was also applied formerly in an aggregate sense to the next. A lime-lover and very rare in Ireland, this is not a likely Manx species.]

J. gerardii Lois. Saltmarsh Rush
N Wet saline ground by the sea. Local, but often abundant where it occurs. Calf.

J. bufonius L. Common Toad Rush
N Damp muddy places, marshes, rock-pools. Common. Calf.

J. foliosus Desf. Western Toad Rush
N Wet seepages. Local, but widely distributed.

Passed over as ***J. bufonius*** till 1967, this is normally told at once by its taller, grass-like habit and dark-bordered perianth segments (there are also seed and chromosome differences). Where the two grow together, as at Port Lewaigue, the distinctness is convincing. Abundant in Ireland and widely distributed in south-west Europe, it is the Toad Rush equivalent of ***J. kochii***. Manx material has been confirmed by Dr S. Snogerup of the University of Lund.

[***J. inflexus*** L. Hard Rush
Indicated for vice-county 71 by Druce (1932). Presumably a clerical slip, as no published record is known. Though so common in England, this species is absent from most of Scotland and northern Ireland, becoming a marked lime-lover at the edge of its range.]

J. effusus L. Soft Rush; Shuin
N Wet pastures, watersides, swamps. Very common both in the lowlands (var. ***effusus***) and the hills (var. ***compactus*** Hoppe). Calf.

J. subuliflorus Drejer (*J. conglomeratus* auct.) Compact Rush
N Base-rich bogs. Frequent. Calf.

J. maritimus Lam. Sea Rush
N Brackish pools by the sea, salt marshes. Very local: mainly Castletown area.

C — Port Cornaa and Gob ny Calla; Port Mooar (to Gob ny Garvain, *MD*). **W** — Creglea, Dalby, *MD*! **S** — Between Scarlett and Castletown, *Forbes*, *Stowell* etc!: Scarlett; Derby Haven, by hotel; W and E Langness; Gansey Point.

J. acutiflorus Ehrh. ex Hoffm. Sharp-flowered Rush
N Wet fields, swamps. Very common. Calf.

The sterile cross with the next is widespread, perhaps common.

J. articulatus L. Jointed Rush; Gollinagh
N Bogs, rock-pools, dune slacks. Common. Calf.

The dwarf dune-slack ecotype, var ***littoralis*** Patze, Meyer & Elkan, has been noted on the Ayres in two places.

J. bulbosus L. Common Bulbous Rush
N Pools, reservoirs, dune-slacks, marshes. Very local. Calf.

N — Ayres by Sartfield, Knock-e-Dooney and E of Rue Point; Curragh-y-Cowle; dub E of The Dhowin; two dubs between Sandygate and Loughdhoo; Sulby Curraghs near Close an Allan. **C** — Baldwin

Reservoir, abundant. **SW** — SE of The Eairy, *BSBI*[1] hb K: Calf, *LSG*: Quayle's Orchard, Grenaby, abundant.

As elsewhere in the North and West, mainly a plant of water and watersides and seemingly much less tolerant of competition than the next. The two sometimes grow together but keep quite distinct — though a fertile hybrid has been raised artificially.

J. kochii F. W. Schultz — Western Bulbous Rush
N Bogs. Very common. Calf.

Luzula pilosa (L.) Willd. — Hairy Woodrush
N Glens, shady banks, open moors. Occasional. Calf.

The moorland occurrences (woodland relics?) are all in the south-west. In this area, too — at Glen Maye — it grows in the open on cliffs.

L. sylvatica (Huds.) Gaud. — Great Woodrush; Leaghyr Vooar
N Shady rocky places, ditches, moorland slopes, sea cliffs. Locally abundant. Calf.

A hardy survivor of deforestation still locally dominant on the slopes of Snaefell and North Barrule summit. On wet coastal rocks and cliffs at Niarbyl, Port Garwick and Pistol (cf. ***Brachypodium sylvaticum***).

L. campestris (L.) DC. — Good Friday Grass; Leaghyr Cheylley
N Dry grassland. Locally abundant. Calf.

L. multiflora (Retz.) Lej. — Many-headed Woodrush
N Curraghs. Local.

N — Berrag dub, Sandygate; Ballaugh Curraghs, in several places; Rhendhoo Curragh, Jurby: Loughcroute; SW of Dhoor, *D & G*. **SW** — Greeba Curraghs W of Crosby. **SE** — Union Mills curraghs, *LSG*.

L. congesta (Thuill.) Lej. — Heath Woodrush
N Heaths, moors, bogs. Common. Calf.

Traditionally lumped with the last but now known to have more chromosomes and to be at least partly intersterile with it, with smaller flowers and seeds as well as the congested inflorescence. Like ***Juncus kochii***, it is the predominant of the two in the West.

Amaryllidaceae

Allium vineale L. — Crow Garlic
NC Sea-shores; dry banks, roadsides. Very local.

N — Ballamanaugh, Sulby; formerly at Kella, Sulby, *RH*: Regaby, *MBB*: by Kimmeragh gravel-pit and near Grenaby, Bride, *D & G*: near

Dog Mills, *MD*. **C** — Maughold shore, *Garner*, *Ralfe*: The Dhyrnane, Port Mooar, *Savage*, *MBB* (probably same locality): Chibbyr Pherric, Lonan, *JMK*. **W** — Ballaterson, Peel, *F. S. Graves*, *Ralfe* hb BM etc!: N Peel, *JK*!: Traie Cabbag brooghs, *JK*: track to Peel battery; by Congary entrance, *D & G*. **SE** — Castleward Farm lane, *LSG*. **S** — Malew churchyard, 1957: railway bank between Ballabeg and Ballakaighen, *LSG*.

Seemingly native in maritime habitats (as in Maughold) only in the West of the British Isles, though in these almost exclusively in Denmark. All plants seen are var. ***compactum*** (Thuill.) Bor., the form supposedly more prevalent in eastern and southern Britain.

A. carinatum L. (Keeled Garlic) is naturalised in Silverdale Glen by the up-stream entrance, *D & G*! ***A. triquetrum*** L. (Three-cornered Leek), first noticed as an escape at Poyllvaaish in 1946, is rapidly overrunning the south-west corner, as it has the Channel Isles and Scilly. It has also been noted at Ramsey, Onchan and Glen Vine.

A. ursinum L. Ramsons; Craue, Garleyd Feie

N or D Glens, plantations. Locally abundant.

Supposedly it is from this plant that the Maughold/Lezayre boundary stream ('Strooan y chraue') and in turn Ramsey itself take their name. Yet Forbes marked it as 'scarce' and a probable introduction and Stowell knew it only in plantations. In Ireland it is but thinly distributed and was formerly much prized there for treating tuberculosis, while Linnaeus found Swedish farmers thought it kept other weeds down (as well as rats and mice) and encouraged it to spread. Once introduced, it multiplies fast by seed. Could the Norsemen have brought it?

Galanthus nivalis L. (Snowdrop; Blaa Niaghtee) is a common escape, abundantly naturalised in many places.

Narcissus pseudonarcissus L. (Lent Lily) is widely naturalised in a form larger than the wild type. Far commoner, however, is the old double variety of this species, 'Van Sion' — the 'Wild Daffodil' of Man (Glioonagh y Ghuiy), from which a yellow dye was anciently extracted and which has attracted folk beliefs. ***N. minor*** L., a dwarf species reputedly from Portugal widespread in old Manx gardens (as 'Jonquils'), especially in the north, is naturalised in the Ballaugh Curraghs in two places, Andreas and Bishopscourt grounds, *D & G*. ***N.*** × ***incomparabilis*** Mill. and ***N. gayi*** (Hénon) Pugsl. 'Princeps' (Trumpet Daffodil) are also naturalised in the Ballaugh Curraghs, the latter elsewhere as well, *D & G*. ***N. poeticus*** L. subsp. ***radiiflorus*** (Salisb.) Baker var. ***exsertus*** (Haw.) Fernandes (*N. majalis* Curt.) (Pheasant's Eye) has been noted at Ballabooie, German (det. Wisley) and at Kirby, *D & G*. ***N.*** × ***mediolatus*** Mill. (*N.* × *biflorus* Curt.) (Primrose Peerless) is naturalised in Silverdale and elsewhere,

D & G. ***Alstroemeria aurantiaca*** D. Don (Peruvian Lily) has spread on the site of an abandoned cottage garden to form a large orange splash in the Greeba Curraghs N of Kennaa.

Iridaceae

Iris pseudacorus L. Yellow Flag; Cleeshag (South), Cliogagh (North)
N Marshes, swamps, ditches. Common.

I. foetidissima L. (Roast-beef Plant; Lus y Vooin, Cliogagh Cliddnagh) is naturalised in Ballaglas Glen, beside the Berrag dub, Sandygate, and in numerous other scattered places. ***Tritonia* × *crocosmiflora*** (Lemoine) Nicholson (Montbretia) has become extensively naturalised in recent years, often far from dwellings. ***Curtonus paniculatus*** (Klatt) N.E.Br. (*Antholysa paniculata* Klatt) has escaped at Cregneish, *LSG*.

Dioscoreaceae

Tamus communis L. (Black Bryony) has occurred, singly, at Poyllvaaish, *Hannay*, Proc (1907) 26. Presumably an accidental import: odd plants turn up elsewhere outside the strict northern and western limits of its native range, but normally prove impermanent.

Orchidaceae

[***Epipactis palustris*** (L.) Crantz Marsh Helleborine
Listed by Gasking. A likely species to occur in the northern 'fens' or dune-slacks (in which it grows profusely on neighbouring coasts).]

Spiranthes spiralis (L.) Chevall. Autumn Lady's Tresses
N Dry, basic turf near the sea. Very rare.

N — Ballaghennie Ayres, *AH & MQ* etc. Discovered in 1965, this colony of 8-12+ spikes is just about the northernmost in the British Isles. **S** — Chapel Hill, Balladoole, 1918, *NHAS*; 1945, *Bersu*; others since (last 1957). Up to 12 spikes.

Listera ovata (L.) R. Br. Common Twayblade
N Damp fields, wet roadsides, railway cuttings, hedges, dune slacks. Local. Calf.

N — Ballaugh Curraghs, locally abundant!; Jurby; St. Jude's; hedge in Andreas, *Paton*: Ballacrebbin, Andreas!; near Kerroogarroo chapel, *MBB*: Ayres W of Ballaghennie, since 1969, *ETL*, *D & G*!: Rhendhoo Curragh, Jurby, *D & G*. **C** — Injebreck, *Cowin*. **SE** — Frequent near

Mount Murray, *Murray*: railway N of Arragon, abundant. **SW** — Glen Rushen, *Paton*: railway, Glen Vine, *Cowin & Megaw*; Ballamodha 'straight', *BSBI*[2]!: Calf, above the Cletts, *PJ*. **S** — Castletown, *Forbes*: Ballamaddrell, Arbory, *Teare*: roadside, Kentraugh, *AC*.

L. cordata (L.) R. Br. Lesser Twayblade

N Bogs in hilly districts, in moss among heather on north-facing moorland slopes. Very rare, perhaps extinct.

C — Hill NE of Snaefell, 1774, *Davies*: 'in the mountains', *Macculloch* (1819 — merely repeating Davies?): Curragh Pot Moin, Maughold, 1880, *Talbot** — presumably the locality variously described as 'above The Dhoon' and 'above Christ Church, Maughold', where Harrison collected it in 1881*, giving specimens to Holt and Murray and showing it to his brother-in-law, P. M. C. Kermode. This must have been on the flank of Slieau Ruy.

This northern species is notoriously inconspicuous and may yet be rediscovered.

[***Neottia nidus-avis*** (L.) Rich. Birdsnest Orchid

Listed for Man in Watson (1832, 277), but not repeated in Watson's subsequent works. Doubtless a mismarking for the next catalogue entry, ***Listera cordata***.]

Coeloglossum viride (L.) Hartm. Frog Orchid

N Short, damp turf of hill slopes and old pastures. Very rare and local.

N — Ballaugh Curraghs, 1942, *Wagstaffe & Williamson*. **C** — Hills near Ramsey, very rare, *Backwell's*: hillside above lower Narradale, one spike, 1965, *JC fide LSG*.

Gymnadenia conopsea (L.) R. Br. subsp. ***conopsea*** Scented Orchid

N Damp pastures, heathy grassland. Rare, but increasing.

N — Ballaugh Curraghs in one field, about 100 spikes, 1943, *Megaw*, *RH* etc!* hb K: Ayres, in three areas, since 1950s, *D & G*: Rhendhoo, Jurby, *MD*.

The recentness of the records, taken with an undoubted spread on the Ayres, suggests a newcomer. It is plentiful in Galloway, whence seeds could readily have blown.

Platanthera chlorantha (Cust.) Reichb. Butterfly Orchid

N Damp pastures (especially under bracken), hayfields. Local, sometimes abundant where it occurs; mainly in the north and round the edges of the central hills.

P. bifolia (L.) Rich. Lesser Butterfly Orchid

N Wet heaths, boggy pastures. Very local.

N — Sulby Curraghs, rare, *Paton*, *LSG*: Ballaugh Curraghs, in one field, *Megaw*, *BSBI*[1]!: **C** — N of Bibaloe, *MD*. **SE** — Near Douglas, *Talbot**: Hillberry, *Cowin*. **SW** — Near Eairy Dam, abundant, *Osvald*, *BSBI*[1]: SW of Ballamodha, *BSBI*[2]!: plentiful in garey, Tosaby.

The south-central focus parallels that of another northern species, ***Rubus infestus***.

Neotinea maculata (Desf.) Stearn (*N. intacta* (Link) Reichb. f.)
Dense-flowered Orchid

N On a fixed dune. Very rare.

N — Ayres near Ballaghennie, a single patch, *MG* etc! hb K. For a full account of this remarkable find and ecological details see Allen (1968). From some 30 spikes in the year of its discovery, 1966, and at least 20 in 1967 the population abruptly dwindled to 9 in 1968. Totals for subsequent years have been 7, 0, 1, 0, 3, ?, 9, 3, 3, 8, 2, 1, 0.

A Mediterranean species, elsewhere in the British Isles known only in the west of Ireland. The dune on which it grows is comparatively recent and a seed must be presumed to have blown there from one of the Irish stations — the nearest some 170 miles away, in the line of the prevailing wind. All the plants are the normal Irish form with whitish flowers and unspotted leaves.

Ophrys apifera Huds. Bee Orchid

N Lime quarries, dry banks. Very rare.

C — Bank in Glen Mona, one spike, c 1910, *ADW*. **SE** — Howstrake, one spike, 1977, *DJ*. **S** — Known in a locality in Malew* since 1957, when only a single spike was seen. From 3 spikes in 1968 it increased to 9 in 1969 and 23 in 1971, crashed to 2 in 1972 and exploded afresh to 46 (in three separate spots) in 1973, rising to 79 in 1976, *D & G*. As the habitat is free from human disturbance, the cause of the fluctuation is presumably climatic.

A typically Germanic species apparently on the increase in the Irish Sea area generally, this may well be a newcomer — though its main locality was unexplored till 1957. It was indicated for vice-county 71 by Druce (1932), but this must be presumed a slip.

Orchis mascula (L.) L. Early Purple Orchid

N Dune heath. Very local.

N — Ayres, frequent for 1½ miles from Rue Point to opposite Ballaghennie, along a narrow belt landward of the highest ridge, favouring the south-facing slope; also in two rear hollows. First noted (at Rue Point) by T. H. Graves in 1934 and apparently spread widely since, suggesting a recent immigration. White-flowered plants also occur.

Several earlier, inland records (eg YLM 1, 124) are apparently errors for

D. purpurella or (YLM 3, 611) ***D. incarnata***. It was also listed by Gasking, on unknown evidence.

Dactylorhiza fuchsii (Druce) Soó subsp. ***fuchsii***
Common Spotted Orchid

N Marshes, wet fields, ditches. Local: frequent in Peel-St. John's area and round Castletown, elsewhere in a few scattered lowland stations. Calf (one plant).

An exceptionally robust form in Knocksharry quarry and a garey W of Grenaby, hb BM, K. The fertile cross with ***D. maculata*** is not uncommon but the sterile one with ***D. purpurella***, common in North Wales, has yet to be recorded.

subsp. ***okellyi*** (Druce) Soó O'Kelly's Spotted Orchid

N Marsh edges, wet pastures, ditches, quarries, dune slacks. Occasional; more thinly but more widely scattered than subsp. ***fuchsii***, with which and ***D. maculata*** it freely crosses. Calf (in two places).

Detected only in 1960, this has since been found in 25 stations, including in great abundance in Scarlett marsh. A sub-albino Irish-Hebridean race, it noticeably favours disturbed habitats and may thus be a newcomer in the course of spread. The tininess of the flower is more diagnostic than its creamy colouring: for a detailed description based on the Manx plants see Allen (1971).

D. maculata (L.) Soó subsp. ***ericetorum*** (E. F. Linton) P. F. Hunt & Summerhayes Heath Spotted Orchid; Bwoid Saggyrt

N Bogs, damp heathy ground. Very common. Calf (oddly scarce).

The cross with ***D. purpurella*** is not uncommon.

D. incarnata (L.) Soó subsp. ***incarnata*** Early Marsh Orchid

N Fens, marshes, dune slacks. Local in the north, elsewhere very rare. Calf.

N — Sulby Curraghs, *Paton corr.:* Ballaugh Curraghs, in two places, *RH*, *BSBI*[1] hb K: curraghs NE of Loughdoo, *BSBI*[1], *D & G*: curragh SW of Cranstal, *WHH*: Ballaterson Curraghs, *MD*: Ayres rear slacks, abundant; Loughcroute, *D & G*: Rhendhoo Curragh, Jurby; The Guilcagh, Andreas. **SW** — Calf, by the mill-pool. **S** — Ballamaddrell, Arbory, *Ralfe*.

Crosses with ***D. purpurella*** in Ballaugh Curraghs, *BSBI*[1] hb K.

subsp. ***coccinea*** (Pugsl.) Soó

N — Two Ayres slacks W of Ballaghennie, *MBB*, *NHAS*!*: rear slacks, with subsp. ***incarnata***, *D & G*.

This dwarfer, western, mainly dune-slack race produces its ruby flowers distinctly later on the Ayres than the flesh-pink type.

D. purpurella (T. & T. A. Stephenson) Soó Northern Marsh Orchid
N Marshes, bogs, road verges, bare lead-mine rubble, damp meadows, dune-slacks. Locally frequent, barely penetrating the hills.

Called 'abundant' by Paton — yet only two stations are known below the Douglas-South Barrule line: on the roadside near Ballanank, Malew, and midway between Cregneish and the Sound. In Ireland this northern species is suspected to be spreading south and the same may be true in Man.

Anacamptis pyramidalis (L.) Rich. Pyramidal Orchid
N Dunes, limestone quarries, dry banks. Very local in the north, elsewhere very rare.

N — Along the Ayres for $3\frac{1}{2}$ miles. First found at Rue Point by Paton* in 1923, since when it has spread from about a mile N of the Point down to The Lhen (also by the Point of Ayre, 1971, *JG*): N of Orrisdale, one spike, 1976, *MD*. **W** — St. John's, 1966, per *LSG*: embankment near Peel Road Station, 1966, per *LSG*. **SE** — Snugborough, 1966, *CB*. **S** — Quarries in Malew (first found 1957): Rushen Abbey verge, 1972, *MD*. A freshly-picked spike by Castletown golf links, 1958, may not have been collected *in situ*.

Evidently a newcomer. It has been increasing elsewhere on the Irish Sea coasts, presumably in response to warmer summers.

Araceae

Arum maculatum L. Lords and Ladies
N Under bushes, especially on base-rich soil. Very rare.

SE — Edge of Douglas on Tromode Road, one clump, *MD*. **S** — Ballahott lane, Ballasalla; railway bank, Castletown, one clump; N end of Billown quarries, in some plenty, apparently spreading, *LSG*.

As elsewhere along the northern margin of this species' range, f. ***immaculatum*** (Schott) Engler occurs almost exclusively, some spotted leaves being found at Billown alone. Apart perhaps from Ralfe's 'fields about Castletown' various earlier records, dating back to 1831, all relate to the next. Despite Bennett's claim in JB (1905) suppl. 88 to have seen a specimen from Holt, hb Holt also contains only that.

A. italicum Mill. (Large Cuckoo Pint) is widely naturalised in plantations and near old gardens. Specimens without the ornamental cream veins, equatable with 'subsp. ***neglectum*** (Towns.) Prime', have been noted at Orrisdale*, Ballakillingan, Braddan, Union Mills* and Michael reservoir*, *D & G*, conf. C. T. Prime; but these are doubtless mere genetic segregants, not a separate native population.

Lysichiton americanus Hultén & St. John (Skunk Cabbage) has been introduced at Port Cornaa and persists in at least two places.

Lemnaceae

Lemna trisulca L. Ivy Duckweed

N Ponds. Very local: north almost wholly.

N — Five ponds in Jurby, six in Andreas and two in Bride. **W** — Spring on sea side of Peel Hill, *FHT*.

L. minor L. Common Duckweed; Gleiy Fannag

NC Pools, ditches, seepages, slow streams. Locally abundant, but scarce south of the Peel-Port Soderick line. Calf.

In rock-pools on the Calf. In artificial pools in Groudle and Garwick Glens, well outside its normal range and probably accidentally introduced.

Sparganiaceae

Sparganium erectum L. Branched Bur-reed

N Ponds, ditches, streams. Locally common in the north, scarce elsewhere.

A series of geographical races which cannot be made to cross and do not differ ecologically, often growing together. Though seemingly rare in Ireland, subsp. ***erectum*** is the prevalent one in Man. The more northern subsp. ***microcarpum*** (Neum.) Domin occurs in the same areas but appears more local:—

N — Ponds W of Sandygate, *MBB*: N of Cranstal, *WFS*!: N of Ballaghaie, Jurby, *LSG*. **SW**— Greeba Curragh near St. John's. **SE** — Port Soderick*: Union Mills Curragh, *LSG*. **S** — Silverburn, below weir and at Castletown, *LSG*.

Paton and workers in the 1950s misidentified this as subsp. ***neglectum*** (Beeby) Schinz & Thell., which (though widespread in Ireland) appears to be absent.

S. emersum Rehm. Small Bur-reed

N Pools, ditches. Local: north only.

S. minimum Wallr. Least Bur-reed

N Peaty pools and ditches. Rare and very local.

N — Ballaugh Curraghs, *Wheldon*!: Sulby Curraghs, plentiful, *Paton*: Penny Pieces, near Ellanrhenny, *Howarth & Osvald*: Ballacain Dubs, Jurby, and pool to E: Lhen trench S of Ballamoar, *D & G*. **SW** — Eairy Dam, *D & G**.

Also listed by Hiern and an unlocalised specimen in hb OXF (W. E. Thompson, 1898, as ***S. angustifolium***, det. R. C. Palmer). ***S. angustifolium*** Michx., to which Paton also mistakenly referred his record, is a plant of mountain tarns and thus (though plentiful in Galloway) unlikely to be Manx.

TYPHACEAE

Typha latifolia L. False Bulrush

H Pools, swamps, river-margins. Local, but spreading: mainly around Douglas and Peel and in the north.

Though its pollen occurs in post-glacial peats at Strandhall (Bruce 1928) and near the Point of Ayre (Phillips 1967), it is hard to believe so conspicuous a plant could have passed unnoticed till the end of the last century had it been present then. The earliest records are by Ralfe (Tromode Dam) and Gasking, shortly before 1900. S. A. P. Kermode, who knew the north well, failed to find it; and even Paton, many years later, could list it there only for the Curraghs. Though abundant now in several northern ponds and on the SW edge of Lough Cranstal, in most of its stations it is clearly a very recent intruder — and destined to have a drastic impact ecologically. It is grown as an ornamental at Great Meadow House, whence may have come the isolated colonies at Billown and near Colby. Suggestively, too, one of the earliest stations was the pond near Government House. That it has no name in Manx and that the Bulrush Wainscot moth, ***Nonagria typhae*** Thunb., was first taken in Man only in 1928 (Chalmers-Hunt 1970) are further indicative of a new colonization, presumably from such planted stocks.

CYPERACEAE

Eriophorum angustifolium Honck.
Common Cotton-grass; Lus y Chadee

N Bogs, fens. Locally abundant.

E. vaginatum L. Harestail; Cannag

N Boggy moorland. Locally common, down to 350ft at The Eairy.

Scirpus cespitosus L. subsp. ***germanicus*** (Palla) Brodd. Deer Grass

N Boggy moorland. Locally abundant.

S. maritimus L. Sea Club-rush

N Brackish ponds, rock-pools. Very local.

[**N** — Lhen, *Stowell*. Correct?] **W** — Creglea, Dalby, *MD*. **SE** — Near Derby Castle, *Backwell's*, *Holt** (now gone): Onchan Harbour: Port Grenaugh (arrived since 1976), *RM*, *D & G*. **S** — Knock Rushen (now gone); NW Langness, plentiful, *Paton**! and spreading south along the driftline, *MD*: Derbyhaven, by hotel: Poyllvaaish, *D & G*.

S. lacustris L. Bulrush

N Pools. Very rare.

N — Near mouth of Lhen trench, *Ralfe*, *Paton** hb BM (now gone): Ballaugh, *Holt**: pool W of Sandygate, with ***Nymphaea***. Other records more probably belong to the next.

S. tabernaemontani C. C. Gmel. Greyish Bulrush; Shuin Vooar

N Peaty pools. Very local.

N — Pools in Andreas, *Forbes* (1848) as ***S. maritimus***, presumably this: (Andreas, *Talbot*): The Pollies, Jurby, (*Ralfe*), *D & G*: two Nappin ponds, Jurby, abundant, (*Ralfe*), *WFS**!: pool, Ballaugh Curraghs, *WFS*!: pool W of Sandygate; dubs by road and behind post office, Sandygate; Regaby dub; marshy field by The Guilcagh, Andreas: dub by Close Chairn, Sulby; Lough Cranstal, *D & G*. (Bracketed records were for ***S. lacustris*** agg.)

Possibly once at the Lhen top, which could explain Stowell's ***S. maritimus*** record. Scarcely maritime in Man: up to two miles or more from the sea.

S. setaceus L. Bristle Club-rush

N Marshes, seepages, dune slacks. Common. Calf.

S. cernuus Vahl Small Bristle Club-rush

N Bogs, marshes, cliff trickles, below 350ft and usually near the sea. Locally frequent: mainly south and south-east coasts. Calf.

S. fluitans L. Floating Spike-rush

N Pools, reservoirs. Local, apparently spreading.

N — Lhaggagh, Smeale; three Curraghs pools NE of Loughdhoo and two E and S of Close Taggart. **C** — Baldwin Reservoir, abundant; Kerrowdhoo Reservoir. **SE** — Union Mills, 1878, *Holt*: old quarry pool, Ballanard, abundant, *Holt*!: Kewaigue tip, brought in silt from Baldwin Reservoir, *BSBI*[2]!

A plant of acid (not, as usually, base-rich) water in Man, characteristically associated with ***Lythrum portula***, ***Veronica scutellata*** and ***Juncus bulbosus***.

Eleocharis quinqueflora (F. X. Hartm.) Schwarz

Few-flowered Spike-rush

N Base-rich marshes, dune slacks. Rare.

N — Andreas, *Backwell's*: near Ballaghaie, Jurby* (with ***Selaginella***) and pool on dunes to N; Ayres N of Keeilthusthag*. **C** — Below Maughold Head, *LSG*.

Holt's specimen which Bennett passed (JB (1896) 449) is ***E. multicaulis***, conf. A. Melderis.

E. multicaulis (Sm.) Sm. Many-stalked Spike-rush
N Bogs, rock-pools. Common. Calf.

E. palustris (L.) Roem. & Schult. subsp. ***vulgaris*** Walters
Common Spike-rush
N Edges of ponds, reservoirs and streams. Common in the north, local elsewhere. Calf.
Abundant in rock-pools at Creglea, Dalby.

E. uniglumis (Link) Schult. Slender Spike-rush
N Wet brackish ground. Very rare.
S — Scarlett, in plenty, *Paton corr.*, *BSBI*[1] hb K!

Blysmus rufus (Huds.) Link Chestnut Sedge
N Wet, saline ground by the sea. Very local near Castletown, elsewhere very rare.
N — Ramsey, *Backwell's*: Port Mooar*. **W** — Creglea, Dalby, *MD*. **S** — Derby Haven, *Backwell's*: NW Langness, *Holt**!: SE Langness, in several gullies, *D & G*.

Schoenus nigricans L. Bog-rush
N Coast marshes, rock-pools; base-rich flushes, fens. Very local.
N — Jurby, *Backwell's*!: Rhendhoo Curragh, Jurby, abundant, *D & G*!: garey and ditch by Ballamoar, Jurby. **W** — Creglea to Dalby Point, abundant, *MD*! **SW** — Cregneish, *Roeder**: two places on Mull Hill; Spanish Head, *LSG*. **S** — Spaldrick Bay, Port Erin, and slabs to W*; along E Langness.

Carex laevigata Sm. Smooth Sedge
N Moist shady places, especially by waterfalls. Local.
C — Meadow near the Dhoon, *Holt**: Dhoon Glen; Port Cornaa; Ballure Glen; near Glenmooar, Sulby Glen; Glen Roy. **SE** — N side of Douglas Bay, *Backwell's*: Groudle Glen; Castleward, *Holt*: cliff near Derby Castle, *AMS*: Garwick Glen. **SW** — Cregneish, *Roeder*: Barnell Reservoir.

C. distans L. Distant Sedge
N Wet coast rocks. Local: mainly east and south coasts. Calf.

C. punctata Gaud. Dotted Sedge
N Wet coast rocks, cliff-top bogs. Very local: central east coast.
C — Two places near Laxey, *Whellan*, *RWD*: Port Mooar, *JEL*. **SE** — Douglas Head, *Backwell's*: Onchan Harbour, abundant, *Holt**, *Whellan* hb K etc!, in bog above, *Holt*! (now overgrown) and on rocky shelf to west, *RWD*.

R. W. David searched all these localities in 1978 but failed to confirm the Port Mooar and Douglas Head records. These may have been errors for a small- and shiny-utricled form of ***C. distans***.

C. hostiana DC. Tawny Sedge
N Base-rich flushes, bogs. Rare.

N — Near Ballaghaie, Jurby*; field S of Cranstal, in plenty: W of The Dhoor*; brooghs S of Dog Mills, *D & G*. **W** — Creglea, *BSBI*[3]. **SE** — Near Groudle, *Holt**: Clay Head. **SW** — Greeba Curraghs NE of Kennaa, *WFS*!: above Fistard, at 450ft: Mull Hill, *MD*.

C. binervis Sm. Moor Sedge
N Heaths, moors. Common. Calf.

C. lepidocarpa Tausch Long-stalked Yellow Sedge
N Base-rich marshes. Very rare.

N — Brooghs S of Dog Mills, an odd dwarf form, *D & G**, det. A. O. Chater. **S** — Strandhall, in very small quantity, *M & S*!* hb K, det. E. Nelmes. A. C. Jermy has determined my material as subsp. ***scotica*** E. W. Davies, a race closer to ***C. demissa*** in fruit characters and probably the product of introgression.

C. demissa Hornem. Common Yellow Sedge
N Bogs, marshes, seepages, wet coast rocks, dune slacks. Common. Calf.

C. demissa × ***hostiana*** **SW** — Above Fistard, in quantity with both parents, conf. E. W. Davies* hb BM.

C. serotina Mérat subsp. ***serotina*** Dwarf Yellow Sedge
N Base-rich flushes. Very rare.

N — Wet field on W side of Ballamoar, Jurby, with ***Schoenus*** and ***Eriophorum***, 1957, hb CGE, conf. R. W. David. By inference (see below) also in field by The Guilcagh, Andreas.

subsp. ***pulchella*** (Lönnr.) Van Ooststr. (*C. scandinavica* E. W. Davies)
N Damp dune hollows. Very local.

N — Inner Ayres between Rue Point and Ballaghennie, locally common* (det. R. W. David & A. O. Chater); Sartfield.

A mainly northern race which continues down the west coasts to Dorset.

C. extensa Gooden. Saltmarsh Sedge
N Rock-pools. Occasional.

C — Port Mooar, *WFS*!: Port Cornaa. **W** — Peel Castle, var. ***pumila*** Anderss. (dwarf, very glaucous)* hb BM; Niarbyl to Creglea. **SE** — Onchan Harbour, *Holt**, *RWD*! **S** — Scarlett, *Paton**!: E Langness, *BSBI*[1], *RWD*!: Port St. Mary Bay; Spaldrick Bay.

Also an unlocalised specimen collected by Jowett in 1836 in hb K.

C. extensa* × *serotina **N** — Boggy field by The Guilcagh, Andreas, 1975, hb BM, det. A. O. Chater, R. W. David & A. C. Jermy. A very rare cross.

C. sylvatica Huds. Wood Sedge

NH Glens, typically by waterfalls. Rare.

C — Ballure Glen, *Backwell's*!: Dhoon Glen, *Holt**, *MBB*!: bottom of Narradale in Ballameanagh grounds, *D & G*!. **SE** — Lhen Coan, Groudle Glen. **W** — Glen Maye, *BSBI*[1]!

Elsewhere probably only naturalised, a relic of sowing as a shade-loving ornamental:—

C — Port Lewaigue, roadside outside house. **SE** — Douglas, *Talbot**!: Summerhill Glen, Onchan; Nunnery grounds: Braddan old churchyard, *WFS*!: near Kirby House, Saddle Road, Braddan, with ***C. pendula***, *LSG*.

C. rostrata Stokes Bottle Sedge

N Peaty ditches, pools, bogs, dune slacks. Common in the northern and central curraghs, rare elsewhere.

Robust plants with narrower fruits from Curragh-y-Cowle, Smeale and Baldwin Reservoir (both hb BM).

C. vesicaria L. Bladder Sedge

N Swamps. Very rare.

SE — Union Mills, *Holt** (as ***C. rostrata***, 1881; as ***C.*** × ***involuta***, 1917) conf. A. C. Jermy.

C. riparia Curt. Great Pond Sedge

N Reedswamp. Very local.

N — Lough Cranstal, locally dominant, *Paton**!

Also an unlocalised record by Holt (Bennett 1896). A Germanic species.

C. acutiformis Ehrh. Pond Sedge

H? Ditches on base-rich soil. Extinct?

S — Great Meadow, near Castletown, 1946, *Paton* hb BM. A patch grew for some years beside Great Meadow House*, the one-time summer residence of the Governor, from which it may well have escaped (it is a popular water-garden ornamental). Presumably Paton's locality was this, not the Great Meadow itself.

Records by Wattam (1901) and Mosley & Wattam (1903) were doubtless errors for ***C. rostrata.***

C. pendula Huds. (Drooping Sedge), a landscape gardening favourite, is naturalised in the Nunnery grounds, Groudle and Bishopscourt grounds and glens, about Cronkbourne, on the Saddle Road, Braddan, and on the Killane bank near Ballacain. It was recorded near Derby Castle in the 1850s.

C. pallescens L. Pale Sedge

N Boggy meadows. Very rare.

N — Rhendhoo, Jurby, 1937, *Paton**: field NNW of Kella, Sulby Curraghs, *WHH* hb BM! **C** — Bottom of Narradale road, *MD*.

C. panicea L. Carnation Sedge

N Bogs, wet grassy places. Common. Calf.

C. flacca Schreb. Glaucous Sedge

N Marshes, bogs, bases of railway cuttings, rock-pools (Onchan Harbour); dry calcareous turf (Billown quarries). Common. Calf.

C. hirta L. Hairy Sedge

NC Marshes, water-sides, glens; bare trampled ground. Locally frequent, in places abundant, avoiding all moister districts and preferring the coast: north, northern west coast, Peel area and south-east.

C. pilulifera L. Pill Sedge

N Dry heather moors, bogs. Locally abundant. Calf.

C. caryophyllea Latourr. Spring Sedge

N Dry turf mainly on the coast. Local.

N — Brooghs W of Ballaugh, abundant: Ayres near Ballakinnag, *MD*. **W** — Peel golf links*; Dalby Point. **SW** — Eairy 'deads', *D & G*. **S** — Bradda Head: E Langness, in two places; Ronaldsway; Scarlett, *LSG*.

Also recorded by Forbes (1831 specimen hb K), as 'common', and Mosley & Wattam (1903).

C. nigra (L.) Reichard Common Sedge

N Bogs, fens, wet grassy places. Common. Calf.

A tall form in Greeba Curraghs NE of Kennaa, *WFS**!, is 'cf var. ***strictiformis*** L. H. Bailey' but another in The Lhaggagh, Smeale, merely the type, det. A. C. Jermy. A similar form was collected by Forbes in 1834 (hb K) and queried as ***C. elata*** All. in Watson (1837). A form with elliptic-lanceolate fruits and cuspidate glumes by Ballamoar, Jurby, is var. ***stenocarpa*** (Kükenthal), det. A. C. Jermy, who considers this a product of ancient introgression with ***C. acuta*** L.

C. paniculata L. Tussock Sedge

N Alder-willow swamps. Rare: mainly central valley.

N — By large pit, Jurby, *Holt**: Berrag Dub, Sandygate, *Paton**!

(same station?) and abundant in boggy hollow nearby, *D & G*. **W** — Ballalough curragh, *Holt**, and Close y Garey curragh, Peel, *D & G*: Congary curragh, Peel, one tussock. **SW** — Greeba Curraghs W and S of Northop and by Crosby, very local.

C. diandra Schrank — Lesser Fox Sedge

N Open fens. Very local.

N — Rhendhoo curragh, Jurby!; by the Guilcagh, Andreas!; Ballaugh Curraghs behind the Wildlife Park; Loughcroute, Jurby East; The Pollies, Jurby; boggy hollow by Berrag Dub, Sandygate, *D & G*.

C. otrubae Podp. — Fox Sedge

N Coast rocks, wet clayey places near the sea. Local: mainly east and south coasts.

N — Ramsey Mooragh, *Holt*: Killane mouth, *WFS*! **C** — Port Mooar (to Gob-ny-Garvain, *D & G*); Port Cornaa. **SE** — Port Groudle; Port Grenaugh: Port Garwick, *RWD*. **S** — Langness; Scarlett; near Ballakeigan, Castletown, one tuft: Gansey Point, Port St. Mary, *MD*.

C. disticha Huds. — Brown Sedge

N Alluvial meadows, ditches. Very local.

SW — By Ballamodha chapel, *D & G*. **S** — Strandhall, abundant, *M & S*!: Great Meadow, abundant*; Scarlett marsh; Grenaby road near Ballakewin.

Indicated for vice-county 71 by Druce (1932), apparently a slip.

C. arenaria L. — Sand Sedge

N Sandy ground mainly near the sea, dry coast turf. Locally abundant in the north and near Castletown, elsewhere rare (on four scattered beaches).

[***C. maritima*** Gunn. — Curved Sedge

A specimen in hb Talbot thus labelled was accepted by Paton (1933). As pointed out by Whellan, BEC (1946-7) 317, it is not this but probably **C. ovalis**.]

[***C. spicata*** Huds. — Spiked Sedge

Bog, Eairy Dam, *BSBI*[1] (Allen, 1954). The specimen proved on re-examination to be ***C. echinata***, a peculiarly robust state of which occurs thereabouts. Osvald (1941) similarly mistook this for ***C. otrubae***.]

C. muricata L. subsp. ***lamprocarpa*** Čelak. (*C. pairaei* F. W. Schultz) — Lesser Spiked Sedge

C Dry banks, roadsides. Local round Castletown, thinly scattered elsewhere; usually only a tuft or two. Apparently spreading. Collected by Talbot c 1866.

[***C. elongata*** L. Gingerbread Sedge
Listed by Wattam (1901) and Mosley & Wattam (1903), without details. Undoubtedly errors.]

C. echinata Murr. Star Sedge
N Bogs, moors. Locally abundant. Calf.

C. remota L. Remote Sedge
N Damp shady places. Local: southern streams and (certain) east coast glens.

C. curta Gooden. White Sedge
N Bogs. Very rare.

C — NW of Ballameanagh Beg, Baldrine, at 350ft, *M & S* hb K.
SW — Greeba Curraghs NW of Crosby Station, one small patch, *D & G**!

C. ovalis Gooden Oval Sedge
N Marshes, wet pastures, bogs, dune slacks. Frequent. Calf.

[***C. pauciflora*** Lightf. Few-flowered Sedge
Wet meadow, Ballaugh Curraghs N of Gob y Volley, *Erdtman* (1925). Not entirely unlikely, but confirmation certainly needed.]

C. pulicaris L. Flea Sedge
N Bogs, especially in the hills. Locally frequent. Calf (unusually common).

C. dioica L. Separate-headed Sedge
N Fens. Very rare.

N — NW corner of Loughcroute, Jurby East*; Rhendhoo Curragh, Jurby, *D & G*.

Discovered in both places in 1978, in tiny quantity. The specimen in hb Talbot accepted by Paton (1933) as this is ***C. pulicaris***.

GRAMINEAE

Phragmites australis (Cav.) Trin. ex Steudel (*P. communis* Trin.) Reed
N Marshes, ditches, hedges, wet cliffs. Locally frequent.

Molinia caerulea (L.) Moench Purple Moor-grass
N Curraghs, wet heaths, moors. Common. Calf.

Sieglingia decumbens (L.) Bernh. Heath Grass
N Dry heathy grassland, cliff turf, railway banks. Common. Calf.

Glyceria fluitans (L.) R. Br. Flote Grass
N Marshes, watersides, bogs. Locally frequent. Calf.

G. fluitans* × *plicata (***G.* × *pedicellata*** Towns.) Locally frequent, in places abundant, mainly in the north and south, often in the absence of both parents. A linear-leaved submerged state is profuse in Baldwin Reservoir.

G. plicata Fr. Sweet-grass
N Marshes, especially on clay near the sea. Local and much less widespread than ***G.* × *pedicellata***.

G. declinata Bréb. Small Flote Grass
N Flushes, muddy margins of streams and pools. Frequent, with a submaritime trend.

Festuca pratensis Huds. Meadow Fescue
D Meadows, sown pastures. Locally common.

F. arundinacea Schreb. Tall Fescue
N Banks of ditches and streams, roadsides. Local: mainly in the south-east (especially in alluvial areas, with ***Carex disticha***) and round the margins of Sulby Curraghs.

F. altissima All. Wood Fescue
N Rocky woods. Very rare.

C — Dhoon Glen, locally abundant, *Whellan*, det. C. E. Hubbard, BEC (1946-7) 320.

F. rubra L. subsp. ***rubra*** Red Fescue
NC Maritime turf; roadsides, walls. Very common. Calf.

Subsp. ***pruinosa*** (Hackel) Piper, with glaucous foliage and glabrous spikelets, is frequent on rocks and cliffs exposed to spray. Var. ***glaucescens*** (Heg. & Heer) Richt., less glaucous and with scabrous lemmas, occurs under Peel Castle* (det. W. O. Howarth) and in a form with spikelets fully pubescent, also on the Cumberland coast, on Dalby Point* (det. Howarth) and the Calf.

Subsp. ***arenaria*** (Osbeck) Syme is abundant on the sandy north coast.

F. ovina L. Sheep's Fescue
N Acid grassland, heather moor, dunes. Very common. Calf.

F. vivipara (L.) Sm. Viviparous Fescue
N Mountains. Very rare, perhaps extinct.

C — Hill NE of Snaefell, 1774 or 5, *Davies.*

× ***Festulolium loliaceum*** (Huds.) P. Fourn. (***F. pratensis*** × ***Lolium perenne***)
N — Ellanrhennie, *D & G**; lucerne field N of Cranstal, *MD.* **S** — Scarlett, *BSBI*[1]! hb BIRM.

Lolium perenne L. Perennial Rye-grass
CD Sown grassland, roadsides, waste ground. Very common. Calf.

Lolium multiflorum Lam. (Italian Rye-grass) and its fertile cross with the above, ***L.*** × ***hybridum*** Hausskn. ('Short Rotation Rye-grass'), are extensively sown in leys and often naturalised on field-margins. ***L. temulentum*** L. (Darnel), a one-time casual in crops recorded by Gasking and Holt, is now staging a come-back as a bird-seed derivative, with four records since 1962.

[***Vulpia fasciculata*** (Forsk.) Samp. (*V. membranacea* auct.) Dune Fescue
Listed by Mosley & Wattam (1903), clearly in error for the next. But this is abundant on some of the coasts opposite and ought to be in Man.]

V. bromoides (L.) Gray Squirrel-tail Fescue
NC Dry heathland; wall-tops, roadsides, cornfields. Frequent, locally abundant. Calf.

V. myuros (L.) C. C. Gmel. Ratstail Fescue
C Walls, bare waste ground. Rare and transient.
N — Andreas, 1924, *Paton*: Ballaugh, 1968, *NHAS*: track, Ballaugh Curraghs, 1974, *D & G.* **SE** — Near Onchan Church, 1957, one plant*. **S** — Malew churchyard, 1965, *LSG.*
Also an unlocalised record by Holt (Bennett, JB (1905) suppl. 107). A southern species spreading rapidly (along railway tracks) in W Wales.

Puccinellia maritima (Huds.) Parl. Sea Meadow-grass
N Salt marshes. Local.

P. distans (L.) Parl. Reflexed Meadow-grass
N Salt marshes. Very rare.
S — By Poyllvaaish farm, one patch, *WFS*!*

Catapodium rigidum (L.) C. E. Hubbard Fern Grass
NC Dry maritime turf, dunes; walls, roadsides. Locally common in Castletown-Ballasalla area, reappearing on the Ayres.

C. marinum (L.) C. E. Hubbard Darnel Fescue

N Bare ground by the sea and on walls up to a mile inland. Locally common but rare along the east coast. Calf.

Poa annua L. Annual Meadow-grass

NCD Mountain summits; artificial grassland, waste ground. Very common. Calf.

Apparently native on the summits of North Barrule (abundant) and Snaefell.

P. nemoralis L. Wood Meadow-grass

H Banks and walls near gardens. Local

N — Farm NE of Ellanbane. **C** — Port Lewaigue!; near Claughbane, *WHH*!: W of Milntown; Glen Roy. **SE** — Keristal, *WFS*!: Nunnery; N Onchan. **SW** — Kennaa, St. John's.

As in Kerry, always near habitations and absent from woodland. It was formerly popular for sowing in shady places (cf ***Carex sylvatica***).

P. compressa L. Flattened Meadow-grass

C Mortared walls, especially of bridges. Rare. First record 1907.

N — The Cronk, *BSBI*[2]! **SE** — Braddan, *Holt**: back of Manx Museum, *BSBI*[1]! hb K: Kewaigue, *WFS*!

P. pratensis L. Smooth Meadow-grass

NCD Rough grassland, meadows, roadsides. Very common.

P. subcaerulea Sm. Blueish Meadow-grass

N Moist hill pastures, dunes. Frequency uncertain, probably common. Best told by its stocky habit, acuminate glumes and hairy-edged leaves.

P. trivialis L. Rough Meadow-grass

NC Marshes, ditches; cultivated and waste ground. Common. Calf.

P. chaixii Vill. (Broad-leaved Meadow-grass), a shade ornamental, formerly grew in Braddan old cemetery, *Holt**.

Catabrosa aquatica (L.) Beauv. Water Whorl-grass

N Marshes near the sea. Rare and very local.

N — [Ditch from Lough Cranstal to Ayres, *Moore* (1931).] SW of Lhen, *D & G*. **S** — NW Langness, *Gasking* hb BM, *Holt** etc! E Langness, near Tower, *MD*.

subsp. ***minor*** (Bab.) Perring & Sell, a dwarf race apparently endemic to the north and west of the British Isles, occurs with the type on NW Langness, *M & S* hb K, and alone at Ronaldsway.

Dactylis glomerata L. Cocksfoot

ND Sea cliffs; roadsides, sown grassland. Very common. Calf.

Glaucous-leaved plants are frequent by the sea, appearing native; but these lack the genetic dwarfness of Atlantic coast populations elsewhere, which approach a Mediterranean subspecies.

Cynosurus cristatus L. Crested Dogstail

NC Damp acid grassland; dry maritime turf. Common.

A regular constituent of the coast sward — perhaps a separate ecotype.

C. echinatus L. (Rough Dogstail) turned up in a large patch under a hedge by Ramsey Harbour, 1979, *RWD*.

Briza media L. Quaking Grass

N Base-rich flushes, damp meadows, calcareous spoil-heaps. Local.

B. maxima L. (Giant Quaking Grass), grown for flower arrangement, is not uncommon on roadsides etc.

Melica uniflora Retz. Wood Melick

N Glens, shady hedgebanks. Local.

C — Ballaugh; Ballure Glen, *Holt*: Glen Shogyl, Ravensdale, *Hoyle*: Churchtown, Lezayre; Albert Tower; Tholt-y-Will, *LSG*. **W** — Glen Maye, *LSG*. **SE** — Groudle Glen, *Holt*, *LSG*: Castletown Road, *Holt*: bottom of Richmond Hill, *LSG*. **S** — Silverdale (N.T.), *LSG*. Also listed by Gasking. Oddly unrecorded by Paton.

Perhaps accidentally introduced in some of these stations. Nowhere in any quantity.

Bromus erectus Huds. (Upright Brome), a native of calcareous grassland, was found singly on Jurby old airfield, 1974, *JH**, det. A. Melderis. A similar solitary clump recently appeared in Guernsey.

B. ramosus Huds. Hairy Brome

N Shady places on basic soils. Very rare.

W — Glen Maye, on clay at foot of relic oak-hazel wood. **S** — Ballahott quarry, Ballasalla, *LSG*, and spinney to E*.

Also listed by Gasking (1890) and probably erroneously by Mosley & Wattam (1903).

B. sterilis L. Barren Brome

N C Roadsides, walls, waste places. Locally frequent.

Once seen on a wet rock-ledge on South Barrule (as in the Highlands and Ireland), *LSG*.

B. hordeaceus L. subsp. ***hordeaceus*** (*B. mollis* L.) Soft Brome
NCD Maritime turf; sown grassland, roadsides. Common.

subsp. ***ferronii*** (Mabille) P. M. Smith
N Cliffs and rocks by the sea. Very local. Calf.

W — Peel Castle* hb BM†. **SE** — Onchan Head, Holt*, *WHH* hb BM†: Port Soderick, *BSBI*[2]!†. **SW** — Calf, fairly plentiful, *SCM*. (†conf. A. Melderis)

A maritime race of S England, W Wales and Kirkcudbrightshire, not yet detected in Ireland.

B.* × *pseudothominii P. M. Smith (*B. thominii* auct.)
C Roadsides, sown grassland. Occasional, usually singly.

A series of hybrid derivatives of ***B. hordeaceus*** subsp. ***hordeaceus*** and ***B. lepidus***, like the latter probably wholly introduced with grass seed. There is a specimen in hb Talbot collected at Ballasalla in 1866.

B. lepidus Holmberg Slender Brome
C Roadsides, leys, walls, waste ground. Occasional, usually singly.

Collected by Holt in 1883 (Port Soderick cliffs, hb BM) and 1913 (Glen Maye*), both as '***B. mollis*** var. ***glabrescens***'.

B. racemosus L. (Smooth Brome) has been collected from a field W of Sandygate, *M & S* hb K, det. C. E. Hubbard. Probably a casual. Other records (eg Hiern 1897) are doubtful.

B. commutatus Schrad. Meadow Brome
C Sown grassland. Rare or overlooked.

SE — Meadows, Union Mills, 1918, *Holt** (as ***B. racemosus***), det. P. M. Smith. **S** — Pastures, Langness, 1918, *Holt**, conf. T. G. Tutin, P. M. Smith.

B. pseudosecalinus P. M. Smith (False Rye Brome), a contaminant of small-seeded pasture grasses, was collected by Holt* in 1883 on field edges above Port Soderick cliffs, det. P. M. Smith.

[***B. secalinus*** L. (Rye Brome) has been recorded in error.]

Brachypodium sylvaticum (Huds.) Beauv. Slender False Brome
N Glens, hedgebanks, stream banks, sea cliffs. Locally abundant.

Widespread on cliffs and dry stony places by the sea in a shorter, more rigid and erect form with shorter and rougher leaves, also on the Cumberland coast and possibly a distinct ecotype.

[***B. pinnatum*** (L.) Beauv. Tor-grass
Listed, without details, by the very unreliable Wattam (1899).]

Elymus repens (L.) Gould Common Couch; Faiyr Voddee
NC Salt marshes, shingle banks (frequent); cultivated and waste ground. Common.

A glaucous form is plentiful in saline turf at Port Cornaa (det. A. Melderis). Awned specimens, sometimes mistaken for ***E. caninus*** (L.) L., are not uncommon.

E. farctus (Viv.) Runemark ex Melderis Sand Couch
N Shores, on sand, stones and mud. Frequent in the north and E of Castletown, very rare elsewhere.

Uncharacteristically, only SW of the Lhen mouth does this form a separate zone in Man and play a part in stabilising fore-dunes, ***Leymus arenarius*** substituting for it in this. A form with ultra-large spikelets occurs on Ramsey foreshore. Watson (1883) claimed to have received from a Liverpool botanist, Robert Brown, a specimen of '***Triticum acutum***', a name then usually given to ***E. farctus*** × ***pycnanthus***; but as ***E. pycnanthus*** (*Agropyron pungens*) has yet to be found in Man, this was surely a mistake.

Leymus arenarius (L.) Hochst. Lyme Grass
N Sandy foreshores. Very local, but spreading: north coast.

Though recorded by Garner (1878, 69), this was not noted again till 1950 — when Howarth found a solitary clump at the mouth of the Killane. In 1952 he located two further patches at Sartfield. By the 1960s it was in plenty at The Lhen and occurred at intervals southwards to beyond The Cronk. It now extends, intermittently, to the Point of Ayre and round to Port Cranstal. As it is known to be spreading round the Irish Sea generally and has arrived on the Galloway and Co Down coasts only in recent years, this evidently represents a recolonisation.

Hordeum secalinum Schreb. (Meadow Barley) occurred as a casual in a ley near Malew church, 1968, *LSG*.

H. murinum L. Wall Barley
C Waste ground, especially near the sea. Locally frequent.

[***H. marinum*** Huds. Sea Barley
Listed by Mosley & Wattam (1903). An error (or misprint) for the above.]

Koeleria macrantha (Ledeb.) Schultes (*K. cristata* (L.) Pers. p.p.)
Crested Hair-grass
N Dry maritime turf, rarely also in hill grassland. Frequent. Calf.

Populations on the Atlantic fringe of Europe, especially on dunes, include strongly hairy plants which were formerly considered a separate species, ***K. supra-arenaria*** Dumort. (*K. albescens* auct.). Specimens corresponding to this were collected in Jurby by Paton* hb BM. The same name was given by Wheldon, Proc LBS (1920) 16, to a gathering from cliffs N of Peel, hb NMW (later det. W. O. Howarth, BEC (1932) 41, as ***K. pseudocristata*** Domin). A specimen of Holt's in hb BM from Douglas Head was also pronounced by Domin to be his ***K. gracilis*** subsp. ***villulosa.*** Although British botanists no longer find these variants worthy of taxonomic recognition, this tendency to ultra-hairiness in Man has interesting parallels in the Manx west coast populations of ***Euphrasia tetraquetra***, ***Thymus praecox*** and ***Festuca rubra***.

Trisetum flavescens (L.) Beauv. Yellow Oat
NC Dry grassland, mainly near the sea; walls. Local.

N — Andreas, *Paton*!: Ayres near Rue Point, *BSBI*[1]. **W** — Glen Maye, *Wheldon*: N Peel. **SE** — Onchan; Douglas Head, abundant, *Holt*: railway bank S of Kewaigue, abundant. **SW** — Eairy, *BSBI*[1]. **S** — Scarlett, *Paton*! (abundant): Castletown links, *BSBI*[1]!: Billown quarries.

Avena fatua L. (Wild Oat) was collected at Laxey in 1912 by *Holt**. Other undocumented records by Watson (1883) and Mosley & Wattam (1903) must be regarded as doubtful. ***A. sativa*** L. (Oat) is common as a casual.

A. strigosa Schreb. Black Oat
C or D Cultivated fields. Very local.

N — Dog Mills, *BSBI*[1] hb K: S of Sandygate, one plant, 1967: weed on Ballaquane and Ballabane farms, Andreas, *JH* (now gone): Ramsey tip, *MD*. **SE** — Cliff near Derby Castle, 1915, *Holt**. **S** — Castletown, rare in one field, 1946, *Whellan* hb K: Ballavell, Malew, 1976, *JB*.

Perhaps a relic of cultivation: known also as 'Sand Oat' or 'Bristle Oat', it was formerly sown with or in place of ***A. sativa*** in harsher areas of the North and West. This, surely (rather than ***Bromus secalinus***, as suggested by Raven, 1950), was the 'Dank or Oat-grass, *Festuca altera*', which Ray and Willoughby noted among corn in the Island on their 1660 visit (*Catalogus*, 103).

[***Helictotrichon pratense*** (L.) Pilg. Meadow Oat
Listed by McNab (Watson, 1832). Clearly an error for the next, which he did not record.]

H. pubescens (Huds.) Pilg. Downy Oat
N Dry banks on or near the coast. Local.

Arrhenatherum elatius (L.) Beauv. ex J. & C. Presl False Oat
NC Artificial grassland, roadsides, beaches. Very common.

As elsewhere on the Atlantic fringe, var. ***bulbosum*** (Willd.) Spenn. overwhelmingly predominates. The type indeed may not be indigenous.

Holcus lanatus L. Yorkshire Fog
NC Meadows, pastures, waste places. Very common. Calf.

H. mollis L. Creeping Soft-grass
N Dry shady and heathy places. Common.
var. ***parviflorus*** Parn. **SW** — abundant on gorse heath, Cronk ny Arrey Laa, *Wheldon & Wilson* hb NMW, BEC (1923) 411.

Deschampsia cespitosa (L.) Beauv. Tufted Hair-grass
N Glens, curraghs, wet fields. Locally abundant.

D. flexuosa (L.) Trin. Wavy Hair-grass
N Heaths, moors. Locally abundant.
The dwarfer arctic-alpine race with large spikelets, subsp. ***montana*** (L.) A. & D. Löve, occurs on the summit slopes of Snaefell, *WHH*!*.

Aira praecox L. Small Hair-grass
N Dry hedgebanks, wall tops, dunes. Locally abundant. Calf.

A. caryophyllea L. Silver Hair-grass
N Sandy ground, wall tops. Very common. Calf.

Ammophila arenaria (L.) Link Marram ('Bent' in Man); Shaslagh
N Abundant along all sandy stretches of coastline.
Moore (1931) noted that on the Ayres the regular uprooting and scything of this for use as thatching inhibited upward growth, thereby enhancing stabilisation of the dunes.

Calamagrostis epigejos (L.) Roth Bush Grass
N Cliff-tops, fens and shady places on clay. Very rare.
N — Andreas, very rare, *Backwell's*. **SE** — Port Soldrick, a large patch, *LSG*!*.
Very rare in Ireland and in scattered isolated stations up the west coast of Scotland.

Agrostis canina L. subsp. ***canina*** Brown Bent
N Marshes, ditches. Common.

subsp. ***montana*** (Hartm.) Hartm.
N Heaths, dry hill grassland. Frequent.

A. tenuis Sibth. Fine Bent
N Dry acid grassland. Very common. Calf.

A. gigantea Roth Black Bent
C Roadsides, cultivated and waste ground. Occasional.

A. stolonifera L. White Bent
N Sea cliffs, salt marshes (var. ***stolonifera***); marshes, swamps, fens (var. ***palustris*** (Huds.) Farw.). Common. Calf.

[***Apera spica-venti*** (L.) Beauv. Silky Bent
Marked for Man in Watson (1832, 313), but not repeated in Watson's subsequent works.]

Phleum bertolonii DC. Catstail
N Dry turf and walls near the sea. Very local: mainly south-east corner.

N — Andreas-Bride road, *MD*. **SE** — Port Grenaugh. **S** — Derbyhaven, *M & S* hb K: S of Cass-ny-Hawin; midway between Ballasalla and Ronaldsway; Chapel Hill, Balladoole, abundant; Poyllvaaish beach; Kentraugh.

A small form of the next is sown in leys and is liable to be mistaken for this.

P. pratense L. Timothy
N?D Meadows; pastures, leys. Frequent.

Perhaps native in alluvial meadows along the south coast.

P. arenarium L. Sand Catstail
N Dunes. Locally frequent.

Also, unexpectedly, by Marine Drive between Douglas Head and Port Soderick, *Holt*, *Paton*.

Alopecurus myosuroides Huds. (Slender Foxtail) occurred casually, in some quantity, in a cornfield near Kiondroghad, Andreas, 1956, *WHH**.

A. pratensis L. Meadow Foxtail
D Artificial grassland. Occasional, usually in small patches, sometimes singly.

A. geniculatus L. Marsh Foxtail
N Marshes, bogs, pools, ditches, damp grassland and tracks. Common. Calf.

Anthoxanthum odoratum L. Sweet Vernal Grass
N Meadows, heaths, moors, marshes. Very common. Calf.

Phalaris arundinacea L. Reed-grass
N Swamps, ditches, stream-banks. Common in the north, local elsewhere.

The ornamental form, var. ***picta*** L. (Gardener's Garters), is naturalised in several places.

P. canariensis L. (Canary Grass), a bird-seed casual, is sometimes abundant on tips and shore-lines near houses. Records for it date from 1866.

Parapholis strigosa (Dumort.) C. E. Hubbard Sea Hard-grass
N Short salt-marsh turf. Rare.

N — Ramsey Mooragh, 1878, *Holt**: river bank near Ramsey station. **C** — Port Cornaa. **S** — Poyllvaaish, *Holt*: inner harbour, Castletown. Also listed by Robinson (1882) from one (?) unstated locality.

In YLM (1902) 20, in an odd lapse, Holt ascribed his two localities to ***Spartina stricta*** (Ait.) Roth — another salt-marsh grass hardly likely to occur in Man. Paton suggested he intended to write ***Nardus stricta***; but he overlooked that the Mooragh plant is in hb Holt, rightly named, and in a later list of Manx grasses in Proc (1911) 466 Holt mentions only ***P. strigosa***.

Nardus stricta L. Mat Grass
N Dry heaths, moors. Locally abundant.

Spartina anglica C. E. Hubbard (*S. townsendii* auct.)
Common Cord-grass
D? Intertidal mudflats. Very rare, but just arrived and spreading.

C — Sea-washed rock shelf E of Port Mooar, 1975. **S** — W Langness, near ruined farm, one patch of some thirty culms, 1972, *MD** hb DBN, det. P. J. Boyle: Derby Haven, 1976; Poyllvaaish, 1977, *D & G*. Dates are when first noticed.

This species originated (by hybridization followed by chromosome doubling) on Southampton Water sometime last century. It has since spread rapidly round the British and Irish coasts, aided by extensive planting as a mud-binder. Its arrival in the Irish Sea is probably due to the latter (Ribble estuary 1932, Galloway 1946), but its rapid spread in Galloway and NE Ireland in recent years has apparently been spontaneous. Its advent in Man has long been expected and its ecological impact could be dramatic.

Panicum mileaceum L. (Common Millet) is an increasing bird-seed casual on tips and waste ground. ***Setaria italica*** (L.) Beauv. (Foxtail Millet), also a bird-seed casual, occurred on Ramsey tip, 1961, *MBB**. ***Arundinaria japonica*** Sieb. & Zucc. (Bamboo) is naturalised in the lanes to Port Garwick and Port Mooar.

APPENDIX ONE

Species and Subspecies which may well occur in Man
(*may occur as a *native* — at present known only as an introduction)

Isoetes lacustris L.	Common Quillwort
Equisetum hyemale L.	Dutch Rush
Hymenophyllum tunbrigense (L.) Sm.	Tunbridge Filmy Fern
Asplenium billotii F. W. Schultz	Lanceolate Spleenwort
Dryopteris assimilis S. Walker	Dwarf Male Fern
Thelypteris thelypteroides (Michx.) Holub	Marsh Fern
Ophioglossum azoricum C. Presl (*O. vulgatum* subsp. *ambiguum* (C. & G.) E. F. Warb.)	Small Adder's Tongue
Ranunculus auricomus L.	Wood Goldilocks
Ranunculus baudotii Godr.	Seaside Water Crowfoot
Corydalis claviculata (L.) DC.	Climbing Corydalis
Fumaria densiflora DC. (*F. micrantha* Lag.)	a Fumitory
Erophila verna subsp. ***spathulata*** (A. F. Láng) S. M. Walters	Broad Whitlow Grass
Rorippa palustris (L.) Bess.	Marsh Yellow Cress
Elatine hexandra (Lapierre) DC.	Waterwort
Stellaria pallida (Dumort.) Piré	Lesser Chickweed
S. neglecta Weihe	Greater Chickweed
Montia fontana L. subsp. ***fontana***	Blinks: northern race
Frangula alnus Mill.	Alder Buckthorn
Geranium pyrenaicum Burm. f.	Pyrenean Cranesbill
Rubus caesius L.	Dewberry
Geum rivale L.	Water Avens
Alchemilla filicaulis subsp. ***vestita*** (Buser) M. E. Bradshaw	a Lady's Mantle
A. xanthochlora Rothm.	a Lady's Mantle
Saxifraga stellaris L.	Starry Saxifrage
S. hypnoides L.	Mossy Saxifrage
Parnassia palustris L.	Grass of Parnassus
Drosera anglica Huds.	Great Sundew
D. intermedia Hayne	Long-leaved Sundew
Apium graveolens L.	Wild Celery
Berula erecta (Huds.) Coville	Lesser Water Parsnip
Ligusticum scoticum L.	Lovage
Oenanthe aquatica (L.) Poir.	Fine-leaved Water Dropwort
Polygonum minus Huds.	Least Water-pepper
Rumex hydrolapathum Huds.	Great Water Dock
Salix triandra L.	Almond Willow
Andromeda polifolia L.	Bog Rosemary
Pyrola rotundifolia subsp. ***maritima*** (Kenyon) E. F. Warb.	Round-leaved Wintergreen

Centaurium pulchellum (Sw.) Druce	Slender Centaury
Lithospermum officinale L.	Common Gromwell
Euphrasia scottica Wettst.	an Eyebright
E. rostkoviana Hayne	an Eyebright
Orobanche hederae Duby	Ivy Broomrape
Utricularia intermedia Hayne	Irish Bladderwort
Clinopodium vulgare L.	Wild Basil
****Scutellaria galericulata*** L.	Common Skullcap
Galium boreale L.	Northern Bedstraw
G. uliginosum L.	Fen Bedstraw
Rubia peregrina L.	Wild Madder
****Viburnum opulus*** L.	Guelder Rose
Senecio viscosus L.	Sticky Groundsel
Chamaemelum nobile (L.) All.	Common Chamomile
Carduus acanthoides L.	Welted Thistle
Cirsium heterophyllum (L.) Hill	Melancholy Thistle
C. dissectum (L.) Hill	Meadow Thistle
Taraxacum palustre (Lyons) Symons agg.	Fen Dandelion
Zostera noltii Hornem.	Dwarf Eel-grass
Potamogeton coloratus Hornem.	Plantain-leaved Pondweed
P. lucens L.	Shining Pondweed
P. gramineus L.	Various-leaved Pondweed
P. praelongus Wulf.	Long-stalked Pondweed
P. pusillus L.	Lesser Pondweed
P. obtusifolius Mert. & Koch	Blunt-leaved Pondweed
Ruppia spp.	Tassel Pondweeds
Juncus inflexus L.	Hard Rush
J. subnodulosus Schrank	Fen Rush
Epipactis palustris (L.) Crantz	Marsh Helleborine
E. helleborine (L.) Crantz	Common Helleborine
E. phyllanthes G. E. Sm.	Green-flowered Helleborine
Hammarbya paludosa (L.) Kuntze	Bog Orchid
Leucorchis albida (L.) Schur	Small White Orchid
Dactylorhiza incarnata subsp. ***pulchella*** (Druce) Soó	Early Marsh Orchid: northern race
D. kerryensis (Wilmott) Hunt & Summerh.	Irish Marsh Orchid
Lemna gibba L.	Fat Duckweed
Eriophorum latifolium Hoppe	Broad-leaved Bog Cotton
Scirpus sylvaticus L.	Wood Club Rush
Eleocharis acicularis (L.) Roem. & Schult.	Needle Spike-rush
****Carex acutiformis*** Ehrh.	Pond Sedge
C. limosa L.	Bog Sedge
C. lasiocarpa Ehrh.	Slender-leaved Sedge
C. elata All.	Tufted Sedge
C. acuta L.	Graceful Sedge

C. aquatilis Wahlenb.	Straight-leaved Sedge
C. bigelowii Torr. ex Schwein.	Stiff Sedge
C. spicata Huds.	Spiked Sedge
Glyceria maxima (Hartm.) Holmberg	Great Water Grass
Festuca gigantea (L.) Vill.	Giant Fescue
Vulpia fasciculata (Forsk.) Samp. (*V. membranacea* auct.)	Dune Fescue
Poa angustifolia L.	Smooth Meadow Grass
Elymus caninus (L.) L.	Bearded Couch
E. pycnanthus (Godr.) Melderis (*Agropyron pungens* (Pers.) Roem. & Schult.)	Sea Couch
Deschampsia setacea (Huds.) Hack.	Bog Hair-grass

APPENDIX TWO

References to Work on the Lower Plants

Mosses and Liverworts

Paton, Jean A. (1971). 'A bryophyte flora of the Isle of Man', *Proc.* 7, supplement. Records for 102 species of hepatics and 287 species of mosses are accepted in this.

Lichens

Hartley, J. W. & Wheldon, J. A. (1927). 'The lichens of the Isle of Man', *NW Nat*, supplement. P. M. Earland-Bennett (1979). 'A preliminary survey and assessment of the lichen flora of the Isle of Man', *Proc.* 8, 139-55.

Fungi

Hartley, J. W. & Wheldon, H. J. (1918) 'Manx fungi', *Proc.* 2, 99-103. Milne, J. E. & Milne, D. J. (1972). 'The Manx fungus flora', *Peregrine*, 4, 7-14. Further lists by the Milnes have appeared in *Peregrine*, 4, 76-8 (1973) and 154-7 (1975). A visit by R. W. G. Dennis in 1970 (*Peregrine*, 4, 149-54 (1975)) and the resident investigations of Dr J. C. F. Hopkins have greatly extended the list of microfungi.

Freshwater Algae

Uninvestigated except for Stoneworts. A full, unpublished list of the latter was furnished in 1979 to the British Museum (Natural History).

Marine Algae

Knight, M. & Parke, M. W. (1931). 'Manx algae', *Liverpool Marine Biol. Comm. Memoir*, 30.

Diatoms

Uninvestigated except for one study of those of Baldwin Reservoir.

BIBLIOGRAPHY

The journal of the Isle of Man Natural History and Antiquarian Society, which for long was the main outlet for the publication of botanical papers and plant records, has been known at different periods as *Transactions*, *Yn Lioar Manninagh* and *Proceedings*. These are abbreviated as *Trans.*, *YLM* and *Proc.* in this bibliography. The chaotic volume numbering of the earlier periods has necessarily been retained.

Since the 1940s most records have appeared in the *Peregrine*, originally the organ of the Manx Field Club.

Allen, D. E. (1953). 'Botanical indications of a possible climatic change in the Irish Sea Area', *Irish Nat. J.* 11, 77-8.

Allen, D. E. (1954). 'Recent work on the Manx flora', *Proc. Bot. Soc. Br. Is.*, 1, 5-20.

Allen, D. E. (1956). 'The vanished forests', *Peregrine*, 2(4), 7-9.

Allen, D. E. (1962a). 'Our knowledge of the Manx fauna and flora in 1961: a statistical summary', *Peregrine*, 3, 93-5.

Allen, D. E. (1962b). 'Railway colonists in the Isle of Man', *Proc. Bot. Soc. Br. Is.*, 4, 502.

Allen, D. E. (1968). '***Neotina intacta*** (Link) Reichb. f. in the Isle of Man', *Proc. Bot. Soc. Br. Is.*, 7, 165-8; reprinted, abridged, in *Peregrine*, 3, 192-3.

Allen, D. E. (1969). *The Flowering Plants and Ferns of the Isle of Man* (Manx Museum handlist). Douglas.

Allen, D. E. (1971). '***Dactylorhiza fuchsii*** subsp. ***okellyi*** (Druce) Soó — behaviour and characters in the Isle of Man', *Watsonia*, 8, 401-2.

Allen D. E. (1972a, misdated 1971). 'History through brambles', *J. Manx Mus.*, 7, 188-92.

Allen, D. E. (1972b). 'Bramble-dating; a promising approach', in *Hedges and Local History*, 30-6. London.

Allen, D. E. (1974). 'Irish and Welsh species of ***Rubus fruticosus*** L. agg. in the Isle of Man', *Watsonia*, 10, 163-4.

Allen, D. E. (1978a). 'The present-day fauna and flora of Man as indicators of the date of the Flandrian severance', in *Man and Environment in the Isle of Man*, ed. P. Davey, 9-13. Oxford: British Archaeological Reports, Series 54(i).

Allen, D. E. (1978b). 'Plant distribution patterns as historical indicators', *ibid.*, 51-9.

Allen, D. E. and Garrad, L. S. (1980). 'Samphire: an overlooked Manx trade', *J. Manx Mus.*, 8, 38-9.

Anon (1836). *A Six Days' Tour through the Isle of Man.* Douglas.

Anon (1883). 'Botany', in *Black's Guide to the Isle of Man.* Edinburgh.

Babington, C. C. (1869). *The British Rubi.* London.

Bennett, A. (1896). 'Additions to the flora of the Isle of Man', *J. Bot.*, 34, 448-9.

Bennett, A. (1901). '***Ulex nanus*** in the Isle of Man', *J. Bot.*, 39, 244.

Bilton, E. and Bostock, E. (1885). *Rep. Trans. N. Staffs. NFC & Arch. Soc.*, 44-5.

Birch, J. W. (1960). 'On the climate of the Isle of Man', *Proc.* 6, 97-121.

Birch, J. W. (1964). *The Isle of Man: a Study in Economic Geography.* Cambridge.

Birks, H. J. B. and Deacon, J. (1973). 'A numerical analysis of the past and present flora of the British Isles', *New Phytol.*, 72, 877-902.

Bruce, J. R. (1928). 'Animal and plant remains in the Manx post-glacial deposits and forest-bed', *Proc.* 11, 154-62.

Chalmers-Hunt, J. M. (1970). 'The butterflies and moths of the Isle of Man', *Trans. Soc. Br. Entom.*, 19, 1-171.

Clapham, A. R., Tutin, T. G. and Warburg, E. F. (1962). *Flora of the British Isles*, Ed 2. Cambridge.

Colman, J. S. (1953). 'Marine zoology', in *A Scientific Survey of Merseyside*, ed. W. Smith, 90-3. Liverpool.

Cooke, M. C. (1867). *A Fern Book for Everybody*. London.

Cowin, W. S. and Karran, A. H. (1945). 'The Great Yellow Loosestrife, an addition to the Manx flora', *Peregrine*, 1(3), 27.

Cumming, J. G. (1848). *The Isle of Man; its History. Physical, Ecclesiastical, Civil and Legendary*. London.

Davies, J. H. (1857). 'Primitiae of the bryology of the Isle of Man', *Phytologist*, NS 2, 20-3, 109-12.

Dickson, C. A., Dickson, J. H. and Mitchell, G. F. (1970). 'The Late-Weichselian flora of the Isle of Man', *Phil. Trans. R. Soc. Lond.*, 258B, 31-79.

Druce, G. C. (1932). *The Comital Flora of the British Isles*. Arbroath.

Erdtman, G. (1925). 'Pollen statistics from Ballaugh and the Curragh, Isle of Man', *Proc. Liverpool Geol. Soc.*, 14, 158-63.

Feltham, J. (1788). *A Tour through the Island of Mann*. Bath.

Forbes, E. (1837a). [records] in G. W. Francis, *An Analysis of the British Ferns and their Allies*, Ed 1. London.

Forbes, E. (1837b). [I.O.M. list] in H. C. Watson, *The New Botanist's Guide to the localities of the rarer plants of Britain*, 2, 407-10. London.

Forbes, E. (1837c). 'On new and rare forms of British animals and plants', *Rep. Br. Ass. Adv. Sci.* sect. 2, 102; *Athenaeum*, 697-8.

Forbes, E. (1842). [Botany] in J. Quiggin, *Quiggin's Illustrated Guide and Visitor's Companion through the Isle of Mann*, Ed 2. Douglas.

Forbes, E. (1845). [List of plants] in J. Train, q.v. 1, 27-8. Douglas.

Forbes, E. (1848) 'Flora of the Isle of Man', in J. G. Cumming, q.v., 360-4.

Forbes, E. (1849). 'On the British forms of ***Daucus carota***', *Bot. Gaz.*, 1, 292-6.

[Garner, R.] (1867). *Holiday Excursions of a Naturalist*. London.

Garner, R. (1878). 'Professor Edward Forbes and his country', *Midland Nat.*, 1, 67-70, 90-4.

Garrad, L. S. (1972a). 'Oak woodland in the Isle of Man', *Watsonia*, 9, 59-60.

Garrad, L. S. (1972b). *The Naturalist in the Isle of Man*. Newton Abbot.

Garrad L. S. (1972c). 'The wildlife of the Ayres', *Peregrine*, 4, 21-41.

Garrad, L. S. (1974). 'Some thoughts on Manx woodland', *Proc.* 7, 666-85.

Gasking, S. (1888-9). 'List of the plants of the Isle of Man', *Research*, 172, 210-11; 40, 66.

Gasking, S. (1890). 'Additions to the list of the plants of the Isle of Man', *Research*, 185-6.

Gill, W. W. (1929). *A Manx Scrapbook*. London.

Gill, W. W. (1963). *A Third Manx Scrapbook*. London.

Gregson, C. S. (1887). 'A day's "scientific" insect-hunting in the Isle of Man in June', *Young Nat.*, 8, 153-5.

Grose, F. (1783-7). *The Antiquities of England and Wales.* London.

Hartley, J. W. and Wheldon, J. A. (1914a). 'The Manx sand-dune flora', *J. Bot.*, 52, 170-5.

Hartley, J. W. and Wheldon, J. A. (1914b). 'Notes on the Manx flora', *J. Bot.*, 52, 213.

Hemsley, W. B. (1886). 'Holiday jottings in the Isle of Man', *Gard. Chron.*, 462-3, 491-2.

Hiern, W. P. (1897). 'Isle of Man plants', *J. Bot.*, 35, 11-15.

Hobkirk, C. P. (1866). 'Notes on some forms of ***Crataegus***', *Naturalist*, 3, 62, 78.

Holt, G. A. (1874). 'Botany', in H. T. Jenkinson, *Jenkinson's Practical Guide to the Isle of Man*, Ed 1. Douglas.

Hudson, W. (1762). *Flora Anglica.* London.

Keegan, P. Q. (1888). 'In the Isle of Man', *Sci. Gossip*, 24, 73-5.

Kermode, S. A. P. (1900). 'The flora of the Isle of Man, 1900', *YLM*, 3, 273-91.

Kermode, S. A. P. (1911). [Botany] in J. Quine, *The Isle of Man.* Cambridge.

Leavett, R. L. (1971). 'A list of the flowering plants and ferns of the Calf of Man', *Calf of Man Bird Obs. Ann. Rep.*, 72-104.

McAllister, H. A. (1973). '***Campanula rotundifolia***: a local race in south-west Scotland', *Glasgow Nat.*, 19, 66.

Macculloch, J. (1819). *A Description of the Western Islands of Scotland including the Isle of Man.* Edinburgh.

Madge, S. C. (1974). 'Additional notes on the flora of the Calf of Man', *Calf of Man Bird Obs. Ann. Rep.*, 68-78.

Marsden-Jones, E. and Turrill, W. B. (1954). *British Knapweeds.* London.

Mitchell, G. F. (1958). 'A Late-glacial deposit near Ballaugh, Isle of Man', *New Phytol.*, 57, 256-63.

Mitchell, G. F. (1965). 'The Quaternary deposits of the Ballaugh and Kirkmichael districts, Isle of Man', *Q. Jl. Geol. Soc. Lond.*, 21, 359-81.

Moore, A. W. (1898). 'Folk-medicine in the Isle of Man', *YLM*, 3, 303-14.

Moore, A. W. (1901). 'Has climate changed?', *YLM*, 2, 237-41.

Moore, E. J. (1931). 'The ecology of the Ayreland of Bride', *J. Ecol.*, 19, 115-36.

Moore, T. (1859a). *A Popular History of the British Ferns*, Ed 3. London.

Moore, T. (1859b). *Nature-printed British Ferns.* London.

Mosley, C. and Wattam, W. E. L. (1903). 'Notes on the natural history of the Isle of Man', *Nature Study*, 12, 48-54.

Munn, S., Crellin, L. V. & Killey, J. (1957). 'Manx plant notes', *NW Nat.*, NS3, 430-2.

Nichols, J. (1822). *Illustrations of the Literary History of the Eighteenth Century*, Vol. 4. London.

Osvald, H. (1949). 'Notes on the vegetation of British and Irish mosses', *Acta Phytogeographica Suecica*, no. 26, 1-62.

Paton, C. I. (1927). MS notes in annotated offprint of Kermode (1900), now in the British Herbarium, British Museum (Natural History).

Paton, C. I. (1933). 'A list of flowering plants, ferns, and horse-tails of the Isle of Man', *NW Nat.*, 8, 547-619.

Perkins, D. F. and Buse, A. (1974). *A Report on an Ecological Survey of the Isle of Man*. Bangor (mimeographed).

Perring, F. H. and Sell, P. D. (1968). *Critical Supplement to the Atlas of the British Flora*. London.

Phillips, B. A. M. (1967). 'The post-glacial raised shoreline around the North Plain, Isle of Man', *Northern Univs. Geogr. J.*, 8, 43-50.

Pollard, E., Hooper, M. D. and Moore, N. W. (1974). *Hedges*. London.

Quayle, G. E. (1973). 'Wild flowers', in *Legends of a Lifetime*, 60-72. Douglas.

Ralfe, P. G. (1892). 'Notes on Manx plants', *Sci. Gossip*, 28, 109-12.

Raven, C. E. (1950). *John Ray, Naturalist, his Life and Works*, Ed 2. Cambridge.

Robinson, J. F. (1882). MS list of additions to Forbes (1837b) donated to Botanical Society of Edinburgh, 12 Jan. 1882 and now in archives of Royal Botanic Garden.

Robson, S. (1777). *The British Flora*. York.

Russell, G. (1967). 'Note on the maritime heath vegetation at the south of the Isle of Man', *Rep. Mar. Biol. Sta. Port Erin*, 79, 37-42.

Shimmin, E. (1915). 'Life in Ballaugh in the Forties', *Mannin*, 3, no. 5.

Stenning, E. H. (1950). *The Isle of Man*. London.

Stowell, H. A. (1856). 'Common plants', *Phytologist*, NS1, 425-9.

Stowell, H. A. (1860). 'Notes on the Isle of Man and its flora', *Phytologist*, NS 4, 161-9.

Stowell, H. A. (1863). 'Botany', in W. Thwaites, *Directory of the Isle of Man*, 97-108. Sheffield.

Tooley, M. J. (1978). 'Flandrian sea-level changes and vegetational history in the Isle of Man: a review', in *Man and Environment in the Isle of Man*: ed. P. Davey, 15-24. Oxford: British Archaeological Reports, Series 54(i).

Townley, R. (1791). *A Journal kept in the Isle of Man*. Whitehaven.

Train, J. (1845). *An Historical and Statistical Account of the Isle of Man*. Douglas.

Turner, D. and Dillwyn, L. W. (1805). *The Botanist's Guide through England and Wales*. London.

Watson, H. C. (1832). *Outlines of the Geographical Distribution of British Plants*. Edinburgh.

Watson, H. C. (1873-4). *Topographical Botany*, Ed 1. Thames Ditton.

Watson, H. C. (1883). *Topographical Botany*, Ed 2. London.

Watson, W. C. R. (1948). In H. J. Riddelsdell et al., *Flora of Gloucestershire*. Arbroath.

Watson, W. C. R. (1958). *Handbook of the Rubi of Great Britain and Ireland*. Cambridge.

Wattam, W. E. L. (1899). 'The Isle of Man in July', *Naturalists' J.*, 8, 16.

Wattam, W. E. L. (1901). 'Botanical finds in the Isle of Man', *Naturalists' J.*, 10, 99.

Wheldon, J. A. (1909-10). 'Flora of the Manx curraghs', *Lancs. Nat.*, NS2, 271-4, 301-4.

Wheldon, J. A. (1918). 'Further notes on the Manx flora', *Lancs. & Ches. Nat.*, NS8, 196-7.

Woods, G. (1811). *An Account of the Past and Present State of the Isle of Man*. London.

References to many other sources not specifically cited are to be found in N. Douglas Simpson's *Bibliographical Index of the British Flora* (Bournemouth, 1960).

ACKNOWLEDGMENTS

In addition to those whose assistance is acknowledged elsewhere in these pages (including the many specialists who have determined critical material) I should like to thank, first and foremost, the Trustees of the Manx Museum for their generosity in sponsoring the publication of this volume. As the Director, Marshall Cubbon, has recalled in the Foreword which he has so kindly contributed, the Museum is where the book substantially had its birth and it is entirely appropriate therefore that it should be from there that it now finally goes out into the world.

Special thanks are also due to Dr. J. W. Birch and Cambridge University Press for permission to reproduce Figures 1–5 from his book *The Isle of Man: A Study in Economic Geography* (1964), to Professor R. Lawton and the Department of Geography of Liverpool University for providing the base-map used in Figure 6, and to the Wild Flower Society for the award of a grant to meet the cost of the colour illustration on the dust jacket. I owe, too, a particular debt to Ann Harrison for seeing the work through the press, to Oliver Turnbull of Titus Wilson and Son for invaluable guidance on typography and to Marjorie Devereau for rounding off all the other help she has given by undertaking the onerous task of compiling the index.

INDEX OF PLANT NAMES (English and Scientific)

Names appearing only as a synonym are in italics.